KT-117-506

Geological maps:

AN INTRODUCTION

Alex Maltman

JOHN WILEY & SONS
Chichester · New York · Brisbane · Toronto · Singapore

Reprinted in August 1992 by
John Wiley & Sons Ltd, Baffins Lane, Chichester,
West Sussex PO19 1UD, England
Reprinted March 1995, November 1996
First published in 1990 by Open University Press

Other Wiley Editorial Offices

John Wiley & Sons, Inc., 605 Third Avenue,
New York, NY 10158-0012, USA

Jacaranda Wiley Ltd, G.P.O. Box 859, Brisbane,
Queensland 4001, Australia

John Wiley & Sons (Canada) Ltd, 22 Worcester Road,
Rexdale, Ontario M9W 1L1, Canada

John Wiley & Sons (SEA) Pte Ltd, 37 Jalan Pemimpin #05-04,
Block B, Union Industrial Building, Singapore 129809

British Library Cataloguing in Publication Data

Maltman, Alex
Geological maps: an introduction
1. Geological features. Analysis. Use of geographical maps.
I. Title
551.8

ISBN 0-471-93241-8 (cased)
ISBN 0-471-93240-X (paperback)

Typeset by Scarborough Typesetting Services
Printed in Great Britain by Redwood Books, Trowbridge, Wiltshire

Geological maps

Contents

Foreword

A recent national survey of geology students indicated that, although they saw the need for a basic training in mapwork, the three-dimensional aspects involved formed the single most difficult part of an introductory geology course, and that it was generally taught in a way both abstract and dull. At the same time, there was no book which puzzled students could turn to for explanations; no book which told them more about real geological maps. This book is an attempt to fill that need. It is based on the view that in these days of increasing specialisation the geological map remains the vital coordinating document, and that the proliferation of computer methods of handling three-dimensional data makes a firm understanding and appreciation of mapwork more imperative than ever.

The book is designed for first year undergraduates. An elementary knowledge of rocks and geological processes is assumed, together with a basic understanding of topographic maps. Geological maps, however, are introduced from first principles, so that some of the material may appeal to anyone with an interest in geology; on the other hand, some of the information may be of use to the more advanced student. Those figures that contain formulae, methods, and information for reference have a frame to enable rapid location. The reference list, in addition to citing the sources of the maps included in the book, indicates much further material of relevance to geological mapwork.

In a subject so fundamental and yet so varied, every geologist will have his own views on geological maps – the matters needing emphasis, the best methods of interpretation, good examples of maps, and so on. Instructors may therefore urge in their taught courses different priorities from those given here, and, although a wide range of maps and map exercises is included, will prefer to continue to use their own 'pet' examples. But this is meant primarily to be a book for the student – to turn to for clarification, for further information, and simply to learn a little more about geological maps.

I acknowledge the years of undergraduate students at the University College of Wales, Aberystwyth, from whose wishes this book was born, and the individual students who commented on early versions of it. The following are also gratefully acknowledged for their constructive criticism and advice: Dr Mark Bentley, Shell Expro; Dr Dave Wilson, BGS; colleagues at UCW, Aberystwyth, in particular Dr Dennis Bates, Dr Bill Fitches, Warren Pratt and Antony Wyatt; and my wife, Jo. For help in the production of the volume I thank Richard Baggaley and Sue Hadden of the Open University Press, and Valerie Grant and Arnold Thawley of the Department of Geology, UCW, Aberystwyth. Finally, I thank my family – Jo, Alastair, and Emily – for putting up with all my nights at the office.

1 Some fundamentals of geological maps

1.1 Introduction

Geological maps show the distribution at the earth's surface of different kinds of rocks. The geological map is a fundamental device of geologists. The patterns on the map record the relationships between the rocks, from which the geologist can deduce much about their arrangement underground and about their geological history. This book is aimed at helping you develop these interpretive skills.

A geological map may be a geologist's first introduction to an area; it may also represent the culmination of investigation. Maps are commonly used to assemble new information as it is obtained; they are also a highly effective way of communicating new data to other geologists. A geological map can act as a synthesis of current knowledge on the geology of an area.

In nature most geological features have three-dimensional arrangements, and a familiarity with them is an essential part of the training of any geologist. The geological map, despite being a flat piece of paper, remains the single most convenient way of representing and working with the spatial arrangement of rocks. The three-dimensional aspect of mapwork is of great industrial use; for example, in dealing with subsurface coal seams, oil reservoirs, and ore bodies. It is a central concern of many of the following chapters.

In both commercial and academic work, maps are much used to help reconstruct the geological histories of areas and the geological conditions that existed in the past. This conveying of information in additional dimensions – underground, and back in geological time – sets geological maps apart from other kinds of maps. Indeed, because so many facts and principles are communicated in a single document, geological maps have been called 'the visual language of geologists' (Rudwick, 1976).

Another fundamental difference from most other kinds of maps is that geological maps are themselves based on interpretation. Constructing a geological map involves several interpretive steps, such that the completed map tends to reflect how well the geology of the area is understood. The map acts as 'an index of the extent and accuracy of geological knowledge at the time of its production, and it is the basis of future research' (North, 1928).

Geology is increasingly becoming a collection of specialised studies, and more and more specialised kinds of maps are evolving. Nevertheless, the conventional geological map continues to provide a common thread. Most specialisations somewhere involve a traditional geological map. However, geological maps themselves are suddenly undergoing very great changes, especially in the way new technologies are being employed in the production of maps and the manipulation of their information. This adds tremendous flexibility to the ways in which maps can be used, but it also makes an understanding of the basic principles behind them more important than ever. It demands that the geologist appreciates both the power and the limitations of presenting geological information on maps.

This book is largely concerned with these fundamental principles. However, it also attempts to give glimpses of why many geologists, in addition to understanding the functional significance of geological maps, have a fondness for them, and a respect for the heritage they represent. This first chapter introduces the basic features of geological maps, expanding on some of the points mentioned above. We begin with a brief consideration of the topographic base on which the geological map is drawn.

1.2 The topographic base map

Normally the geological data are added to a topographic base map in order that the geology can be located. The base may consist simply of some recognisable features, such as the shape of a coastline or the position of major towns, or the geology may be superimposed on a complete topographic map. Therefore, a first requirement for working with geological maps is a familiarity with the principles of topographic maps, as discussed in standard textbooks on cartography. The most important aspects of topographic maps for geological purposes are summarised in the following sections.

SCALE:	*1:10 000 000* and smaller
USE:	Maps of entire continents, oceans, or planets, on single sheets.
SCALE:	*1:5 000 000* and *1:1 000 000*
USE:	Synoptic views of continents or countries, sometimes on several sheets.
SCALE:	*1:500 000*
USE:	Maps of countries, provinces, states (depending on size); little detail but of use for general planning and overviews.
SCALE:	*1:250 000*
USE:	Regional geology, e.g. the conterminous U S in 472 sheets (2° long. × 1° lat. quadrangles); Australia in 544 sheets; Canada in 918 sheets; U K and adjacent shelf in 106 sheets. Usually have topographic base.
SCALE:	*1:50 000, 1:25 000*, and thereabouts
USE:	The standard scales for reasonably detailed published geological maps of well-investigated countries, e.g.: the previous 'One-Inch' maps of the B G S at 1:63 360; the 'Classical areas' maps of the B G S at 1:25 000; U S G S 15′ quadrangles at 1:62 500; U S G S 7′ quadrangles at 1:24 000
SCALE:	*1:10 000* and larger
USE:	1:10 000 the standard scale for B G S field surveying and detailed investigations. Generally unpublished, apart from coalfields, but copies available to the public. Larger scale maps or plans (true dimensions shown) of sites of scientific or commercial interest: mines, quarries, etc.

Fig. 1.1 Some notes on typical scales of geological maps.

1.2.1 Scale

The **scale** of geological maps is highly variable: from very small-scale maps of entire continents or even planets, to very large-scale maps which show fine details of a particular locality, perhaps one of special scientific or commercial interest. Scale is most usually specified as a ratio, for example 1 : 100 000, where one unit on the map represents 100 000 of the same units on the ground. Thus 1 cm on a map at this particular scale would be equivalent to 100 000 cm, that is 1000 m or 1 km. Examples of the kinds of scales typically used for geological maps are given in Fig. 1.1.

Older, non-metric maps were sometimes referred to by a comparative scale, such as 'one inch equals one mile'. USGS* maps are commonly called 'quadrangle maps', as they show a quadrangular area defined by lines of latitude and longitude. The spacing of the lines implies the scale of the map (Fig. 1.1). Maps may also have a linear or graphic scale, that is, a bar or line divided into segments which correspond to specified distances on the ground. This kind of scale is useful in these days of rapid enlargement and reduction of maps by photocopying machines because the scale will still be valid at the modified size.

1.2.2 Map projection

In small-scale maps, say at 1 : 500 000 and smaller, the way in which the curved surface of the earth has been projected onto the flat paper is important because of the distortions of angles and areas that can result. The various projection methods that are used are summarised in the introductory pages of most atlases; they are considered in detail by Snyder (1987). However, the maps normally used for quantitative geological work are at a sufficiently large scale for the effects of projection to be negligible for most purposes.

1.2.3 Grid systems and location

The direction of north is specified on most maps and is normally towards the top of the sheet. Many maps are divided by a **grid system** running north–south and east–west to aid in locating particular features. Small-scale maps commonly employ latitude and longitude; large-scale maps may involve some arbitrary but standardised system. For example, the UK uses a 'National Grid', summarised in Fig. 1.2. In the USA the most frequently used method of specifying localities remains the 'township and section' system (Fig. 1.3). There are, however, increasing attempts to apply the metric Universal Transverse Mercator (UTM) system. This grid already appears on USGS $7\frac{1}{2}$′quadrangles and, together with the National Grid, on BGS† 1 : 250 000 sheets.

* United States Geological Survey.

† British Geological Survey.

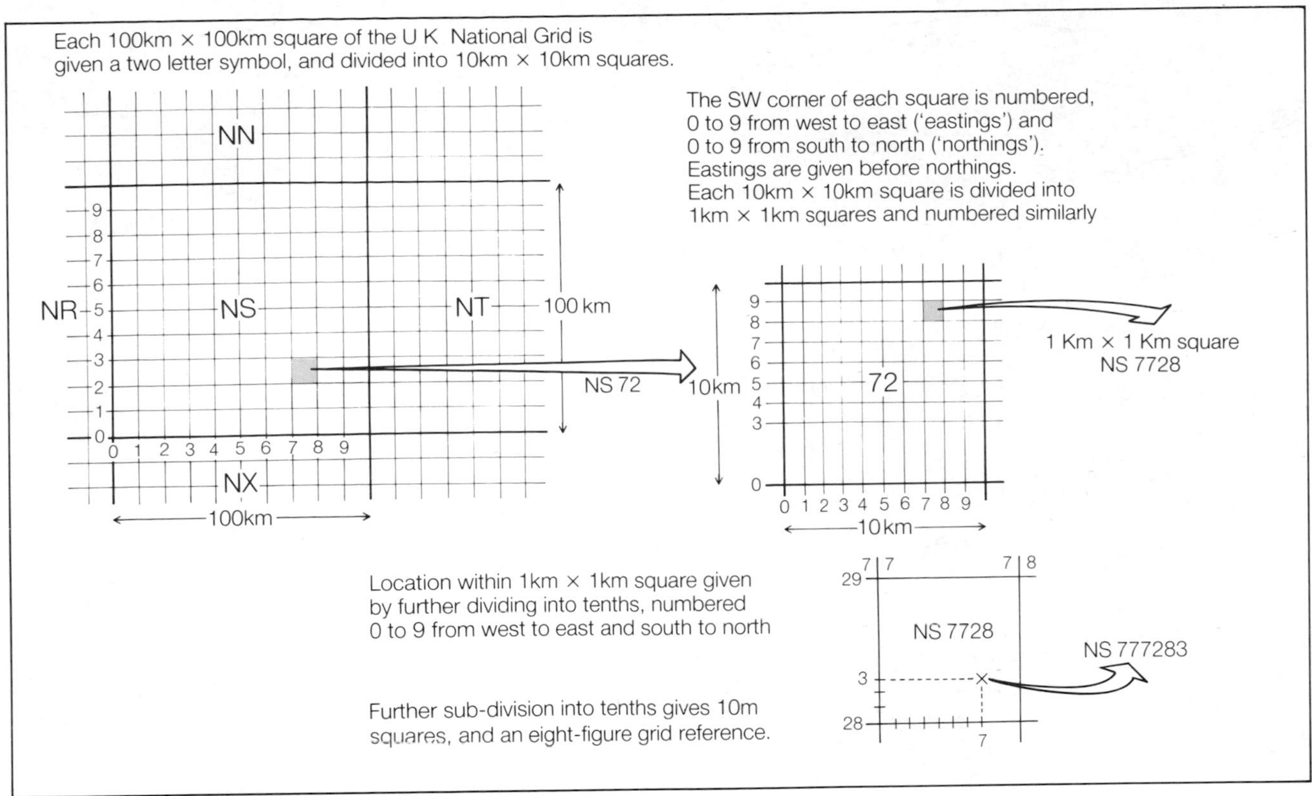
Each 100km × 100km square of the U K National Grid is given a two letter symbol, and divided into 10km × 10km squares.
NN
NR
NS
NT
NX
100 km
100km
NS 72
The SW corner of each square is numbered, 0 to 9 from west to east ('eastings') and 0 to 9 from south to north ('northings'). Eastings are given before northings. Each 10km × 10km square is divided into 1km × 1km squares and numbered similarly
72
10km
1 Km × 1 Km square
NS 7728
Location within 1km × 1km square given by further dividing into tenths, numbered 0 to 9 from west to east and south to north
NS 7728
NS 777283
Further sub-division into tenths gives 10m squares, and an eight-figure grid reference.

Fig. 1.2 Finding locations on maps using the UK National Grid.

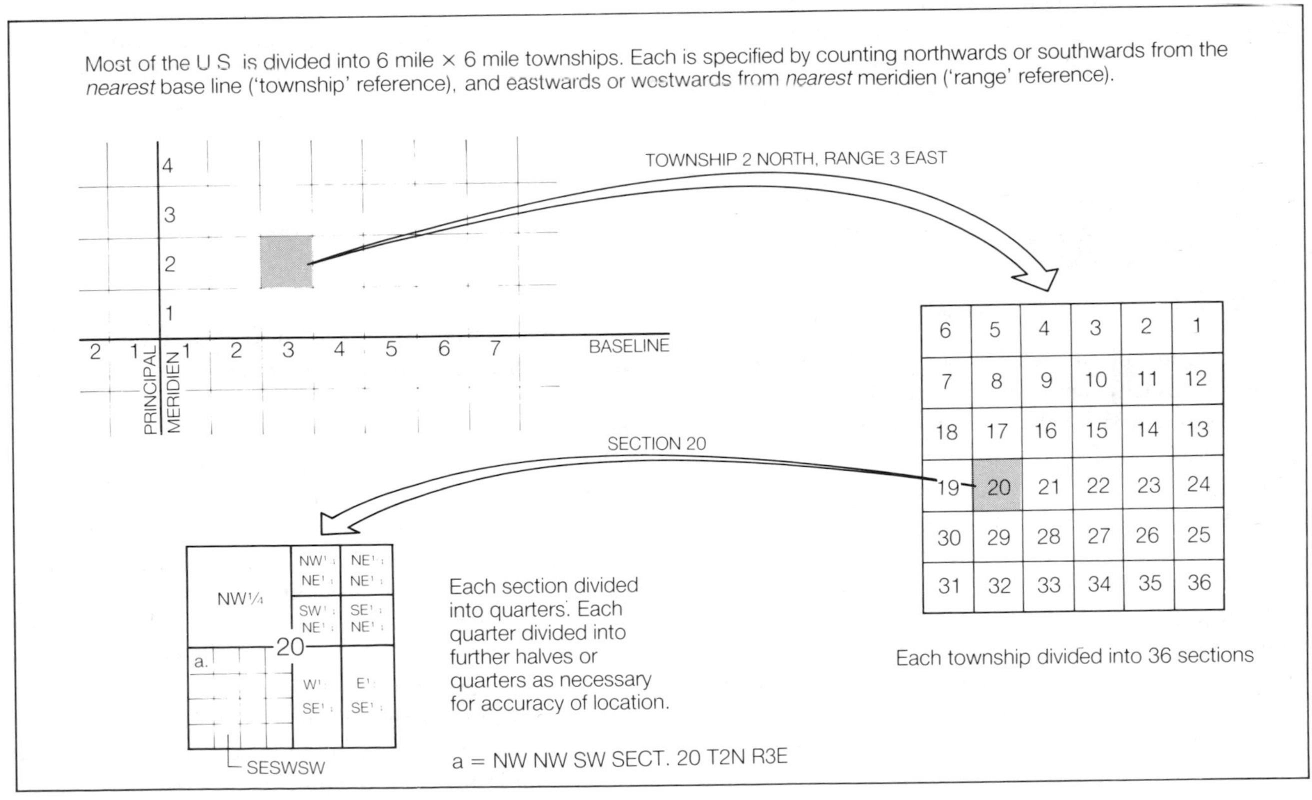
Most of the U S is divided into 6 mile × 6 mile townships. Each is specified by counting northwards or southwards from the *nearest* base line ('township' reference), and eastwards or westwards from *nearest* meridien ('range' reference).
TOWNSHIP 2 NORTH, RANGE 3 EAST
BASELINE
PRINCIPAL
MERIDIEN
SECTION 20
Each township divided into 36 sections
NW¼
20
a.
SESWSW
Each section divided into quarters. Each quarter divided into further halves or quarters as necessary for accuracy of location.
a = NW NW SW SECT. 20 T2N R3E

Fig. 1.3 Finding locations on maps using the US township and section system.

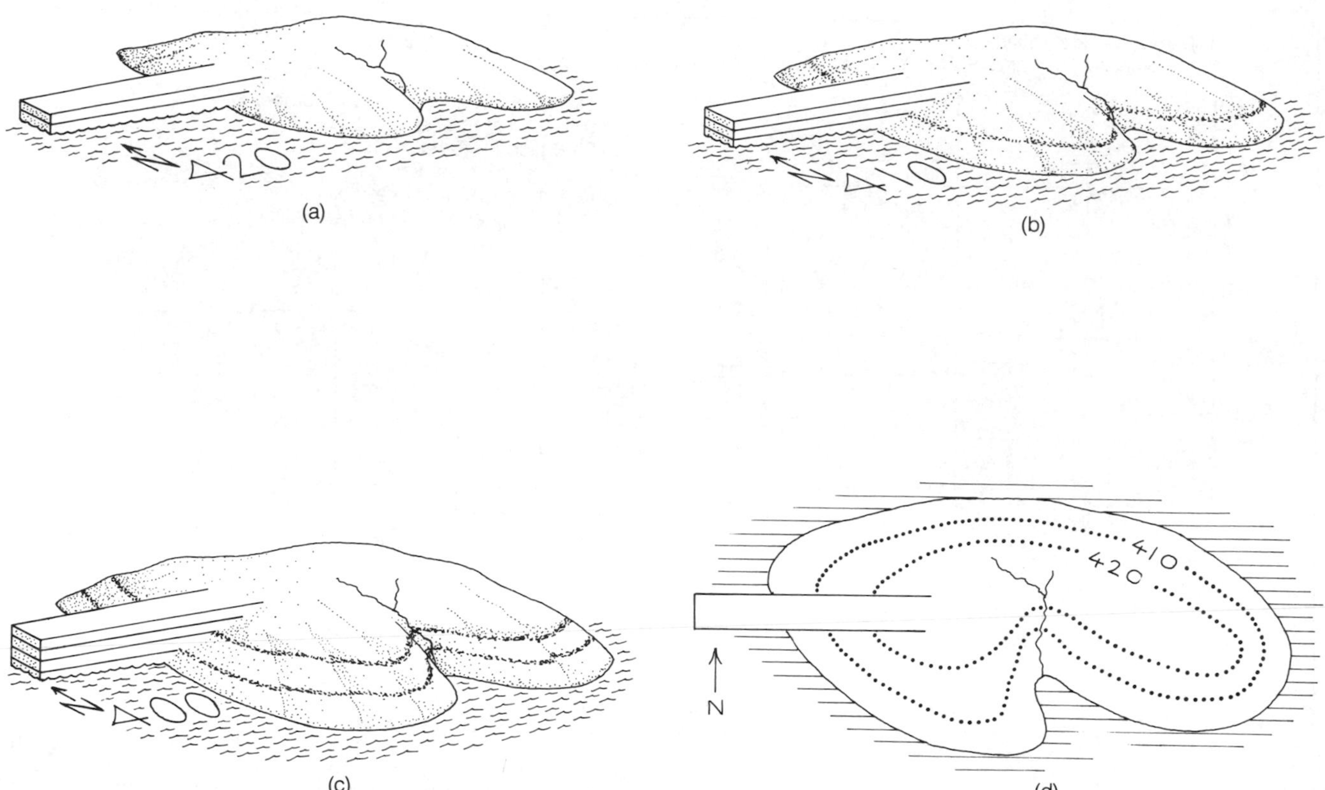
420
(a)
410
(b)
400
(c)
410
420
N
(d)

Fig. 1.4 The concept of topographic contours, illustrated by a small island in a lake with dropping water level. (a) Lake level at 420 m altitude. (b) Lake level dropped to 410 m. (c) Lake level dropped to 400 m. Note that the previous lake levels are represented by strand lines on the island. These, like the lake levels, are horizontal, and at 420 m and 410 m. (d) Topographic map of the island, lake level at 400 m. Contour interval 10 m. The topographic contour lines, being horizontal, coincide with the strand lines shown in (c).

1.2.4 Relief

Representation of the relief or topography of the land surface is usually omitted from small-scale geological maps. The systems of colour shading commonly employed in small-scale relief maps, for example in many atlases, would interfere with the colours or ornaments used to depict the geology. However, it may be possible to gain some idea of the relief on such maps from associated features such as river drainage patterns and lakes.

On larger scale maps it is extremely useful to indicate the topography. Older maps employed **hachures**, which can look attractive when executed well and if they do not interfere with the geology. However, they are not quantitative. Hachuring gives a visual impression of relief without specifying the altitude or steepness of slopes. **Spot heights** give very localised information on altitude and are employed on some small-scale maps.

The most successful method of representing relief is by **topographic contour lines** (Fig. 1.4). These join together points of equal height above some datum, normally sea-level. The contour interval is the height difference between adjacent contours. Interpolation between the contour lines enables the altitude at any point on the map to be estimated. The spacing of the lines indicates the slope of the land. Closely spaced lines reflect steep gradients, curved lines indicate rounded slopes, and so on. Figure 1.5 gives examples. It is vital that you do not memorise a series of 'rules' about the patterns of contour lines, but mentally visualise the relief they are depicting. With a little practice the ups and downs of the land surface should be apparent in your mind's eye simply by looking at the contour shapes. If more precise information is needed, topographic cross-sections are easy to construct from contour lines; Fig.1.6 shows the method.

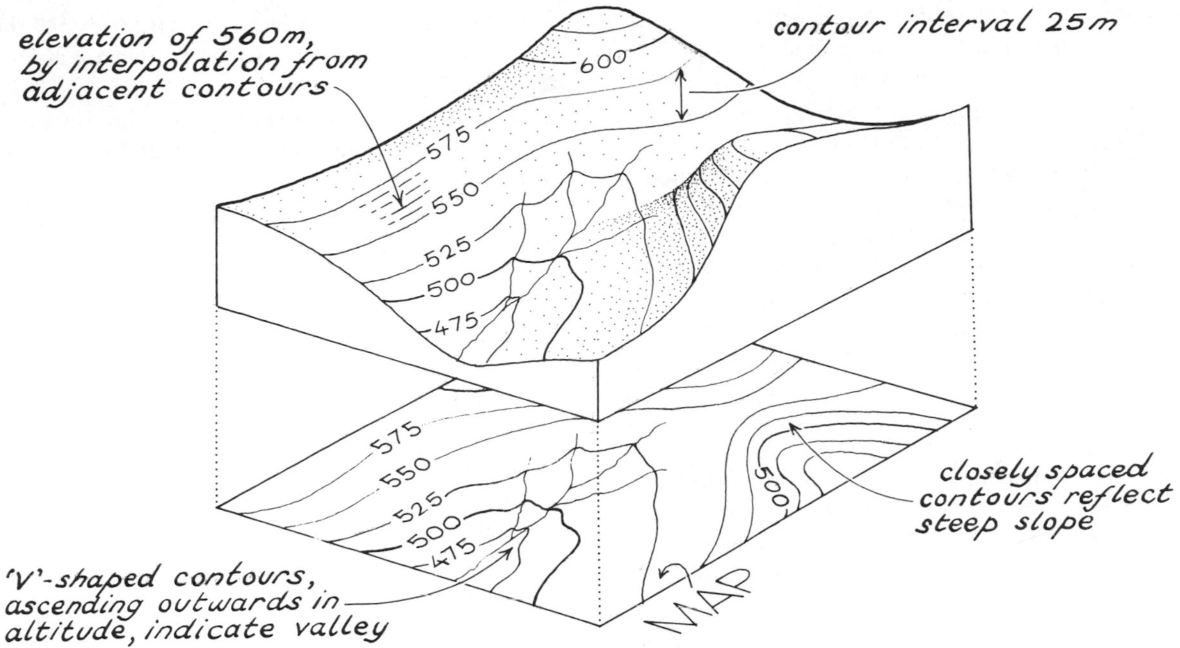

elevation of 560m, by interpolation from adjacent contours
contour interval 25m
600
575
550
525
500
475
575
550
525
500
475
500
closely spaced contours reflect steep slope
'V'-shaped contours, ascending outwards in altitude, indicate valley
MAP

Fig. 1.5 Diagram showing relationships between topographic contours and relief.

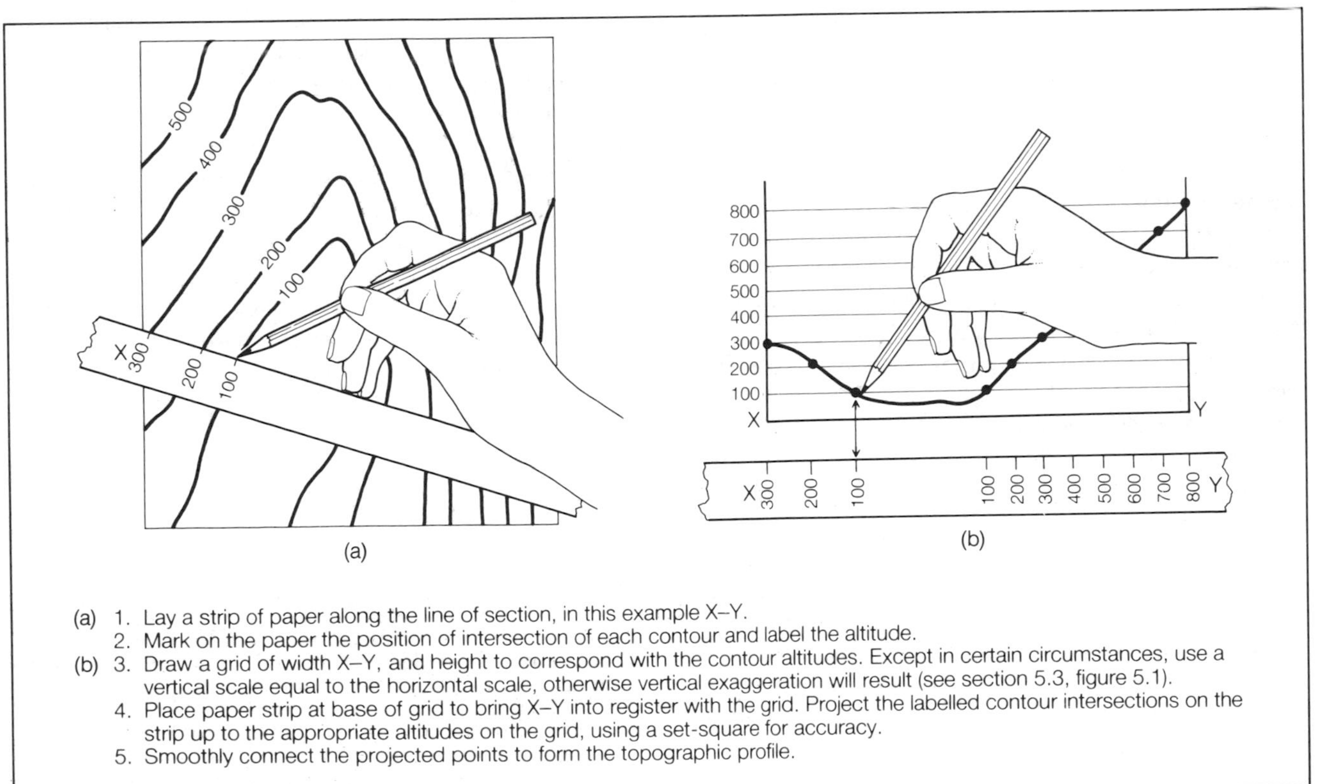

500
400
300
200
100
X 300 200 100
(a)
800
700
600
500
400
300
200
100
X
Y
X 300 200 100 100 200 300 400 500 600 700 800 Y
(b)
(a) 1. Lay a strip of paper along the line of section, in this example X–Y.
2. Mark on the paper the position of intersection of each contour and label the altitude.
(b) 3. Draw a grid of width X–Y, and height to correspond with the contour altitudes. Except in certain circumstances, use a vertical scale equal to the horizontal scale, otherwise vertical exaggeration will result (see section 5.3, figure 5.1).
4. Place paper strip at base of grid to bring X–Y into register with the grid. Project the labelled contour intersections on the strip up to the appropriate altitudes on the grid, using a set-square for accuracy.
5. Smoothly connect the projected points to form the topographic profile.

Fig. 1.6 Instructions for drawing a topographic profile from a map.

It is important to realise that the topographic contour lines are being employed to represent the shape of the land surface, which is three-dimensional, on a flat, two-dimensional, piece of paper. In geology, the problem commonly arises of depicting some three-dimensional geological feature on a two-dimensional map, and contours are used for this also. In this book the lines used for the relief of the land surface will always be referred to as *topographic* contours, in order to avoid any confusion with the contour lines to be introduced later for various geological surfaces.

1.2.5 Key or legend

There may be further cartographic information provided on the geological map, for example some details of the surveying and production of the topographic part of the map, but it is not normal to provide a full topographic key. The user is assumed to be familiar with the portrayal of roads, political boundaries, rivers and the like. Most of the map key is given over to geological matters.

1.3 Geological aspects

1.3.1 Key or legend

Probably the most striking thing about a typical geological map is its numerous patches of colour. Uncoloured maps have equivalent areas of black and white **ornament**. These colours and ornaments indicate the distribution of the **map units** into which the rocks have been divided for the purpose of the map. The map **key**, also referred to as a **legend**, **explanation**, or **index**, specifies the geological meaning of the colours and ornaments, together with any symbols used on the map. It can also contain much additional information, and should be one of the first things to consult when you examine a map.

On some maps, particularly those at a small-scale, the map units represent rocks of different stratigraphic ages, and on some large-scale maps the units are named according to particular fossils that the rocks contain. However, the majority of maps have units divided according to rock type – the **lithology**. The unit may comprise a single kind of rock or a convenient grouping of different rock types. A map unit is commonly loosely referred to as a **formation** or as 'beds' of rock, and this will be done here, even though these words may not correspond with their strict stratigraphic definitions. The narrow line that separates two colours or ornaments on a map represents the surface of contact between two adjacent units. The map key may well provide information on the stratigraphic age of the formations, and may make some additional remarks on fossil content, mode of origin, etc. of the beds, but the basic separation of the map units is normally made according to the type of rock.

The units may be presented in the key as spaced rectangles, or arranged in a kind of stratigraphic column. sometimes drawn to scale to reflect the thicknesses of the formations and the relationships between them. Whatever the design of the key, it is conventional to show, as far as possible, the oldest units at the bottom and successively younger formations above. The differences between the rock units on the map may be further clarified by adding symbols, usually letters or numbers, to the ornament. Symbols are commonly chosen which convey added information, for instance a letter which acts as an abbreviation for the stratigraphic age of the rock unit. Stratigraphic information is commonly not available for igneous and metamorphic units and so these are listed separately at the foot of the key.

1.3.2 Superficial and bedrock maps

Most geological maps show the distribution of the different types of bedrock, and omit any thin cover of soil, concrete, or whatever. However, if superficial deposits of geological interest, for example, dune-sand, till, or peat, are significantly developed, they are normally also shown on the map and explained in the key. Alluvium, in particular, tends to be shown in order to emphasise river courses and hence drainage patterns. The BGS has traditionally produced its maps in different versions, variously called 'solid', 'solid and drift', and 'drift' editions according to which aspects are given most emphasis.

Where a bedrock unit or structure reaches the land surface it is said to **outcrop**, even though it may actually be covered by a thin veneer of superficial material ignored on the geological map. Any parts of the outcrop that are not covered but are seen as bare rock are known as **exposures**. Some geologists use the terms 'outcrop' and 'exposure' interchangeably; in this book their use will be as given above.

1.3.3 The third dimension: geological cross-sections

Geologists often have to deal with the fact that the rocks and structures of the earth are arranged in three-dimensions. The distribution of rocks at the earth's surface, which is responsible for the shapes and patterns that are such a striking aspect of geological maps, is simply a function of how this three-dimensional configuration happens to intersect with the present-day earth's surface, that is, how it outcrops. With practice a geologist can visualise from the **outcrop patterns** on a map how the rocks are arranged in three dimensions, and can picture how the rocks lie below the earth's surface, and how they would once have been above the present land surface before erosion.

As well as the horizontal map surface, the geology can be depicted in a vertical plane by means of a geological **cross-section**. Most geological maps are accompanied by cross-sections, and the two together are a powerful means of communicating the three-dimensional arrangement of the geology. Maps and sections are two facets of the same thing – the spatial arrangement of the rocks. Many of the general statements made in this book concerning 'maps' really refer to 'geological maps and cross-sections'.

Geological maps and sections are so closely interrelated that, although cross-sections can be interpreted from finalised maps, in practice the two are usually developed together, and in some cases the geological sections are obtained first and the map is derived from them. An example of this is the exploration for oil below the sea. In this situation there is no accessible bedrock to plot on the map from which sections can be drawn! The seismic and drill-core data yield information readily in the vertical plane, enabling a series of geological sections to be built up, and from these sections the geological map is constructed.

1.3.4 The interpretive nature of maps

Although much of this book is concerned with deducing information from completed maps, it is important to understand at the outset that the geological map itself is a highly interpretive document. Numerous interpretive steps are involved in its production. Right from the moment the geological surveyor stands at an exposure of bedrock at the earth's surface, or examines a piece of drill-core, subjective judgement is exercised. The surveyor has continually to decide to which formation, eventually to be a particular colour on the completed map, each rock exposure will be assigned. The map units may be somewhat arbitrary, and because rarely will the bare rock be observable at the land surface, the locations and courses of the geological boundaries between the units will have to be judged. Even the nature of the boundary may be questionable.

How the boundaries are depicted on the map has implications not only for the three-dimensional relationships, as mentioned above, but also for portraying what is thought to be the geological evolution of the area. The completed map therefore reflects the surveying team's state of knowledge of the map area; even to some extent the state of geological science at the time (Harrison, 1963). This is why the geological surveying of a country can never be finalised. Because it is an interpretive document, there can never be an ultimate geological map of an area, as long as geological knowledge continues to improve.

1.3.5 Aesthetics

Geological maps can embody a tremendous amount of observational data, and at the same time have the capacities mentioned above of enabling projection into three dimensions and into past geological times. Nevertheless, despite being such a powerful scientific document, a geological map should be visually pleasing to work with. A good geological map is both scientifically sound and artistically attractive. Indeed, when looking at a map it is often the colours and the design of the map that make the first impact. However, there is no ideal or universally agreed way of presenting information on a geological map. This is one reason why many of the maps reproduced in this book look so different from one another.

Willats (1970) chose to express the aesthetic aspect of maps in a poem entitled 'Maps and Maidens':

> They must be well-proportioned and not too plain;
> Colour must be applied carefully and discreetly;
> They are more attractive if well dressed but not over dressed;
> They are very expensive things to dress up properly;
> Even when they look good they can mislead the innocent;
> And unless they are very well bred they can be awful liars!

1.4 Summary of chapter

1. Geological maps show the distribution of different rocks at the earth's surface.
2. Normally the geological data are added to a topographic base map.
3. On a large-scale map it is useful to depict the relief of the land surface, which is best done by topographic contours.
4. The key or legend to the geological map explains the ornament and symbols used to represent the geology, and can contain much information.
5. From the outcrop patterns on the geological map the three-dimensional arrangement of the rocks can be interpreted.
6. Geological cross-sections are complementary to maps in helping portray the three-dimensional arrangement of rocks.
7. The geological map is itself an interpretive document.
8. As well as being a powerful scientific device, a geological map should be pleasing visually.

1.5 Selected further reading

Thompson, M. M. (1979). *Maps for America*, USGS.
(A well-illustrated review of the map products of the USGS, including a short section on geological maps.)

Open University (1983). S236 Geology Course, Block 1 *Maps*, Milton Keynes, Open University Press.
(A highly readable self-tutoring manual on the fundamentals of geological maps.)

2 The nature of geological maps: the Ten Mile map of the UK and the 1:2 500 000 map of the USA

2.1 Introduction: cartographic matters

This chapter will use portions of two real examples of geological maps, one of the UK and one of the USA, to introduce some aspects of map interpretation. It provides a preliminary glimpse of the kinds of interpretations that can be made before the various concepts are examined more closely in succeeding chapters. We begin by noting some of the cartographic matters; first, the scale. Despite its time-honoured name, the Ten Mile UK map (Plate 1) is actually at a scale slightly larger than ten miles to the inch, at 1:625 000. There is a north sheet and a south sheet to cover the whole of Great Britain. The US map (Plate 2) is at 1:2 500 000 and comes in three sheets: the east and west halves of the map and a separate sheet showing the legend.

The UK sheets show latitude and longitude at the margins of the map, and also the ten kilometre squares of the UK National Grid. The US map shows degrees of latitude and longitude. Note that the equal area projection used for these maps results in the parallels of latitude being more widely spaced than the meridians of longitude. There is no attempt on the relatively small-scale US map to indicate topography directly; the UK map shows spot heights in feet. For example, at [SN709806] the summit of the hill Plynlymon is shown as 2470 ft.

The key on the UK map is called an 'Index and Explanation' and is hybrid in nature – it uses different kinds of map units for different kinds of rocks. Intrusive igneous rocks are divided on the basis of lithology – gabbro, granite, rhyolite, and so on – whereas extrusive igneous rocks are divided by rock type and stratigraphic age. Thus basalt, for instance, appears several times on the key, according to its geological age. The sedimentary rocks are arranged in ascending stratigraphic order, almost wholly using time-stratigraphic names as far as the Devonian period, where there comes in a mixed system involving time, rock type, and the location of the deposits.

The US map is divided into units on the basis of stratigraphic age. Within some of the stratigraphic intervals the igneous and metamorphic rocks are named by their lithology. There is, in addition, an attempt to divide the sedimentary rocks of a particular stratigraphic age according to their overall environment of formation, that is, whether they are 'eugeosynclinal' (marine, with volcanic material) or 'continental' deposits. Close attention has therefore to be paid to the letter symbols and subscripts of each of the numerous subdivisions. This explains why, given the size of the country involved, the legend has to occupy its own sheet.

2.2 Interpretation of the maps: geology and relief

Let us begin our attempt to see how these geological maps are more than just arrays of fine colours by interpreting some aspects of how geology and topography interact. Starting with the US map (Plate 2), and the region centred on long. 110° 30′, lat. 43° 0′, those parts to the northeast are drained by rivers that flow towards the northeast and the southwest district is drained by southwest-flowing rivers. This drainage divide suggests a central area of upstanding relief, and because many of the rivers originate in small, adjacent but isolated, lakes, it is probably an area of irregular topography.

The reason for an area having much higher relief than adjacent ground may well be something to do with contrasting rock types. Here, the apparently higher area is made of granites and gneisses (Wg and Wgn), which are likely to be more durable than the surrounding Tertiary (Tec) materials. However, toughness alone might not account for the relative elevation of such ancient, Precambrian rocks, which could have been subject to erosion for a very long time. The thick black lines on the map indicate major faults, and it would seem likely that some of these, such as the ones to the SW of the granite–gneiss area, indicate sites of uplift of the masses of resistant rocks. Note that one major fault has been shown as a dotted line where its presence is suspected but covered by a veneer of Tertiary and Quaternary deposits. (In fact, this region is the heavily glaciated Wind River Mountains, which are thought to have been uplifted in Tertiary times along a very major fault.)

In contrast to the last instance, the region shown in pink (Qu) centred on long. 113° 0′, lat. 43° 15′, shows no drainage at all, except at its margins. Volcanic rocks occupying such a large area are likely to be bedded volcaniclastic rocks or lava flows. Such recent rocks, especially in view of the drainage being off the flanks of the area, may well be lying horizontally. Any rainfall presumably dissipates through pore spaces and underground fissures, which may be common if the rocks are lavas. A picture emerges from the map of a very flat, featureless, volcanic plain, lacking in surface water. (It is the Snake River Plateau. It is no coincidence that this flat empty area of lava flows was used for carrying out the early experiments on nuclear power.)

2.3 Map patterns and geological structure

2.3.1 Dipping formations

On the UK map (Plate 1) divisions 70–74 are units of successively younger Ordovician and Silurian ages. They are sedimentary rocks, and so were deposited, back in Lower Palaeozoic times, one on top of the other in a roughly horizontal arrangement (Fig. 2.1a). During the time since the Silurian, the sediments have been buried, lithified, and eventually brought back to the earth's surface. But if we were to journey from, say, the town of Llandovery [SN7734] to Trecastle [SN8829] we would travel not across the one unit that happens to be at the present erosion level but successively across all five units. The most likely explanation for this is that the rock units have been tilted, as depicted in Fig. 2.1b. It shows which way the beds of rock must be inclined, for any other direction of tilt would not explain the arrangement seen on the map. It is a general rule that rocks become successively younger in the direction towards which they are inclined. We do not know anything yet, though, about the magnitude of the tilting. The rocks could be gently or steeply inclined, or even rotated to vertical.

On a journey from Abbeycwmhir [SO0571] to Knighton [SO2971] the same five units are also successively crossed. but over a longer distance. It seems that each unit occupies a greater area at the land surface. One immediate explanation for this is simply that the units are thicker here than to the southwest – there could have been more of the sediment deposited. The continuing increase in the width of each formation as we look further to the north could suggest a progressive increase in sediment thickness northwards. However, this could be illusory. The units west of Knighton have to be tilted, as explained in the previous paragraph, but the angle might only be small. If the units near Abbeycwmhir are inclined more steeply than those near Llandovery, then, as Figs 2.1b and 2.1c show, they would appear narrower at the earth's surface, even if they have similar thicknesses. It may be that both factors are operating; the units could be both thicker and less inclined. It is difficult to gauge on small-scale maps the relative importance of each factor.

If the journey eastwards were continued between Bosbury [SO6943] and Great Malvern [SO7745], the units would be crossed in a very short distance. The reduced width at the surface is so marked that it would seem likely that both the effects mentioned above are operating. The formations are probably relatively thin, and may well be steeply inclined. That the environment of deposition of the sediments was somewhat different here is supported by the development of a limestone unit (coloured turquoise on the map) between divisions 73 and 74. Notice also that the units are here crossed in the reverse sequence from the previous traverses – they become successively younger from east to west. This does not account for their narrowness but it does tell us that the beds here are inclined towards the west (Fig. 2.1d).

Any tilting from the horizontal shown by beds of rock is referred to as the angle of dip, and the direction towards which the beds are inclined is known as the direction of dip. At right angles to the dip direction is the direction of strike, often just called the 'strike' of the beds. These important concepts of strike and dip will be defined and examined more rigorously in section 4.2. For the moment, we can simply note that the strike direction is reflected by the outcrop patterns, at least on small-scale maps. For example, the rock units just discussed around Great Malvern [SO7745] dip to the west, and the strike, at right angles to the dip, is N–S, as shown by the N–S arrangement of the outcrops. At Llandovery [SN7734], the outcrops have a NE–SW pattern, indicating a strike in that direction (Fig. 2.1e). The dip is to the southeast.

2.3.2 Unconformities

Along an irregular line running southwestwards from long. 110° 20′, lat. 44° 20′ on the US map (Plate 2), NW–SE striking outcrops of rocks, varying in age from Precambrian (W) through Upper Paleozoic to Cretaceous (K), are obliquely cut across by the Quaternary volcanics (Qf) of Yellowstone Park. This appearance – referred to as a **discordant relationship** – came about in this case because the latter rocks are younger and were laid down as a series of volcaniclastic rocks and lava flows on a land surface which already consisted of the NW–SE striking Cretaceous and older rocks. The junction therefore represents a period of geological time (between the Cretaceous and the Quaternary) for which no rocks are present.

A discordant junction which represents a period of non-deposition is known as an unconformity (Fig. 2.2a). It is commonly recognisable on a map as an irregular line along which younger rocks appear to truncate older rocks. The rocks above an unconformity are markedly younger than those below, and were laid down on a surface developed on the older rocks. In the present example, the surface was the landscape of Yellowstone at the time the volcanic material was deposited. Where that preserved surface meets today's

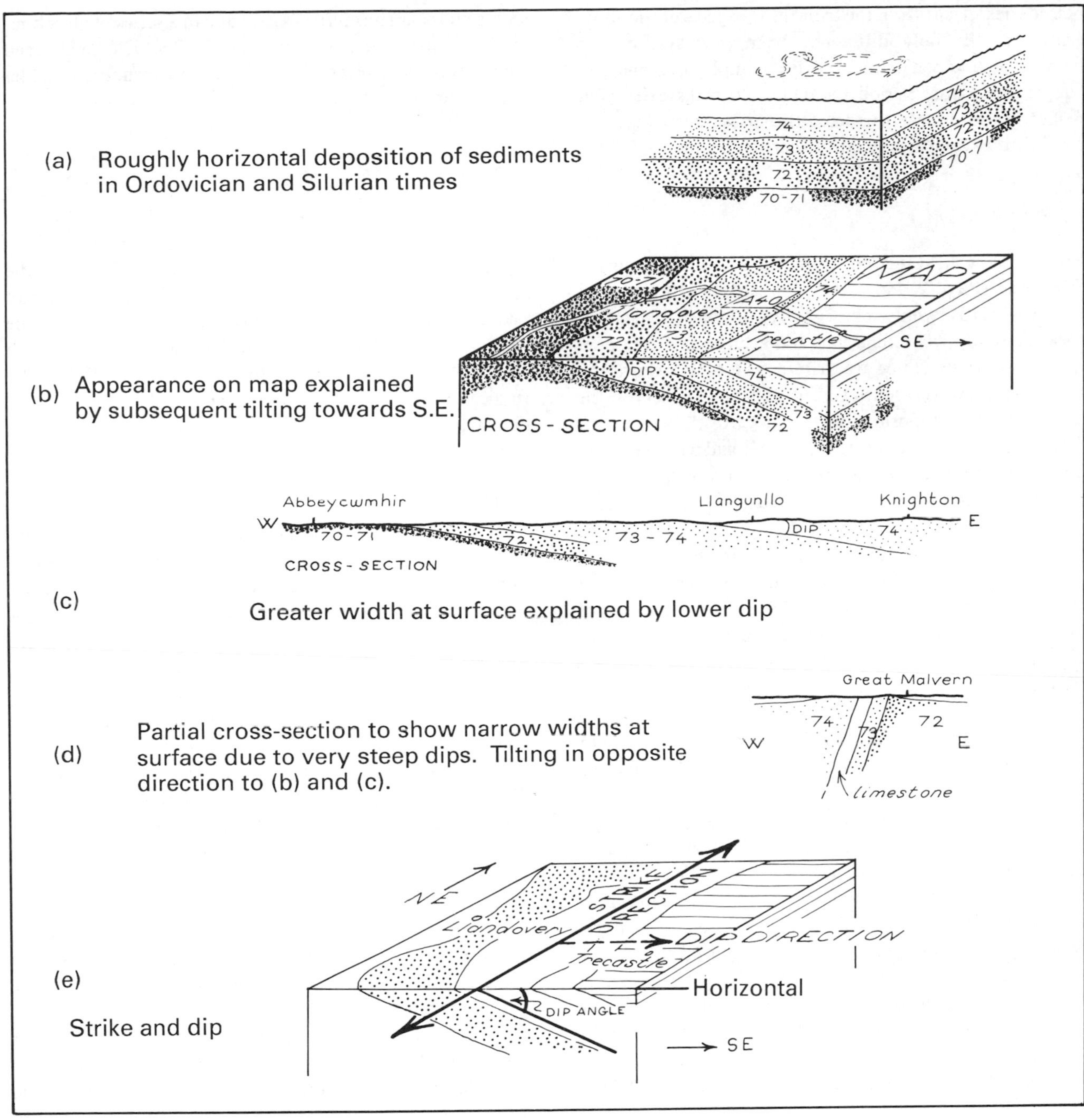
(a) Roughly horizontal deposition of sediments in Ordovician and Silurian times
74
73
72
70-71
(b) Appearance on map explained by subsequent tilting towards S.E.
MAP
70-71
A40
Llandovery
72
73
74
Trecastle
SE
DIP
CROSS - SECTION
Abbeycwmhir
Llangunllo
Knighton
W
E
70-71
72
73 - 74
DIP
CROSS - SECTION
(c)
Greater width at surface explained by lower dip
Great Malvern
(d) Partial cross-section to show narrow widths at surface due to very steep dips. Tilting in opposite direction to (b) and (c).
limestone
NE
STRIKE DIRECTION
Llandovery
DIP DIRECTION
Trecastle
Horizontal
DIP ANGLE
SE
(e)
Strike and dip

Fig. 2.1 Sketches to show aspects of the geology seen on Plate 1, part of the BGS Ten Mile map of the UK.

landscape, a linear trace is formed, as always with the intersection of two surfaces. Thus, on the map we see the **trace of unconformity**.

A further example of an unconformity occurs on the northeast flanks of the Wind River Mountains discussed earlier (section 2.2) around long. 109° 15′, lat. 43° 20′. The Tertiary deposits (coloured yellow) appear to be truncating the Cretaceous and older NW–SE trending units (coloured green, blue, and pink). Just here the Cretaceous and Palaeozoic sequence must be dipping northeast because the units become younger in that direction (see section 2.3.1). The Tertiary material was presumably deposited horizontally on top of the older rocks after they had been tilted and eroded. The resulting discordant junction therefore represents a span of geological time unrepresented by any rocks (Fig.2.2a).

Notice that these lines of unconformity are drawn on the map with the same thickness as ordinary geological boundaries. Apart from the truncating aspects of the above examples, the only difference from normal junctions between sedimentary rock units is the implication of a time gap, a substantial period for which no rocks exist. The reader has to deduce this from the map and its key. Unconformities are considered further in chapter 7.

2.3.3 *Folded rocks*

From Yellowtail Reservoir in the Big Horn Mountains of Wyoming (Plate 2, long. 108° 10′, lat. 45° 10′), a route northeastwards would take us from Upper Palaeozoic rocks across Lower Cretaceous and a succession of Upper Cretaceous units. They are therefore dipping towards the northeast. However, southwest of Yellowtail Reservoir the units dip in the opposite direction towards the southwest. The simplest explanation of this rather sudden reversal of dip direction is that the units are flexed into an upwarp, the reservoir being situated in the middle (see Fig. 2.2b). This idea is supported by the fact that to the northwest of the reservoir the same units curve round on the map to link up the two oppositely inclined sequences. This curving outcrop pattern, with the oldest rocks in the central part of the arc, is characteristic of beds which are unwarped. Where the curvature of the outcrops is complete, to give a circular aspect to the map pattern, the beds may well be forming a dome.

Continuing southwest from Yellowtail Reservoir into the area around the Greybull River, rocks of Tertiary age (TeC) are reached. But then the sequence reverses again and, further southwest, units of Palaeocene (Txc) and progressively older Cretaceous age (uK3, uK2) are crossed. These units, too, curve around, southeast of Worland, to produce an arcuate pattern but here with the youngest rocks in the middle. This is the kind of outcrop pattern associated with downwarped units (Fig. 2.2b). Downwarps on this scale (tens of kilometres or more across) are referred to as **basins**, and the upwarps as **arches** or **domes**. Just as with a dome, a completely formed basin will give a roughly circular pattern, concentric around the centre of the structure. A small-scale example occurs at long. 109° 0′, lat. 43° 30′ and there are several incomplete examples in the vicinity.

This warping of rocks, particularly on a smaller scale, say a few kilometres and less, is known as **folding**. Folds with the oldest rocks in the middle are called **anticlines** and those with the youngest rocks in the middle are called **synclines**. They are detected on maps by the roughly symmetrical reversal of dip direction (Fig. 2.2c). If the crest or trough of the fold structure is inclined to the ground surface, it will produce arcuate outcrop patterns like those mentioned above in the Bighorn Mountains.

To give an example from Plate 1, in E Wales around Llanfyllin [SJ1419], the curving outcrop patterns of Silurian rocks (units 70–74) are due to a series of anticlines and synclines, the crests and troughs of which are inclined towards the southwest. Folded rocks are examined further in chapter 8.

2.3.4 *Faulted rocks*

Faults are fractures in rocks, along which the rocks have been displaced. Materials of different ages can therefore be brought next to each other. Rather like unconformities, the effect of a time gap is produced, indeed the two kinds of structures can be difficult to tell apart. However, where the geological surveyor has decided that the junction between two different units is a fault, it is usual for this to be indicated on the map by some special symbolism. The UK and US maps both do this, on the former by a dot–dash line and on the latter by a heavy line, dotted where concealed by younger deposits.

The fault in Teton County, Wyoming (Plate 2, long. 110° 40′, lat. 43° 40′) brings Precambrian rocks (Wg) next to Quaternary deposits (Q). In view of the rock displacement required to explain this age contrast, this rather isolated fault must be a major one. Moreover, unlike most of the boundaries of the Quaternary outcrops, which are shown to represent normal depositional surfaces, the fact that this boundary is a fault means that the Quaternary deposits themselves have been displaced (Fig. 2.2d). It is therefore a very young fault and conceivably may still be active. (In fact this fault, the Teton Fault, has displaced the Precambrian rocks by over 8 km, continues to produce tremors, and has a profound effect on the landscape.)

Eighty miles to the south, around the Idaho–Wyoming state line (Plate 2, long. 110° 45′, lat. 43° 0′), a closely spaced system of faults interrupts the upper Palaeozoic (blue, uPz) to lower Cretaceous (green, lK) succession. Most of the normal geological boundaries that are shown indicate an overall dip to the west (Mesozoic rocks follow the upper Palaeozoic westwards). But towards the west of the area, instead of the upper Palaeozoic rocks being at depth and therefore not shown on the map, a number of these faults have displaced the Palaeozoic rocks back to the surface. Such systems of closely spaced faults which can bring older rocks up from depth are typical of what are called thrust belts, which are looked at more closely in section 10.2. Notice two points regarding the age of these faults: (a) in places the faults curve, together with the outcrops of the rocks, suggesting that the faults themselves have been folded; (b) these faults pass underneath deposits of Tertiary and Quaternary age, indicating that movement along the fractures had ceased before Tertiary times. (These are actually contraction (thrust) faults; part of the important Cretaceous-age Idaho-Wyoming thrust belt.) Faults are looked at in more detail in chapters 9 and 10.

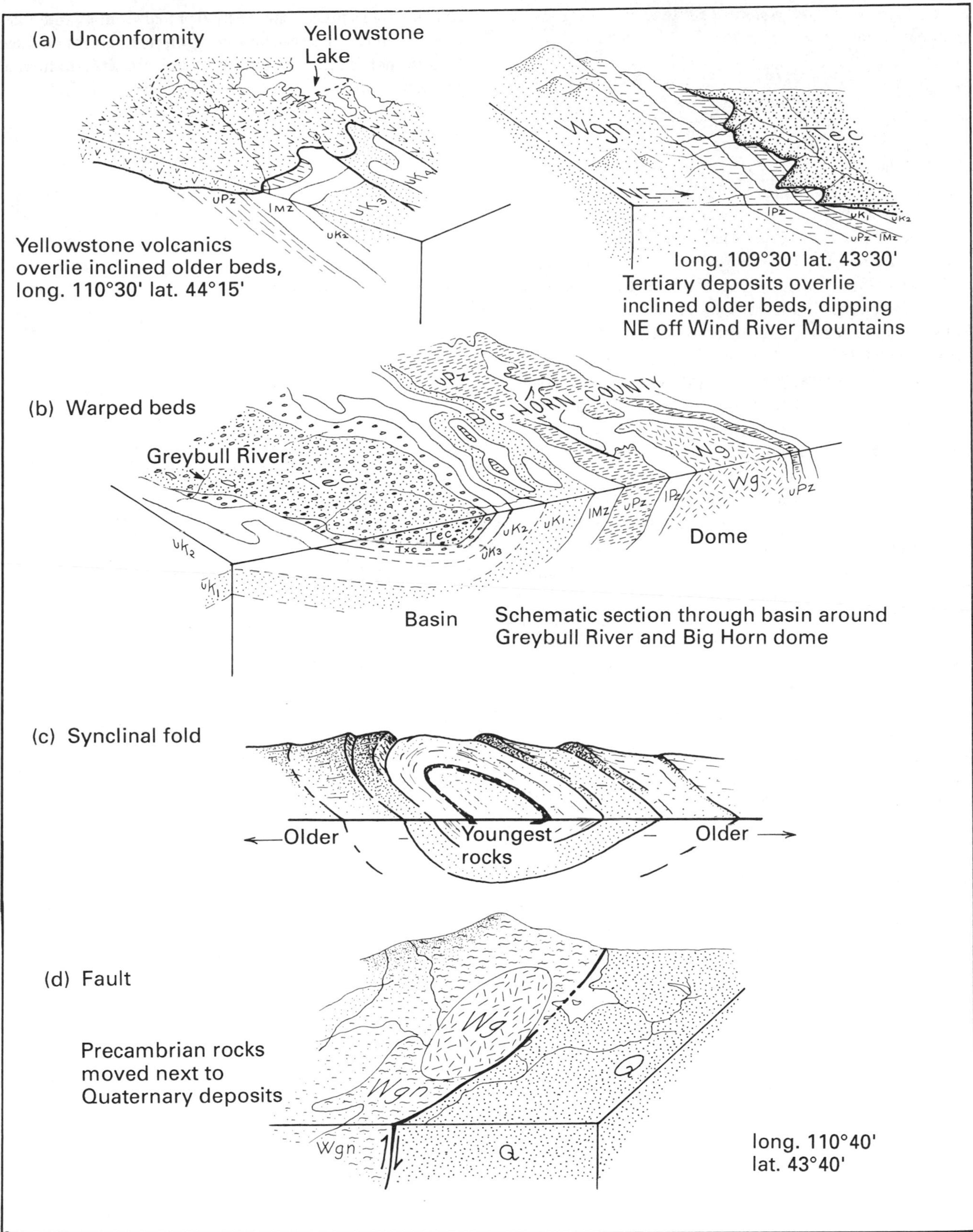
(a) Unconformity
Yellowstone Lake
uPz
lMz
uK2
uK3
uK4
Yellowstone volcanics overlie inclined older beds, long. 110°30' lat. 44°15'
Wgn
Tec
NE
lPz
uK1
uK2
uPz
lMz
long. 109°30' lat. 43°30'
Tertiary deposits overlie inclined older beds, dipping NE off Wind River Mountains
(b) Warped beds
Greybull River
Tec
BIG HORN COUNTY
uPz
Wg
uK2
uK1
lMz
uPz
lPz
Wg
uPz
Txc
uK3
uK1
Dome
Basin
Schematic section through basin around Greybull River and Big Horn dome
(c) Synclinal fold
Older
Youngest rocks
Older
(d) Fault
Wg
Wgn
Q
Precambrian rocks moved next to Quaternary deposits
Wgn
Q
long. 110°40' lat. 43°40'

Fig. 2.2 Sketches to show aspects of the geology seen on Plate 2, part of the USGS 1:2 500 000 map of the USA.

2.3.5 Igneous rocks and geological histories

On Plate 1, the long, narrow strips of basalt and dolerite around Dolgellau [SH7317] parallel the nearby sedimentary and volcaniclastic rocks and are therefore likely to be the concordant igneous bodies known as **sills**. In contrast, the igneous rocks on Plate 2 around long. 110° 20′, lat. 46° 10′ outcrop with no relation to the surrounding rocks. These must be the discordant sheets called **dykes**. In this example, they are **radial dykes**, arranged like spokes around a hub of igneous material.

It is common with igneous rocks to be able to deduce something from a map about their relative ages. For example, the dykes in the last example cut across Tertiary rocks, and must therefore have been intruded at some more recent geological time. The principle that a geological feature that cuts another must be the younger of the two, often called **cross-cutting relationships**, is a fundamental one in deducing geological histories. It is by no means confined to igneous rocks. For example, the concentric outcrops centred on long. 106° 15′, lat. 42° 10′ become younger outwards, and are therefore folded in a dome form. However, they are also faulted, the movement of the units being recorded by the offsets of the outcrops along the fault lines. But it is the *folded* units that are faulted, that is, the folding must have preceded the faulting of the rocks. An example of deducing information on the relative ages of faults was given at the end of section 2.3.4. Interpretation of the sequence in which events took place is an important aspect of geological map work and is explored further in chapter 2.

2.4 Conclusion

Even at this preliminary stage, we have begun to see the variety of things that can be interpreted from a geological map. From the relationships between rocks and structures of different ages, we can interpret something of the geological history of the area. Some idea of the three-dimensional nature of the rocks can be obtained, especially by noting particular outcrop patterns. All these concepts will be explored more fully in succeeding chapters. We begin by considering in more detail one of the most powerful and useful aspects of large-scale geological maps: the accurate representation of rocks in three dimensions.

2.5 Summary of chapter

1. Uncontoured geological maps may yield information on geology and topography, especially from drainage patterns.
2. Rocks become successively younger in the direction in which they are dipping.
3. Relatively narrow outcrops may reflect steeper dips or thinner units, or some combination of both.
4. Unconformities represent missing stratigraphy, and may appear as discordant junctions between units of different geological ages.
5. Folds produce symmetrically repeated outcrop patterns. The units become younger outwards from the centre of domes and anticlines, and older outwards from the centre of basins and synclines.
6. Faults, fractures along which the rocks have been displaced, are commonly depicted on maps by a particular line symbol.
7. The form of igneous bodies, such as dykes and sills, may be deduced from maps.
8. Aspects of the geological history of an area can be interpreted from maps.

3 The three-dimensional aspect: structure contours

3.1 Introduction

The problem of representing three-dimensional things on a flat piece of paper has exercised minds for many years, nowhere more so than with regard to maps. Many atlases begin by discussing the question of how to represent the spherical earth in a book. A similar problem is the portrayal of the undulations – the relief – of the earth's surface. Early map-makers attempted to depict relief by drawing humpy little hills, often wildly exaggerated in height and steepness. Better pictorial methods gradually evolved, such as shading and hachuring, but in general these are unsuited to geological maps. By far the most successful means yet devised are topographic contour lines. These are now common on larger scale geological maps, say 1:100 000 or larger. Figures 1.4 and 1.5 illustrated the concept of topographic contours, and Fig. 1.6 showed how to construct topographic profiles from them. It is important that you are completely familiar with topographic contours.

This chapter is concerned with applying all these principles to *underground* surfaces. It begins by emphasising the similarity between topographic contours and those drawn for underground surfaces, called structure contours. The chapter explains how structure contours are derived, and illustrates their use. Although these days the routine construction and manipulation of structure contours are increasingly being carried out by computer methods, the understanding of the three-dimensional principles behind them remains fundamental.

3.2 The nature of structure contours

Contour lines can be used to represent on a piece of paper any three-dimensional surface, not necessarily the relief of the land. The contours drawn in Fig. 3.1a could equally represent the shape of the earth's surface or, say, the surface* of a rock formation. Although the formation may be underground, it still has an altitude, and the contour lines simply join the points on either its top or bottom surface that have equal height.

It is possible, therefore, to draw on a map contour lines which portray not the land surface but the position and undulations of some underground surface. Such contour lines are called **structure contours**. Without labels, the lines on Fig. 3.1a could be topographic contours representing a hill, but they could equally well be structure contours depicting a map unit that has been upwarped into a dome. The structure contours sketched in Fig. 3.1b are of a surface which has the form of a basin, and in Fig. 3.1c they depict a dome. Note that because the dome in Fig. 3.1c is deeply buried, the altitudes are negative with respect to sea-level.

If the structure contours of a surface are known, a cross-section can readily be constructed, in an exactly analogous way to a topographic profile (Fig. 1.6). Instead of marking on a strip of paper where the *topographic* contours meet the line of the section, the position and altitude of the *structure* contours are marked and transferred to the section grid. This has been done to produce the cross-sections shown in Figs 3.1b and 3.1c. Some published maps include structure contours, normally of a surface that is considered representative of the structure of the area, but it usually falls to the map reader to construct them. Structure contours can be drawn for any geological surface, for example, a fault or the boundaries of an igneous intrusion.

3.3 Examples of structure contours on maps

Figure 3.2a is a structure contour map of the Ekofisk oilfield, the first of the giant oilfields to be discovered in the North Sea. The surface for which the structure contours are drawn is the top of the rock unit which contains most of the oil. The contours show this formation to be in the form of a deeply buried dome, slightly elongate in a

* Note that the word 'surface' has two slightly different meanings in the map context. In addition to meaning *land* surface – the outer surface of the earth – the term also applies to the boundary of *any* geological body or curving geological plane, and these can be underground. Thus geologists talk both about 'the beds outcropping *at* the land surface', the ground on which we live, and 'the outcrop *of* a surface', such as the boundary of a map unit or a fault.

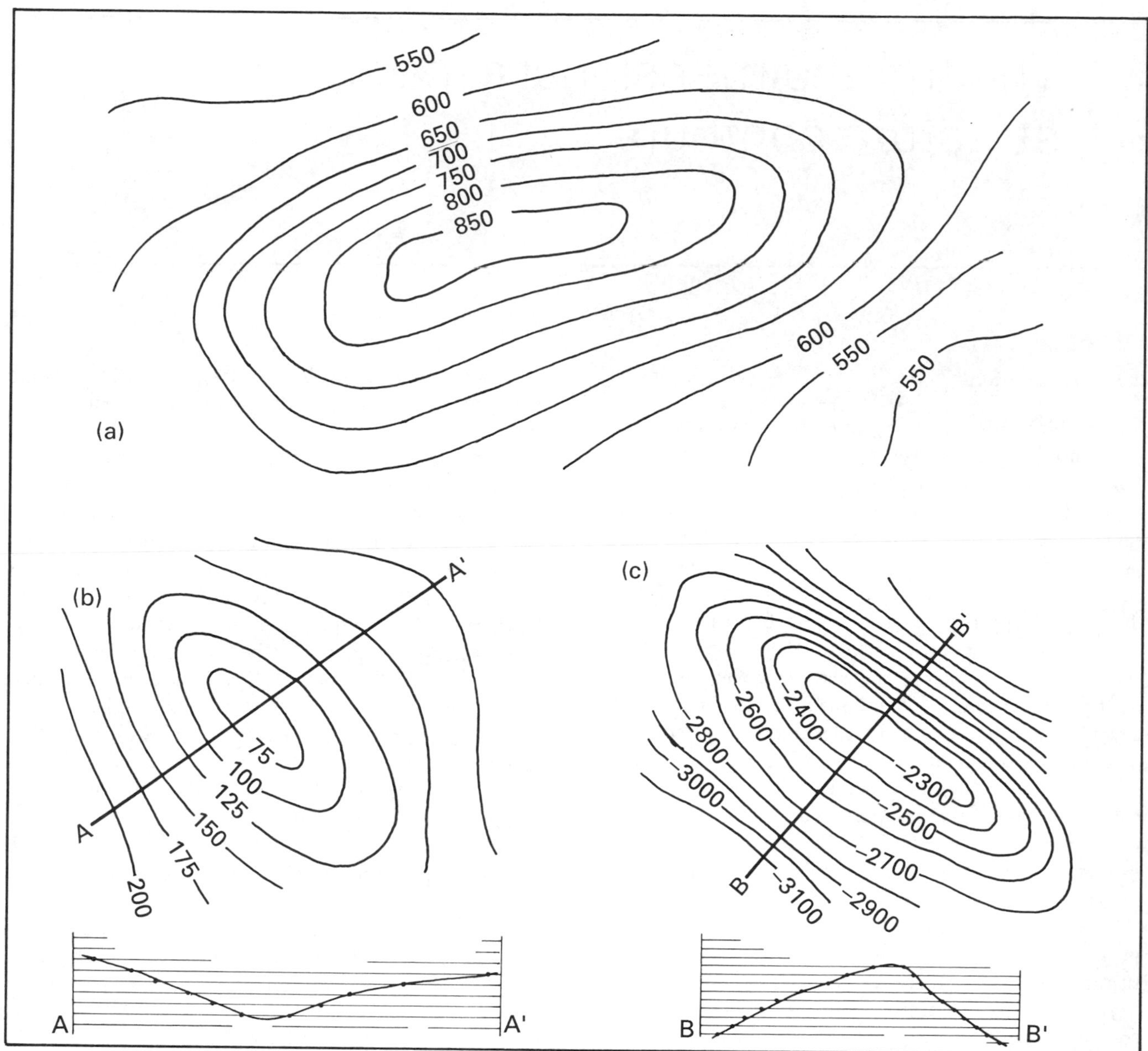
550
600
650
700
750
800
850
600
550
550
(a)
(b)
A'
A
75
100
125
150
175
200
(c)
B'
B
2300
2400
2500
2600
2700
2800
2900
3000
3100
A
A'
B
B'

Fig. 3.1 The similarity between topographic and structure contours. The lines in (a), if they are regarded as topographic contours, represent a hill. Equally they could be regarded as structure contours representing a dome-shaped geological surface, buried beneath some higher land surface. The lines in (b), without information on whether they are topographic or structure contours, could represent either a depression in the land surface or a buried structure of basinal form. The lines in (c), although similar in form to topographic contours representing a hill, are likely in view of their negative altitudes, to be structure contours representing a subsurface dome. In practice, different line symbolisms are used on maps to differentiate the two kinds of contours.

N–S direction. It is in the upper part of this dome that the oil is trapped.

Figure 3.2b is an inclined view of the structure which may help you see how the structure contours are representing the dome. It is vital that you become used to visualising structure contours in three dimensions. Map 1 provides an exercise. Figure 3.2b also shows the location of the main oil wells, positioned to penetrate the oil in the crest of the dome. Perhaps it is becoming apparent to you why structure contours are of such value in applied geology. In fact, it was for practical reasons that the device was originated in the anthracite fields of Pennsylvania.

Figure 3.3 illustrates an unusual practical use of structure contours, as well as a very irregular contour pattern

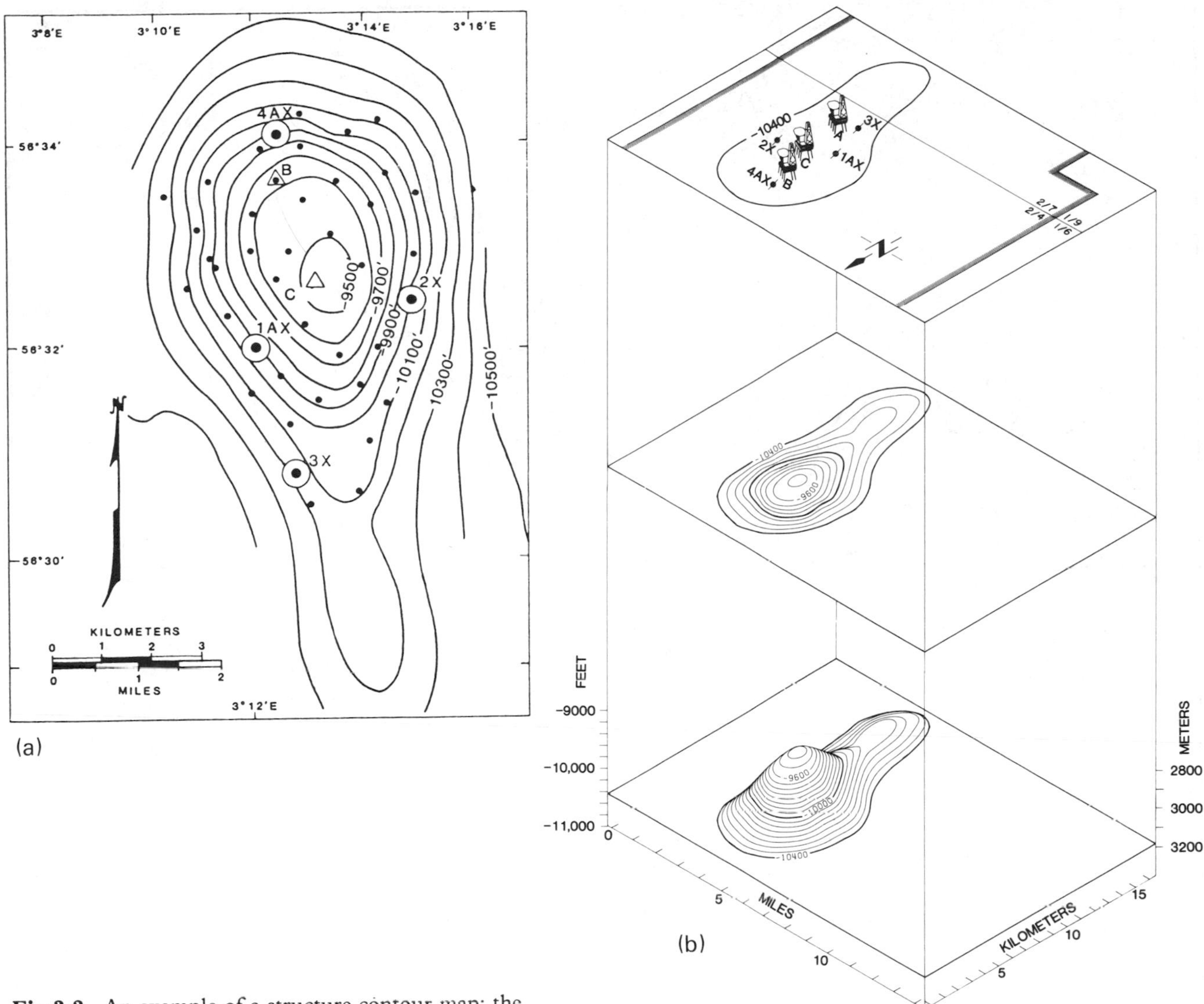
3°8'E
3°10'E
3°14'E
3°16'E
56°34'
56°32'
56°30'
3°12'E
KILOMETERS
MILES
4AX
B
C
1AX
2X
3X
-9500'
-9700'
-9900'
-10100'
-10300'
-10500'
(a)
FEET
-9000
-10,000
-11,000
METERS
2800
3000
3200
MILES
KILOMETERS
(b)

Fig.3.2 An example of a structure contour map: the Ekofisk oilfield, North Sea. (a) Structure contour map of the top of the oil-bearing formation. (b) Oblique view of the form of the contoured surface (bottom level of drawing), in comparison with the structure contours (drawn at some arbitrary middle level) and the sea-bed (top level). Reproduced with modification from van der Bark and Thomas (1980), by permission of the American Association of Petroleum Geologists.

(see section 4.2 for the reasons for the irregularities). In the area south of Bordeaux, France, the quality of the grapes depends upon the soil, which in turn depends upon the depth to a particular limestone, known as the Calcaire à Astéries. Better wine is likely to be made where the limestone is buried by no more than a few metres. The structure contours for the top surface of the limestone allow, by comparison with a map showing topographic altitudes, determination of the depth to the limestone at any locality of interest. This provides an initial guide to the likely value of a specific locality for wine-making.

3.4 Structure contours derived from borehole/well information

But how are structure contours known if the surface they represent is out of sight underground? The most common method of deriving them, especially in industry, is to use information obtained by drilling (e.g. Bishop, 1960). If the elevation of the land surface where the drilling starts is known, the depth at which the bedding surface of interest is encountered can be measured, and, by subtraction, its elevation derived. Such boreholes, usually called wells in

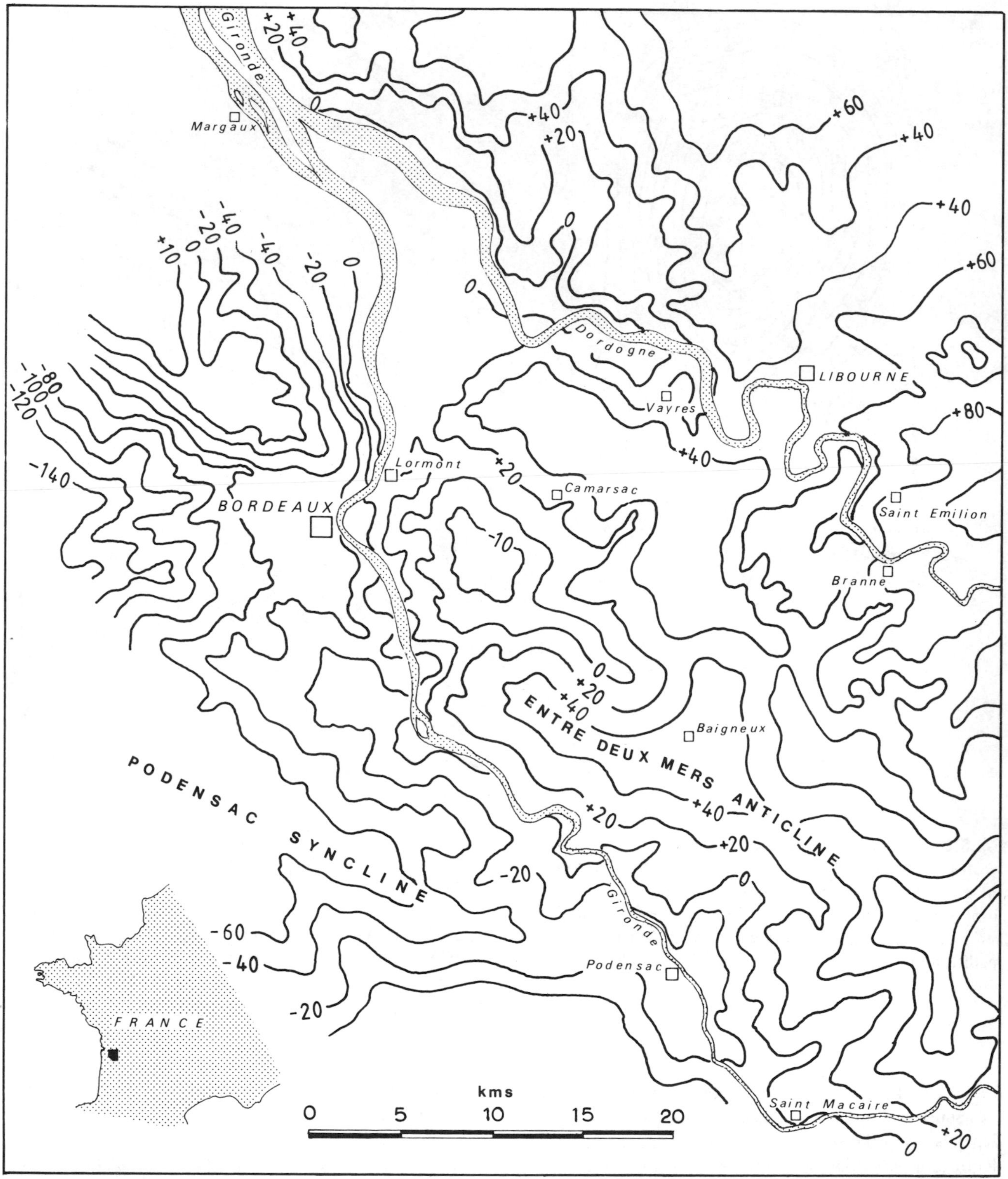
Gironde
Margaux
Dordogne
LIBOURNE
Vayres
Lormont
Camarsac
BORDEAUX
Saint Emilion
Branne
Baigneux
ENTRE DEUX MERS ANTICLINE
PODENSAC SYNCLINE
Podensac
Saint Macaire
FRANCE
kms
0 5 10 15 20

Fig. 3.3 An example of a structure contour map: the Calcaire à Astéries, Entre-Deux-Mers, France. Note the shallow-burial levels of the contoured surface. Reasons for the irregularity of the contours are mentioned in section 4.2. Based on Vigneaux and Leneuf (1980).

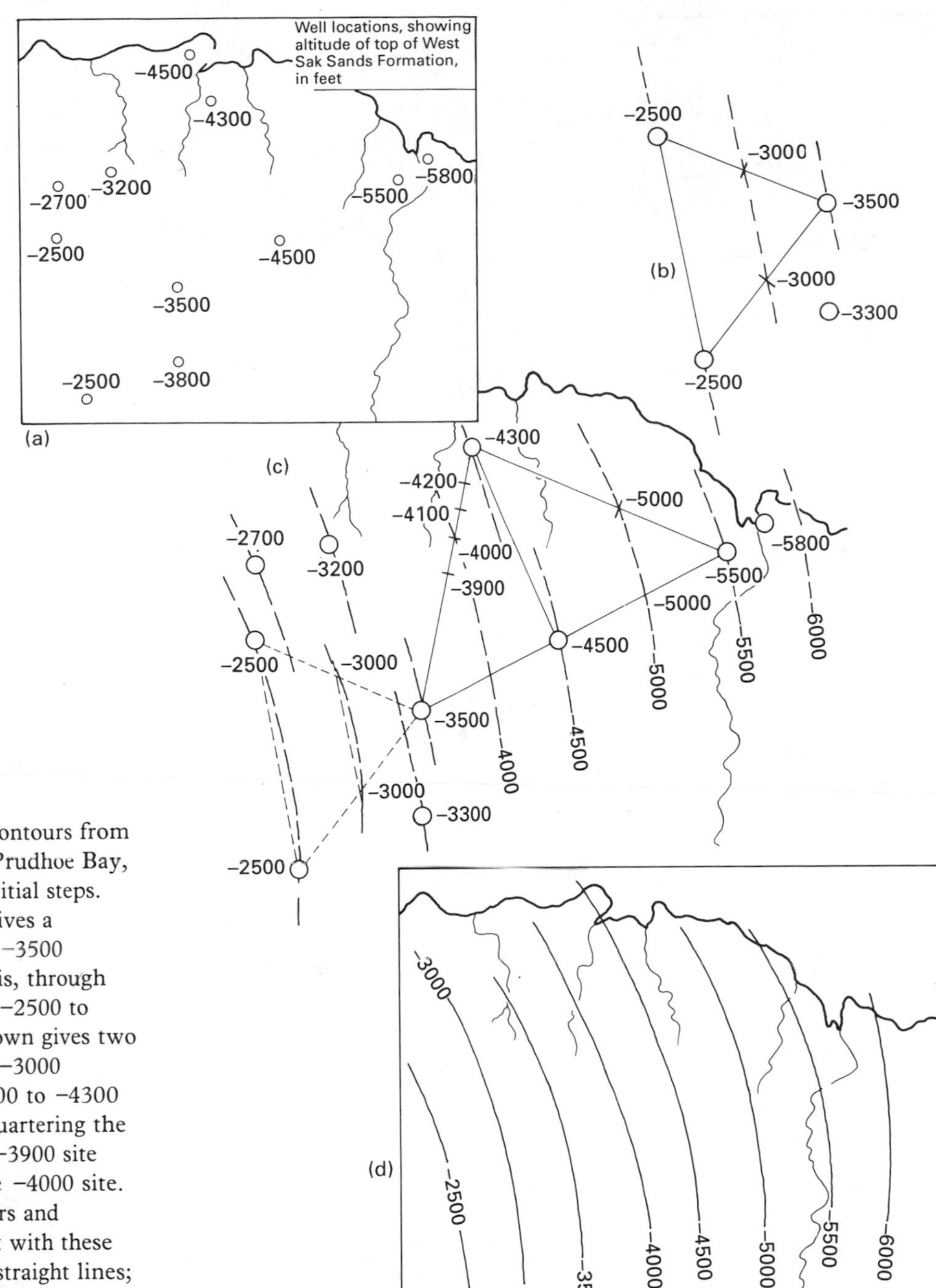
Well locations, showing altitude of top of West Sak Sands Formation, in feet
-4500
-4300
-5800
-2700
-3200
-5500
-2500
-4500
-3500
-2500
-3800
(a)
-2500
-3000
-3500
(b)
-3000
-3300
-2500
-4300
(c)
-4200
-4100
-5000
-2700
-3200
-4000
-5500
-5800
-3900
-5000
-6000
-2500
-3000
-4500
-3500
-5000
-5500
-4000
-4500
-3000
-3300
-2500
-3000
(d)
-2500
-4000
-4500
-5000
-5500
-6000
-3500

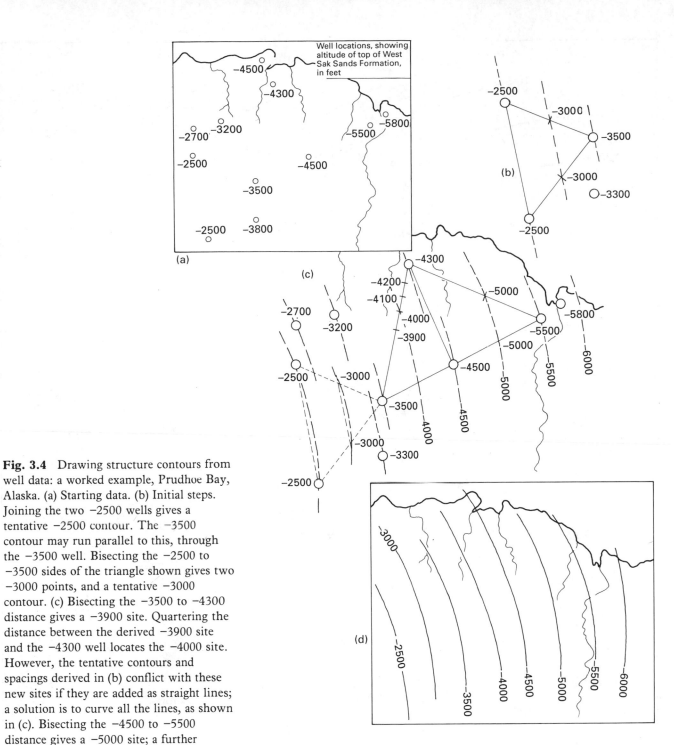

Fig. 3.4 Drawing structure contours from well data: a worked example, Prudhoe Bay, Alaska. (a) Starting data. (b) Initial steps. Joining the two −2500 wells gives a tentative −2500 contour. The −3500 contour may run parallel to this, through the −3500 well. Bisecting the −2500 to −3500 sides of the triangle shown gives two −3000 points, and a tentative −3000 contour. (c) Bisecting the −3500 to −4300 distance gives a −3900 site. Quartering the distance between the derived −3900 site and the −4300 well locates the −4000 site. However, the tentative contours and spacings derived in (b) conflict with these new sites if they are added as straight lines; a solution is to curve all the lines, as shown in (c). Bisecting the −4500 to −5500 distance gives a −5000 site; a further −5000 point is derived by dividing the −4300 to −5500 distance into twelfths, and hence the −5000 contour. Parallel to this, presumably, is the −5500 contour and, beyond the −5800 well, the −6000 contour. (d) Completed map, omitting well data but showing structure contours at 500 ft intervals. Base data highly simplified from Jamieson *et al.* (1980), by permission of the American Association of Petroleum Geologists.

the oil industry, are important sources of much subsurface information. Of course, to assess a buried undulating surface with any accuracy, many holes would be needed with interpolation between the known values. Figure 3.4 is a worked example, and Map 2 provides an exercise. Any other available information will be added in to help control the accuracy of the structure contours. In oil exploration, especially, the data from seismic sections will be included.

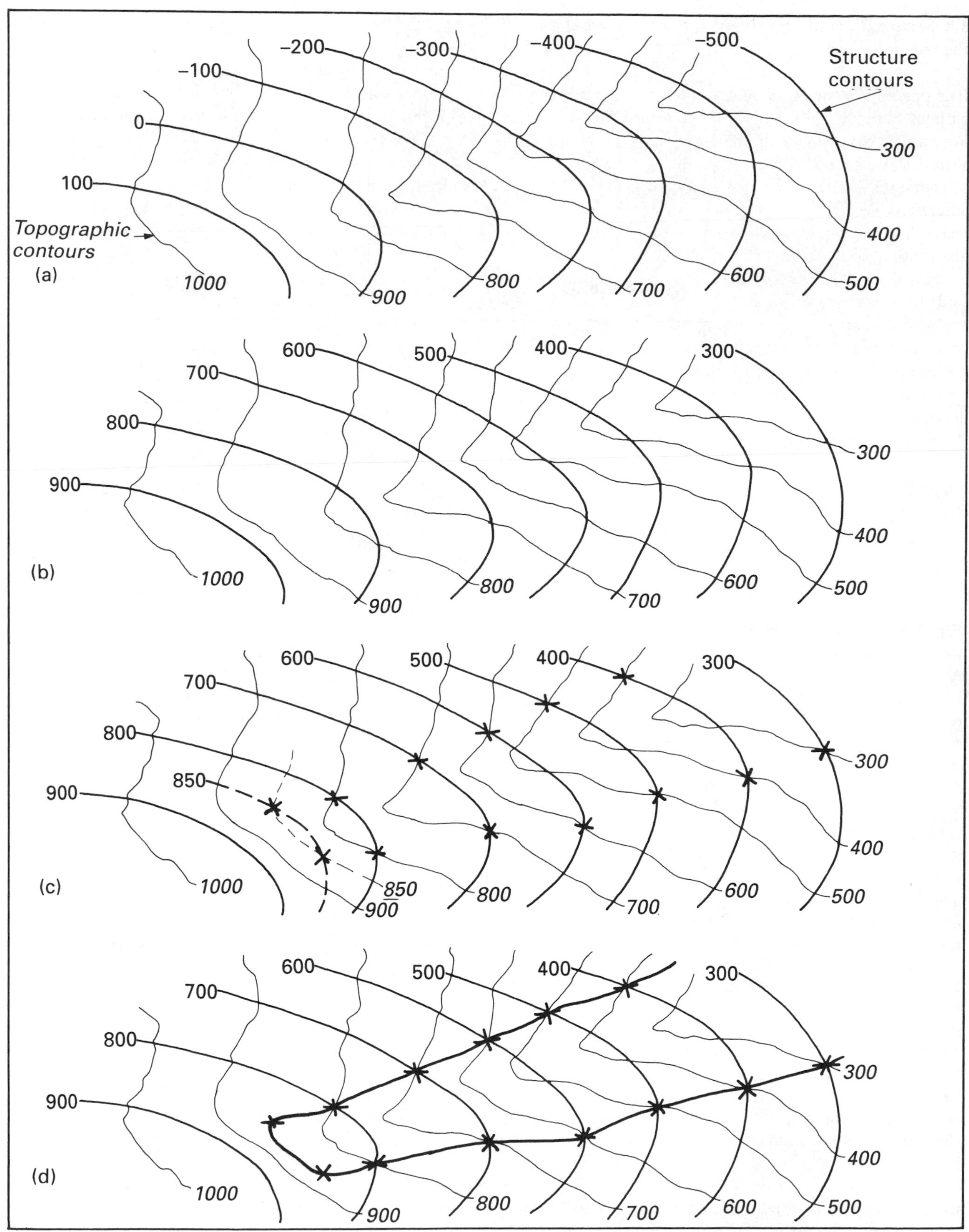

Structure contours
Topographic contours
(a)
(b)
(c)
(d)

Fig. 3.5 The relationship between topographic contours (narrow lines), structure contours (medium lines) and outcrop (broad lines). Section 3.5 explains this figure in detail.

3.5 Structure contours derived from topography: the theory

It is possible to construct contours for near-surface rocks without borehole information, if the formation outcrops. For this, it is necessary to know the various topographic altitudes at which the unit reaches the land surface. This, of course, is exactly what is shown on a geological map. Therefore, this technique is much used, both in academic research and commercial work. In fact, the three-dimensional thinking that the method involves is relevant to many kinds of subsurface work. However, beginners can find the concepts difficult. Therefore, the following explanation starts with a broader consideration of the problem and develops the method step-by-step.

Topographic contours and structure contours both work on the principle of connecting points of equal elevation, differing merely in the particular surfaces they represent. They can be shown together on a single map. In Fig. 3.5a the topographic contours are depicting a land surface ranging between 300 and 1000 m in elevation, whereas the structure contours are showing a curved formation boundary at an altitude of between −500 and 100 m. The formation surface is therefore underground. You should look at Fig. 3.5a and make sure you can see in your mind's eye the two separate surfaces represented: the land surface and the formation at depth.

Figure 3.5b shows a rather similar situation – exactly the same land surface, and structure contours for a curved formation surface – but there is an important difference from Fig. 3.5a. The particular formation boundary shown, although of the same shape as before, is at a higher altitude and so is less deeply buried. In fact, in some places the topographic contours and the structure contours intersect at precisely the same value of altitude. Where this is the case, the formation surface cannot be buried at all. The formation will actually outcrop at the earth's surface. Figure 3.5c is exactly the same as Fig. 3.5b except that it includes the points where the contours are showing that the formation boundary must outcrop.

The values of the contours given on the map depend on the contour interval; there may well be intermediate elevations where the bed also reaches the surface. Figure 3.5c shows in addition the interpolated 850 m contours, and hence further points where the bed would be expected to outcrop. Figure 3.5d shows the logical extension of this – *all* the points where the bedding surface should reach the land surface. These merge together to form a linear trace. This line is the trace of where the bedding intersects with the land surface: it is the *outcrop* of that bedding surface. Thus, by knowing the structure contours for a geological surface and the topographic contours we have predicted what should be the outcrop of that surface. This is a procedure which finds some use in field surveying (section 13.2), but it is a variation on this approach that allows us to make the more valuable construction of deriving structure contours from topography.

For most purposes it is much more useful to construct not the outcrop from known structure contours and topography, but structure contours from known outcrop and topography, for these last two factors are available at the land surface. It is possible for just the same reasons as developed above. Figure 3.6a shows a small part of the outcrop of a geological surface and it shows topographic contours. Figure 3.6b shows locations through which the 200, 300, and 400 m structure contours must pass, and Fig. 3.6c represents the only way in which the structure contours can be drawn satisfactorily in this example. Section 3.6 discusses further why this is the only possible path. (An alternative interpretation involving all the boundaries being wholly vertical is also possible here, but would normally be identifiable if more of the map were seen.)

A large-scale geological map will usually supply the information on topography and outcrop, and so in principle we can construct on it structure contours for surfaces of interest. We are therefore in a position to predict *from a map*, the three-dimensional arrangement of an outcropping formation. Imagine the practical applications of this: a hydrogeologist can derive the location and form of an aquifer; a mining geologist can estimate the length of tunnel or drill-hole necessary to reach the material of value; an engineering geologist can assess the nature of the rocks he is considering excavating for a building foundation. If we derive structure contours for the top and bottom of a formation of commercial value, we will be able to calculate its volume, that is, we can estimate reserves. We have arrived at one of the great practical uses of geological maps.

3.6 Structure contours derived from topography: the practice

Begin by locating on the map the outcrop of the surface that is to be contoured. If you are interested in the top of a formation, make sure you are dealing with the top surface and not the base! The top will be adjacent to the next youngest formation, and the dip direction of the unit, if it is known, will be towards it (section 2.3.1).

Look for places where the outcrop of the surface crosses topographic contours, and start your construction in an area where there are plenty of intersections. Leave until last those areas where there are few intersections and therefore least control on the route of the structure contours. Where the outcrop crosses or meets a topographic contour, you know the surface must be at the same altitude as that topographic contour. If you can locate two or more reasonably close intersections with the same altitude, you can tentatively connect them to produce the structure contour for that altitude.

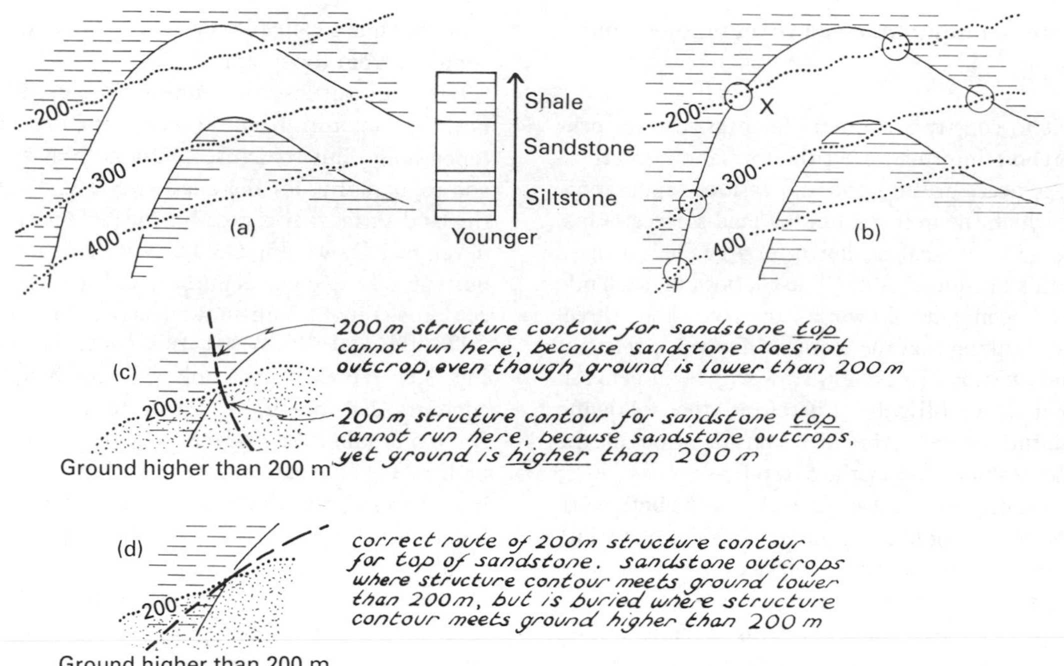
200
300
400
(a)
Shale
Sandstone
Siltstone
Younger
200
X
300
400
(b)
(c)
200
Ground higher than 200 m
200m structure contour for sandstone top cannot run here, because sandstone does not outcrop, even though ground is lower than 200m
200m structure contour for sandstone top cannot run here, because sandstone outcrops, yet ground is higher than 200m
(d)
200
Ground higher than 200 m
correct route of 200m structure contour for top of sandstone. sandstone outcrops where structure contour meets ground lower than 200m, but is buried where structure contour meets ground higher than 200 m

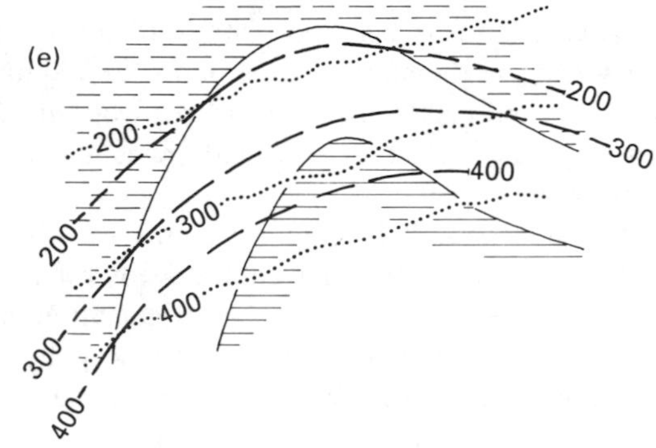
(e)
200
300
400
200
300
400
200
300
400

Fig. 3.6 Constructing structure contours from topography and outcrop. (a) Portion of a hypothetical geological map, showing topographic contours (dotted) and the outcrop of a sandstone unit. The top of the sandstone is to be contoured. (b) Preliminary steps. Reference to the stratigraphic sequence shown in the key enables the *top* of the sandstone to be located on the map. Circles indicate where the altitude of the top of unit is known, from intersections with topographic contours: the structure contours will pass through these circles. Consider the circle at X. At first it may seem that there are two possible routes for the 200 m structure contour to pass through the outcrop/200 m topographic contour intersection, as illustrated in (c) and (d). However, the route shown in (c) is not compatible with the map information, and only the route shown in (d) can be correct. (e) shows the 200, 300 and 400 m structure contours completed from the map information.

It may seem at first that there are several courses the structure contour could take through the point of known altitude (e.g. see Fig. 3.6b). However, only one of them will correspond with the actual outcrop that is shown on the map (Fig. 3.6d). For example, if the structure contour (drawn for the *top* of a unit) of a certain altitude crosses an intersection into ground of a lower altitude, then the formation that is being contoured will be outcropping there. On the other hand, if the same structure contour enters ground of higher altitude, then the outcrop there will be of material stratigraphically above the contoured formation.

The structure contour of a surface can cross a topographic contour of the same altitude only at a point where that surface outcrops. There is nothing wrong with it crossing topographic contours of higher altitudes, provided the surface at those places is buried. Conversely, it can cross topographic contours of lower altitudes, provided the map shows the surface being contoured to have been eroded away at those points.

Another help in drawing the course of a structure contour is to sketch in lightly some interpolated intermediate altitudes to obtain more control points. In most cases the structure contour will curve smoothly; if it makes violent twists it is likely to be wrong, or there has been faulting of the rocks. Experience counts a lot in drawing satisfactory structure contours and there is usually a fair amount of trial and error involved.

When the tentative structure contour seems to be obeying all the topographic and outcrop information in the starting area, it can be firmed up. Further structure contours in that vicinity can then be added, using the same

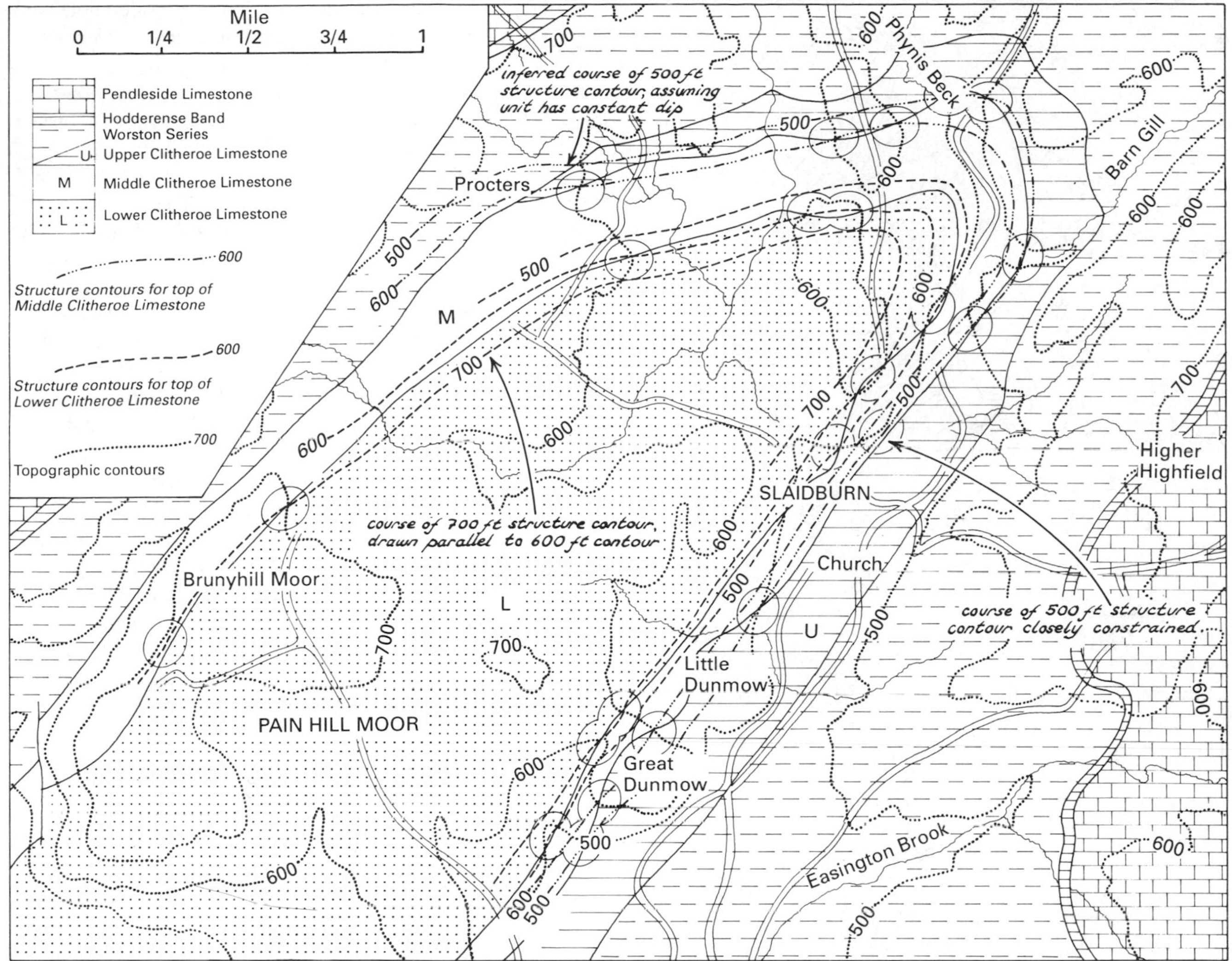
Mile
0
1/4
1/2
3/4
1
Pendleside Limestone
Hodderense Band
Worston Series
Upper Clitheroe Limestone
Middle Clitheroe Limestone
Lower Clitheroe Limestone
Structure contours for top of Middle Clitheroe Limestone
Structure contours for top of Lower Clitheroe Limestone
Topographic contours
inferred course of 500 ft structure contour, assuming unit has constant dip
course of 700 ft structure contour, drawn parallel to 600 ft contour
course of 500 ft structure contour closely constrained
Procters
Phynis Beck
Barn Gill
Higher Highfield
SLAIDBURN
Church
Brunyhill Moor
PAIN HILL MOOR
Little Dunmow
Great Dunmow
Easington Brook

Fig. 3.7 Deriving structure contours from outcrop and topographic contours: a worked example, Slaidburn, Yorkshire. The ellipses enclose areas of information particularly useful in drawing the structure contours. With the contour patterns established, additional subsurface contours, say 400, 300 and 200 ft, could be added to allow subsurface predictions. Geological map based on Parkinson by permission of the Geological Society, on 'The Carboniferous succession in the Slaidburn district, Yorkshire', D. P. Parkinson, *Quart. J. Geol. Soc. London*, **92**, p. 294–331.

methods. Adjacent structure contours tend to be parallel, so that once one is drawn with confidence, it serves as a guide for the nearby ones. They are likely to be evenly spaced. Structure contours can touch each other only where the surface is vertical. These latter guides take priority over any interpolated points, which, after all, are only hypothetical. Developing several adjacent contours together usually gives better results than completing each line in turn. There is normally little point in adding structure contours of *higher* altitude than the present-day land surface, that is, representing where the contoured surface used to be before erosion. On the other hand, adding *subsurface* contours is of immense practical use, as mentioned earlier, in predicting the underground location of materials.

It is usually easiest to work progessively outwards from the starting area, but with some maps it is necessary to sketch the structure contours for several separated areas where there is good topographic control, and then to extrapolate between them. A look at the outcrop patterns on the map should give you some idea of the form of the rocks (section 2.3) and therefore the kind of overall shape the structure contours are likely to have. With practice you will develop your own way of tackling these constructions.

Figure 3.7 shows a worked example of structure contours derived from the intersection of outcrops and topography on a real geological map. Some explanatory comments are added. The important thing when drawing stucture contours is not to try and apply a series of memorised rules, but to *understand* the procedure. Always

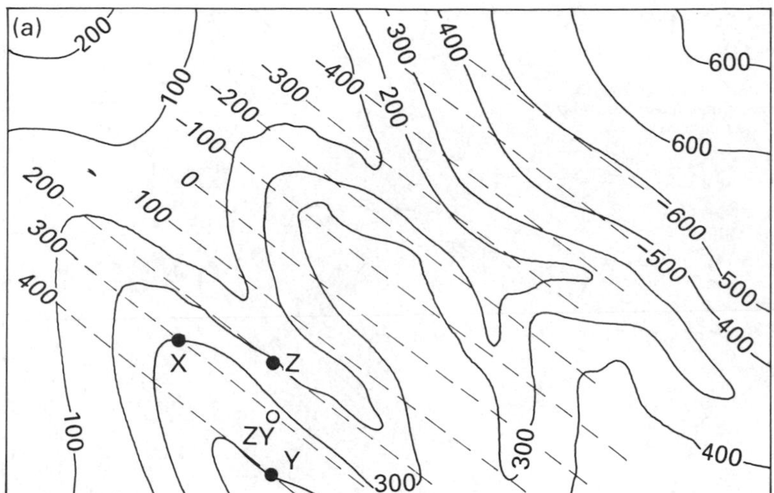
(a)
200
100
-200
-300
-400
300
400
200
-100
0
100
200
300
400
600
600
600
-500
500
400
X
Z
ZY
Y
100
300
300
400

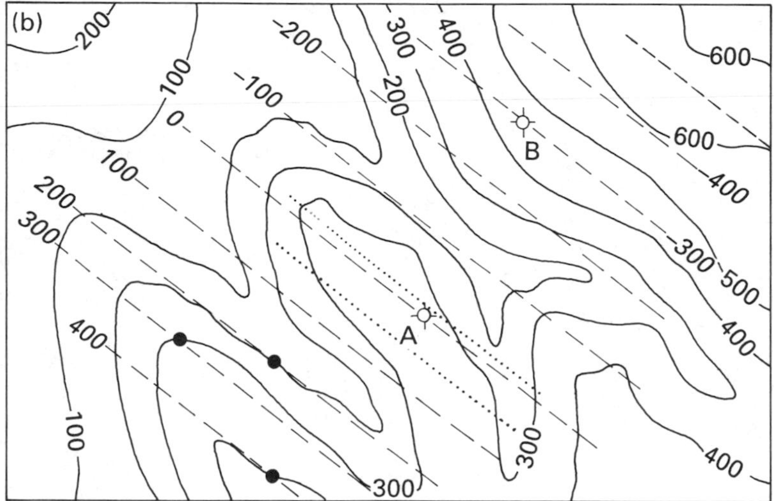
(b)
200
100
0
-100
-200
300
400
200
100
200
300
400
B
600
600
400
-300
500
400
A
100
300
300
400

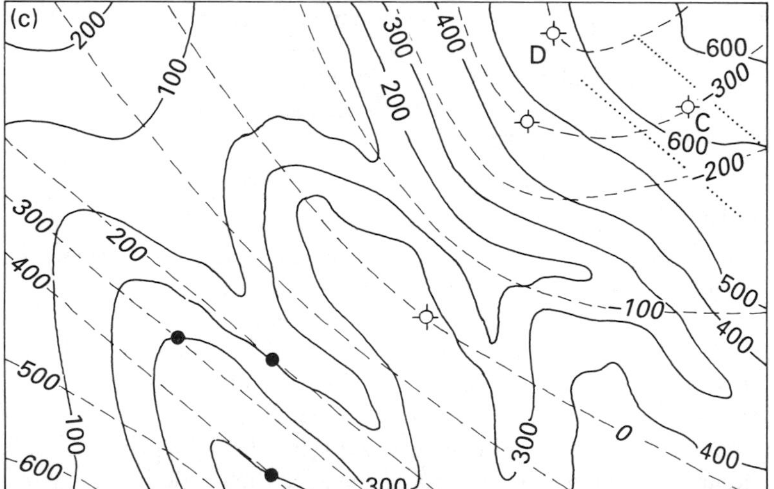
(c)
200
100
300
400
200
D
600
300
C
600
200
300
200
400
500
600
100
500
-100
400
0
300
300
400

Fig. 3.8 An example of the use of borehole/well information to constrain the routes of structure contours drawn from topography. (a) Topographic contours (solid lines) and known outcrops of coal seam at X, Y and Z (solid black circles). At location ZY, halfway between Z (200 m) and Y (400 m), altitude of seam is presumably 300 m, enabling 300 m structure contour to be drawn through ZY and X. Parallel to this, 400 m structure contour is drawn through Y and 200 m structure contour through Z. Additional structure contours are equidistant, assuming uniform dip of the seam. (b) Borehole at A encounters coal seam not at the 80 m predicted from (a) (0 and −100 m structure contours of (a) shown as dotted lines), but at 0 m. This suggests dip increases north-eastwards; structure contours in (b), with increased spacing, reflect this new information. Borehole at B confirms seam at −300 m, as predicted. Structure contours of (b) are best interpretation of information from three outcrops and two boreholes. (c) Further borehole at C fails to encounter seam at −460 m as predicted from (b). (−400 and −500 m structure contours of (b) shown in dotted lines), but at −300 m. This could indicate a reversal of dip direction in the north-east of the area (i.e. seam dips south-west), in which case borehold D should encounter seam at about −320 m. However, seam at D is met at −400 m, suggesting that structure contours are not parallel, leading to the refined interpretation shown in (c).

try to visualise in three dimensions what you are doing. Working geologists do not spend vast amounts of time carrying out these constructions, especially in these days of assistance from computers, but an understanding of how the methods work is paramount.

3.7 Structure contours from topography and boreholes

Deriving structure contours from outcrop and topography is useful in near-surface operations, but the reliability of

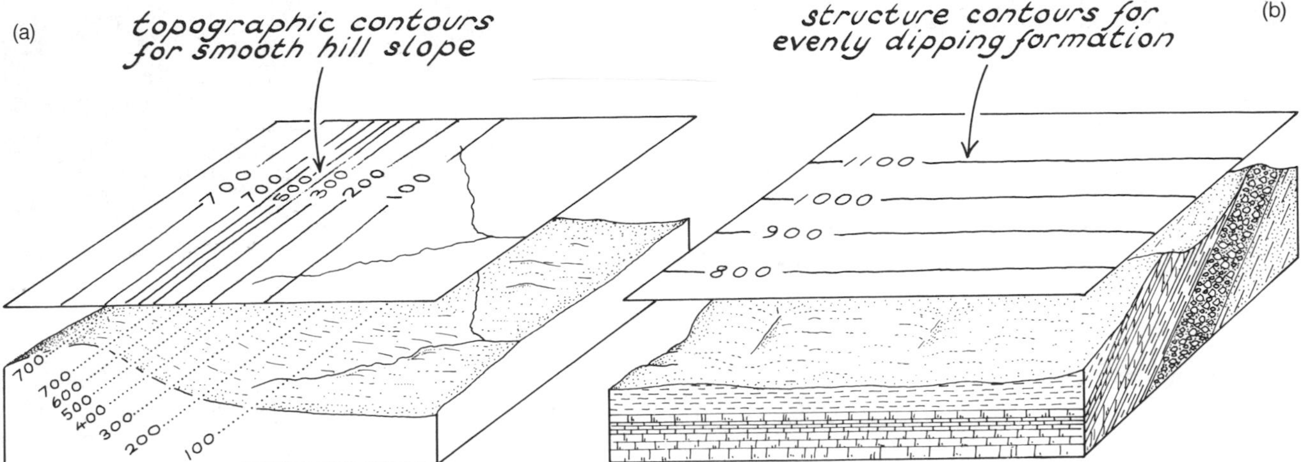
(a)
topographic contours for smooth hill slope
700
700
600
500
300
200
100
structure contours for evenly dipping formation
(b)
1100
1000
900
800

Fig. 3.9 The significance of straight structure contours (strike lines). (a) Straight topographic contours resulting from smooth hillslope with consistent direction. The varying gradient is represented by the spacing of the contours. (b) Straight structure contours representing a smooth geological surface; the even spacing reflects a uniform angle of dip.

underground predictions falls off as increasing extrapolation becomes necessary. It may become too approximate for commercial work on more deeply buried rocks. Then it becomes necessary to supplement the map information with some direct underground data. Drilling is expensive, but a carefully sited borehole or two can greatly constrain where the structure contours can be drawn. Figure 3.8 gives an example. Map 5 provides an exercise using outcrop and borehole information in conjunction.

3.8 Straight structure contours

Structure contours are exactly the same as topographic contours except that they represent some underground surface. They can, however, look a bit different. Figure 3.9a shows the topographic contours for some hypothetical smooth hill slope of fairly even gradient. The topographic contours are straight and evenly spaced, merely becoming closer where the gradient is steeper. Rarely are topographic contours actually like this on maps because natural hill slopes usually have various irregularities due to erosion. Bedding surfaces, however, can have this appearance on large-scale maps if the inclined plane is smooth and non-undulating (Fig. 3.9b). Here, the structure contours will appear as straight lines. They are, however, unlikely to be dead straight. You should not construct contours with a ruler; natural planes are not that smooth!

Straight structure contours are sometimes referred to as *strike lines*. This is because structure contours everywhere parallel the strike of the surface they are representing, which is conspicuously constant in direction if the lines are straight. The strike direction is therefore readily visualised and measured from them. Knowledge of the strike direction is essential in assessing the orientation of geological surfaces. The idea of strike and dip was introduced in section 2.3.1. but we now need to look more closely at this much used geological concept.

3.9 Summary of chapter

1. Structure contours are similar to topographic contours, but represent some underground surface such as the boundary of a rock unit rather than the land surface.
2. They depict in map view the position and form of the underground surface, and are therefore a highly useful construction.
3. They can be constructed from borehole/well information by interpolating the elevations of the surface between the holes.
4. Structure contours for outcropping surfaces can be constructed from the topographic elevations at which they outcrop.
5. The drawing of structure contours from outcrop elevations is more closely controlled if there is borehole information in addition.
6. Structure contours for smooth, uniformly-inclined surfaces are straight, and are also called strike-lines.

3.10 Selected further reading

Badgley, P. C. (1959). *Structural Methods for the Exploration Geologist*, New York, Harper and Brothers. (Chapter 4 of this excellent, advanced book is about structure contour maps. It includes a list of properties of structure contours and constructing hints.)

Ragan, D. M. (1985). *Structural Geology. An introduction to geometrical techniques*, 3rd edn, New York, Wiley. (Chapter 18 is a brief treatment of structure contours.)

MAP 1 Raton, New Mexico, USA

Location of
map 1

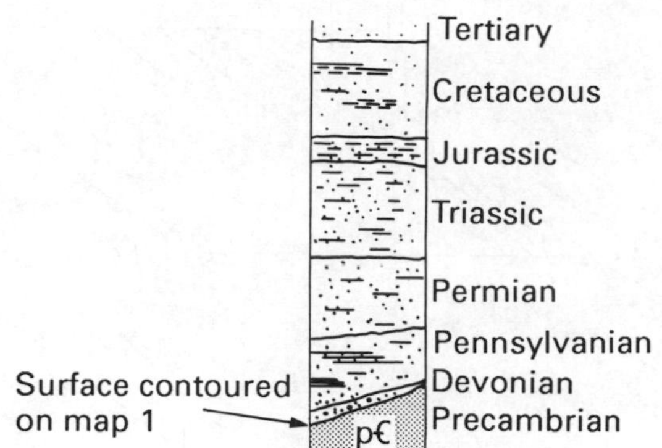
Tertiary
Cretaceous
Jurassic
Triassic
Permian
Pennsylvanian
Devonian
Precambrian
Surface contoured
on map 1
p€

In northeastern New Mexico, between the towns of Las Vegas and Raton, is a thick sequence of Palaeozoic and Mesozoic clastic sedimentary rocks. Gas has been extracted from some of the Cretaceous rocks. In fact, there are signs that hydrocarbons have been widely generated in the area, but suitable traps have proved elusive. In the search for oil and gas traps, numerous structure contour maps have been constructed for various stratigraphic horizons.

It turns out that the overall control on the form of the sedimentary basin is the Precambrian basement. On its surface the sedimentary pile accumulated. The form of this surface is depicted in the structure contour map opposite, reproduced with slight modification from Woodward (1984), by permission of the American Association of Petroleum Geologists.

Where in the area is the thickest accumulation of sediments likely to be? If the present-day land surface at that site is 2000 m above sea-level, how thick are the sediments there? Describe in words the form of the Precambrian basement in the vicinity of that site.

Away from the structure just discussed, where is the next thickest sedimentary accumulation likely to be? How does the structure here differ from that described above? What kind of structure separates the two areas? Describe its orientation.

Where in the map area is the highest point on the Precambrian surface? Where does it show the steepest gradient? Where is it least steep?

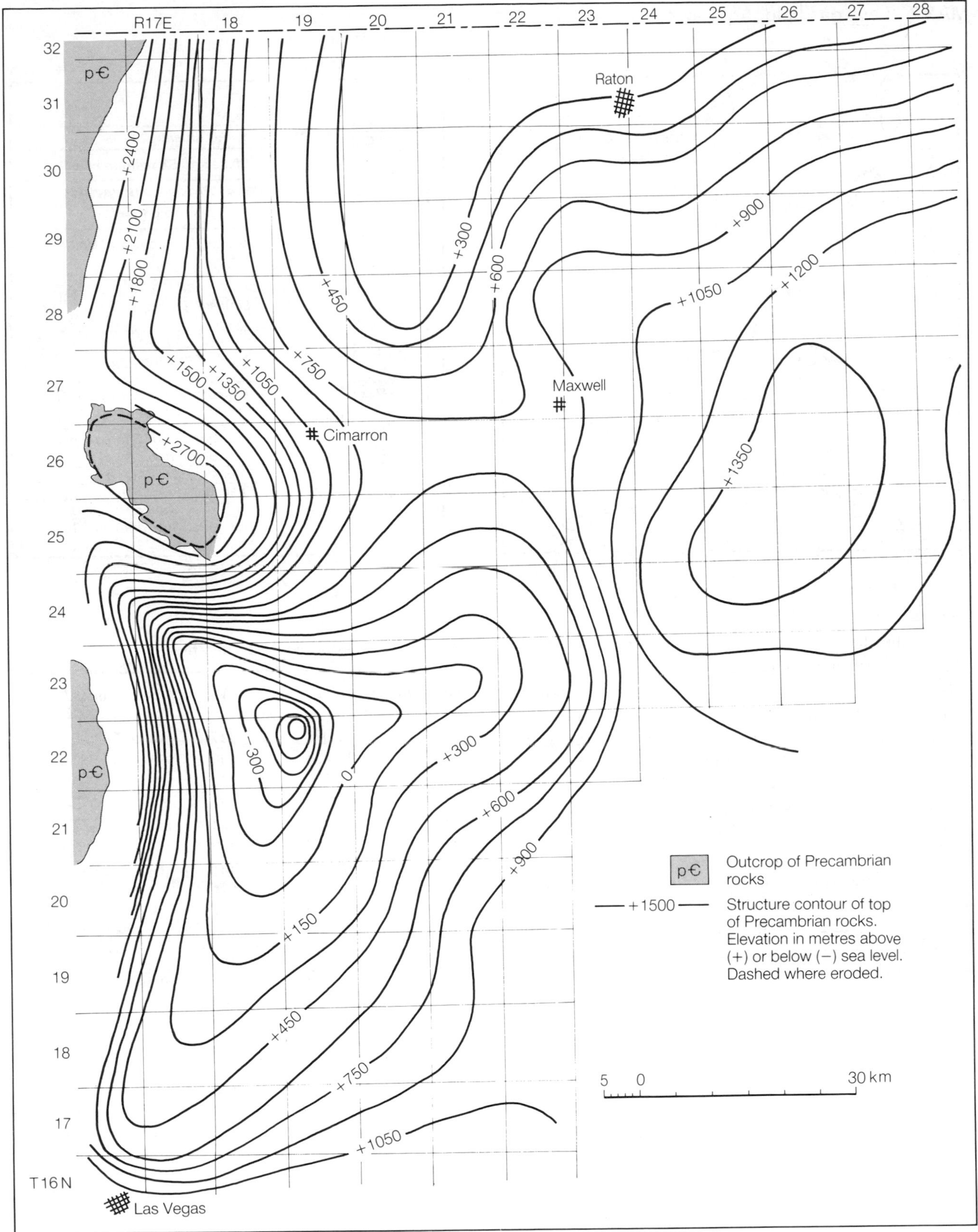
R17E
18
19
20
21
22
23
24
25
26
27
28
32
31
30
29
28
27
26
25
24
23
22
21
20
19
18
17
T16N
pЄ
Raton
Maxwell
Cimarron
Las Vegas
+2400
+2100
+1800
+1500
+1350
+1050
+750
+450
+300
+600
+900
+1050
+1200
+1350
+2700
−300
0
+300
+600
+900
+150
+450
+750
+1050
Outcrop of Precambrian rocks
+1500
Structure contour of top of Precambrian rocks. Elevation in metres above (+) or below (−) sea level. Dashed where eroded.
5 0 30 km

MAP 2 Lacq gas field, Aquitaine, France

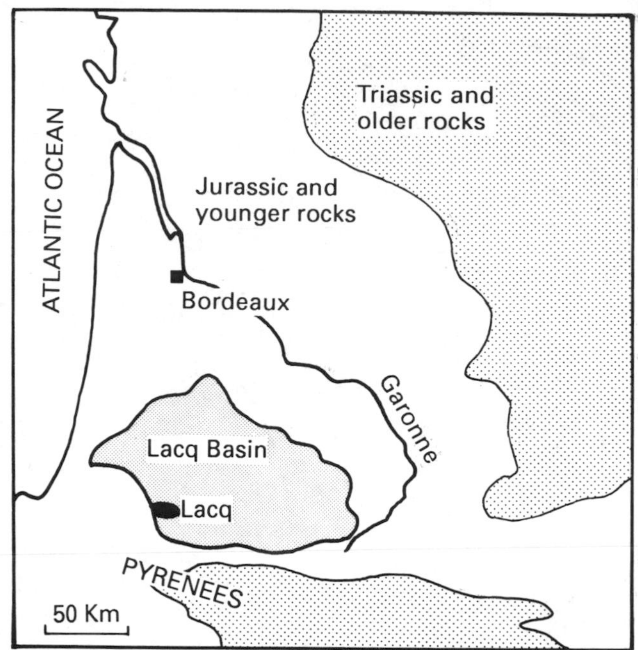

Triassic and older rocks
Jurassic and younger rocks
ATLANTIC OCEAN
Bordeaux
Garonne
Lacq Basin
Lacq
PYRENEES
50 Km

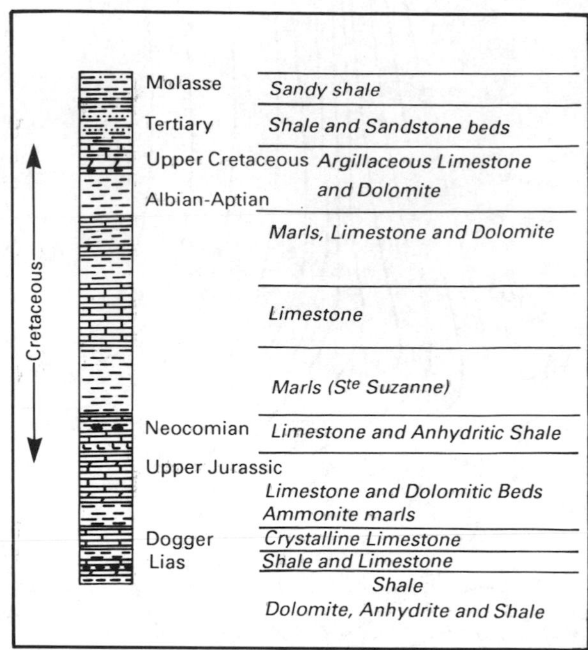

Molasse
Sandy shale
Tertiary
Shale and Sandstone beds
Upper Cretaceous
Argillaceous Limestone and Dolomite
Albian-Aptian
Marls, Limestone and Dolomite
Limestone
Marls (Ste Suzanne)
Cretaceous
Neocomian
Limestone and Anhydritic Shale
Upper Jurassic
Limestone and Dolomitic Beds
Ammonite marls
Dogger
Crystalline Limestone
Lias
Shale and Limestone
Shale
Dolomite, Anhydrite and Shale

During the decade 1950–60, extensive drilling defined what was to become France's largest gas field. On the map opposite, slightly modified from Winnock and Pontalier (1970), by permission of the American Association of Petroleum Geologists, the locations of some of the wells are shown. The table opposite gives the depth at which each well encountered the top of the Neocomian rocks (a division in the lower Cretaceous), within which gas is trapped.

From these data draw a structure contour map of the upper surface of the Neocomian. Describe in words the form of the Lacq structure. Sketch a NE–SW cross-section, say through wells 118 and 126, to illustrate the structure.

Lacq gas field, Aquitaine: well depths.

Well number	*Depth**	*Well number*	*Depth**
3	11 070	117	14 420
101	11 250	118	11 960
102	12 300	119	11 790
103	11 390	120	11 040
104	10 730	121	13 150
105	10 300	122	11 590
106	12 070	123	12 200
107	13 010	124	12 640
108	12 360	125	12 490
109	14 300	126	14 000
110	13 880	127	12 740
111	12 950	128	11 810
112	11 540	129	11 370
113	10 500	130	11 790
114	12 850	131	11 690
115	12 950	132	12 940
116	13 460	133	10 680

* Depth quoted is to top Neocomian, in feet below sea-level.

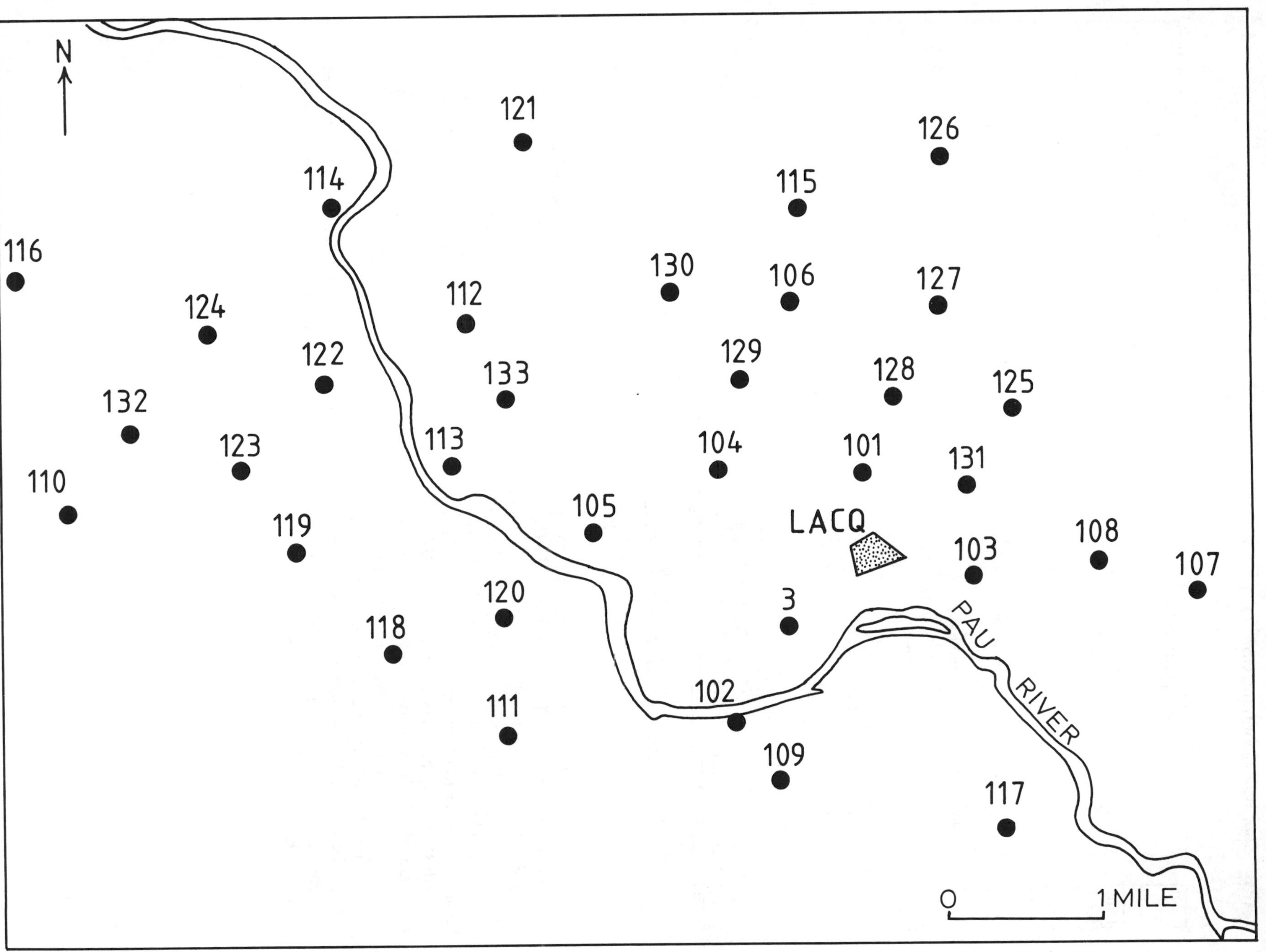

N
121
126
114
115
116
130
106
127
112
124
122
129
128
125
133
132
123
113
104
101
131
110
105
LACQ
119
108
103
107
120
3
PAU RIVER
118
102
111
109
117
0
1 MILE

MAP 3 Bear Hole, Montana, USA

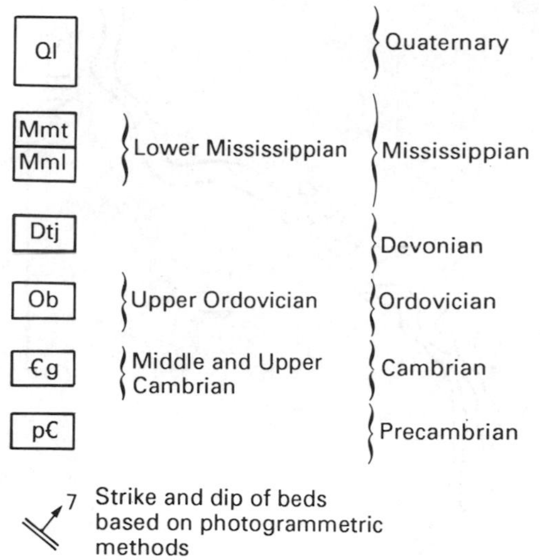

Ql
Quaternary
Mmt
Mml
Lower Mississippian
Mississippian
Dtj
Devonian
Ob
Upper Ordovician
Ordovician
€g
Middle and Upper Cambrian
Cambrian
p€
Precambrian
7
Strike and dip of beds based on photogrammetric methods

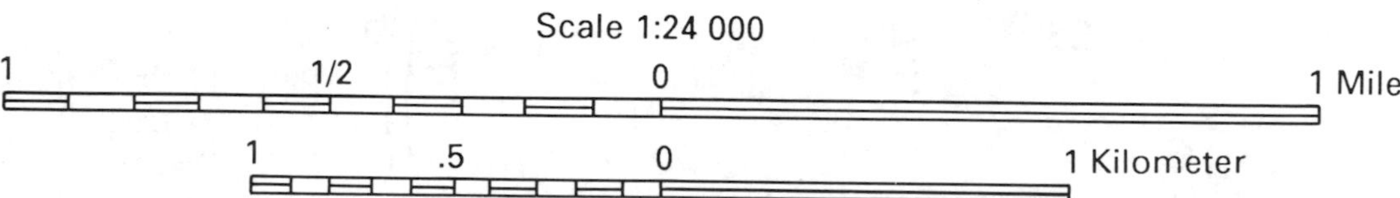

Scale 1:24 000
1
1/2
0
1 Mile
1
.5
0
1 Kilometer

The map opposite is of an area in south-central Montana, in the Big Horn Mountains. The land is part of the Crow Indian Reservation. The geology also appears, in very simplified form, on Plate 2 (note the values of latitude and longitude). The map is part of the USGS 1:24 000 Preliminary Geological Map of the Bear Hole Quadrangle, Map MF-1885, reproduced by permission of the USGS. It was produced using a combination of field reconnaissance and air photo interpretation, together with a computer-assisted method of determining the strike and dip of units from the air photos. The technique was feasible because the units are uniformly dipping and of reasonably consistent thickness. The formations in the area range in age from Precambrian to Mississippian (Lower Carboniferous), as indicated on the above key.

Identify the Upper Devonian by adding colour to its outcrop. Locate its top and its base. Draw structure contours, say the 8200, 8400, and 8600 ft values, for the top and bottom surfaces of the Upper Devonian. Comment on the form and spacing of the structure contours, and hence the form of the Upper Devonian.

The formations appearing in the northeast corner of the area are unlabelled. Deduce what they should be.

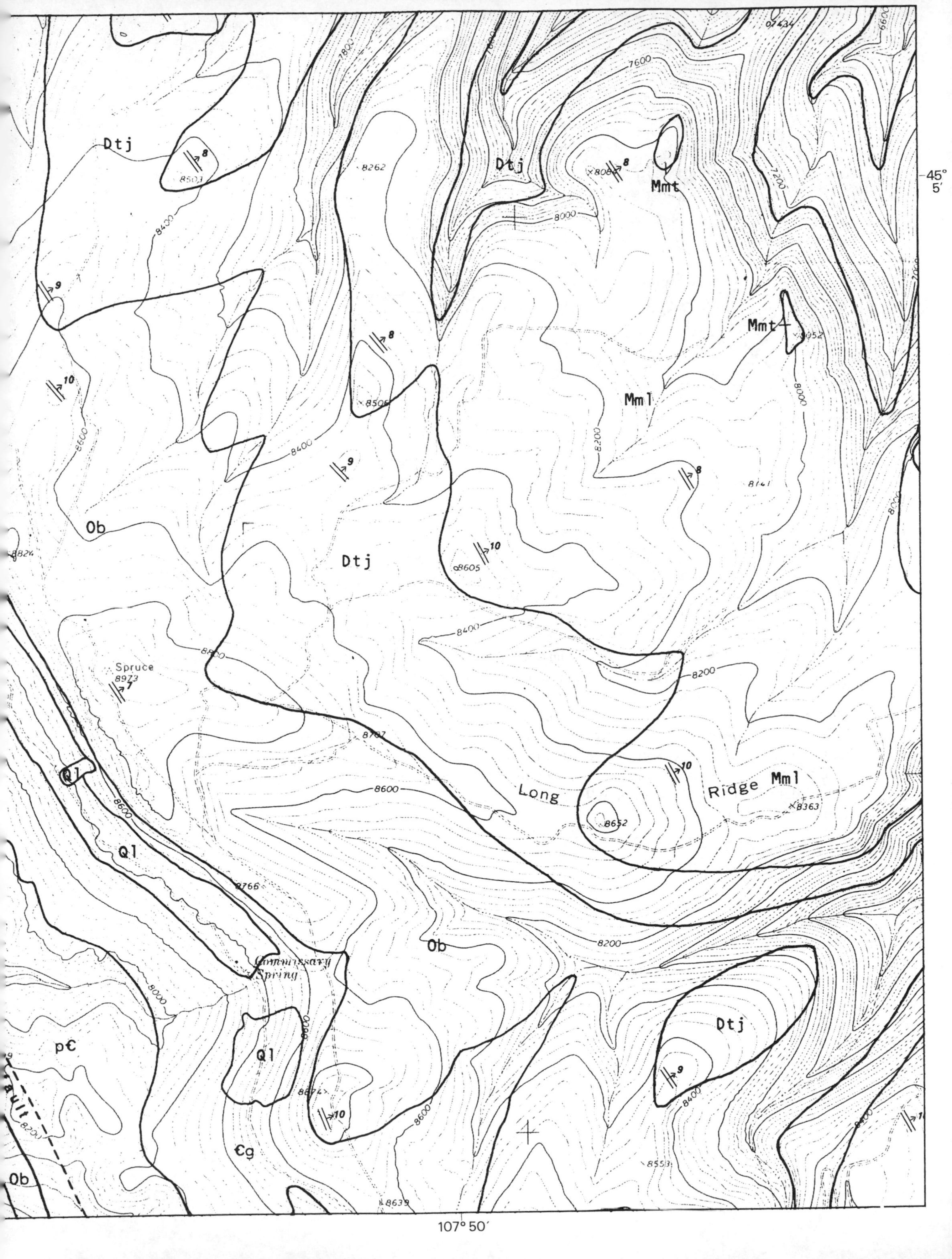

Dtj
Dtj
Mmt
Mmt
Mml
Ob
Dtj
Spruce
Ql
Ql
Long
Ridge Mml
Commissary
Spring
Ob
pЄ
Ql
Dtj
Єg
Ob
fault
45°
5′
107° 50′

MAP 4 Maccoyella Ridge, Koranga, New Zealand

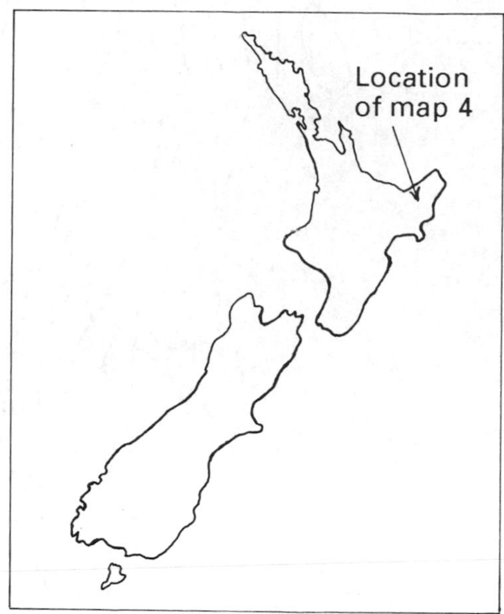
Location
of map 4

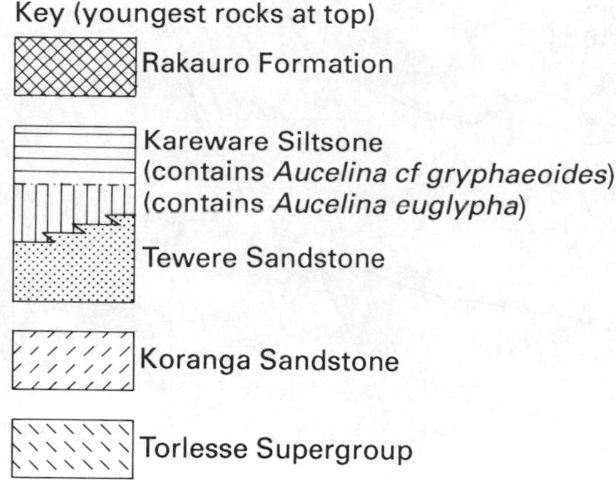
Key (youngest rocks at top)
Rakauro Formation
Kareware Siltsone
(contains *Aucelina cf gryphaeoides*)
(contains *Aucelina euglypha*)
Tewere Sandstone
Koranga Sandstone
Torlesse Supergroup

The facing map is based on part of the New Zealand Geological Survey PTS Sheet N87/9, N88/7: Geology of Koranga, Raukumara Peninsula, by permission of the New Zealand Geological Survey. It is enlarged here from the 1:15 840 (four inches to a mile) of the original to approximately 1:10 000. The grid reference numbers can be used in an analogous way to the UK National Grid.

The map shows a sequence of sedimentary rocks of Jurassic–Cretaceous age. There is some variation in thickness, shown particularly by the Koranga sandstone, which in some places is absent altogether. Also, the units are slightly folded, so that structure contours will tend to curve, and their spacing may vary, reflecting differing amounts of inclination.

From the age relations given in the key, in what overall direction are the units dipping?

On the map, is the top surface or the base of the Te Were sandstone further towards the southeast? Carefully draw structure contours for the base of the Te Were sandstone.

Describe in words the form of this surface.

Assuming all the other units dip by the same amount as the Te Were base, sketch a cross-section across the area to show the overall geological structure.

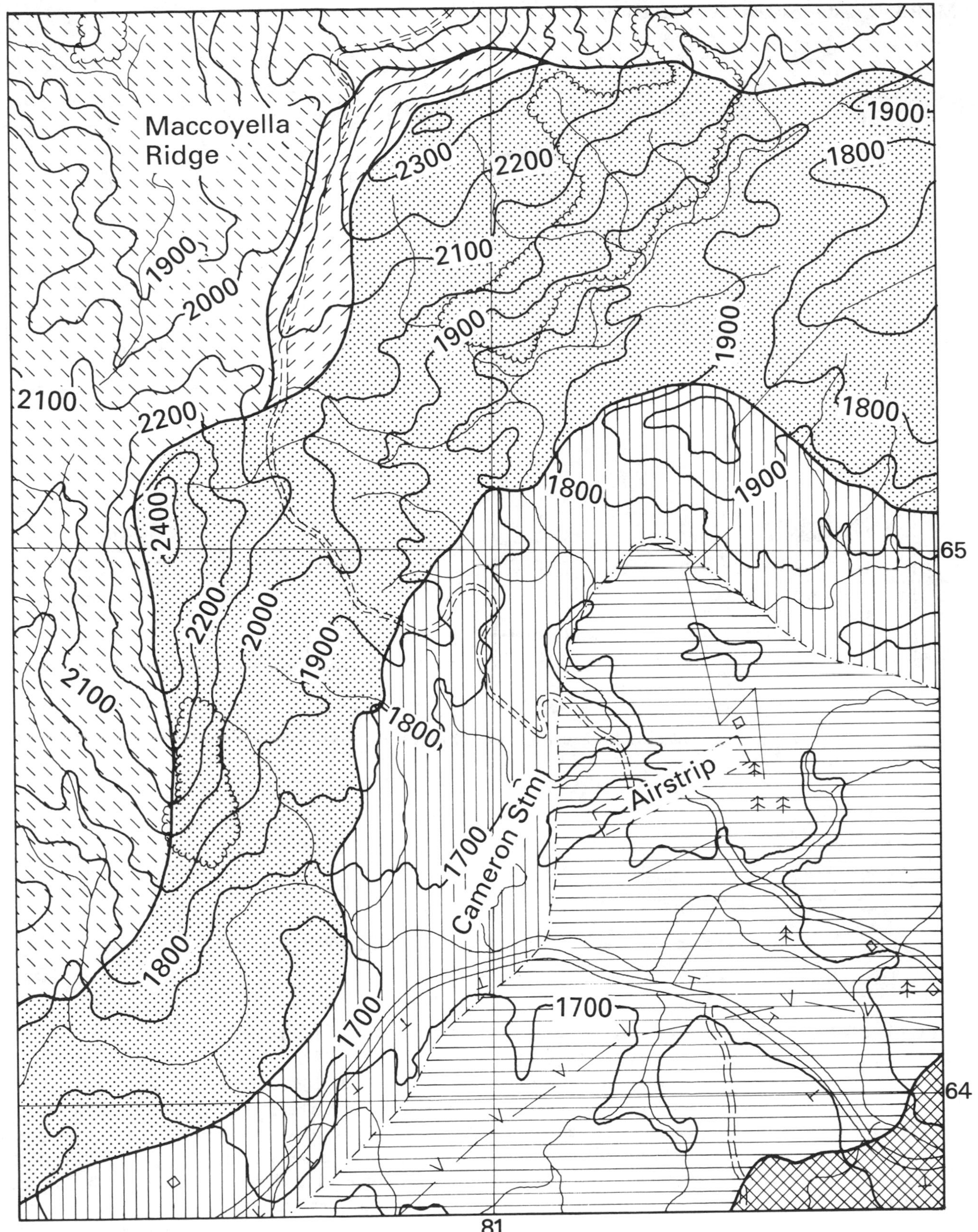

Maccoyella
Ridge
2300
2200
2100
1900
1800
1900
2000
2100
2200
2400
2200
2000
1900
1800
1900
1800
1900
1800
2100
1900
1800
1700
Cameron Stm
Airstrip
1800
1700
1700
65
64
81

MAP 5 Coalbrookdale Coalfield, Shropshire, England

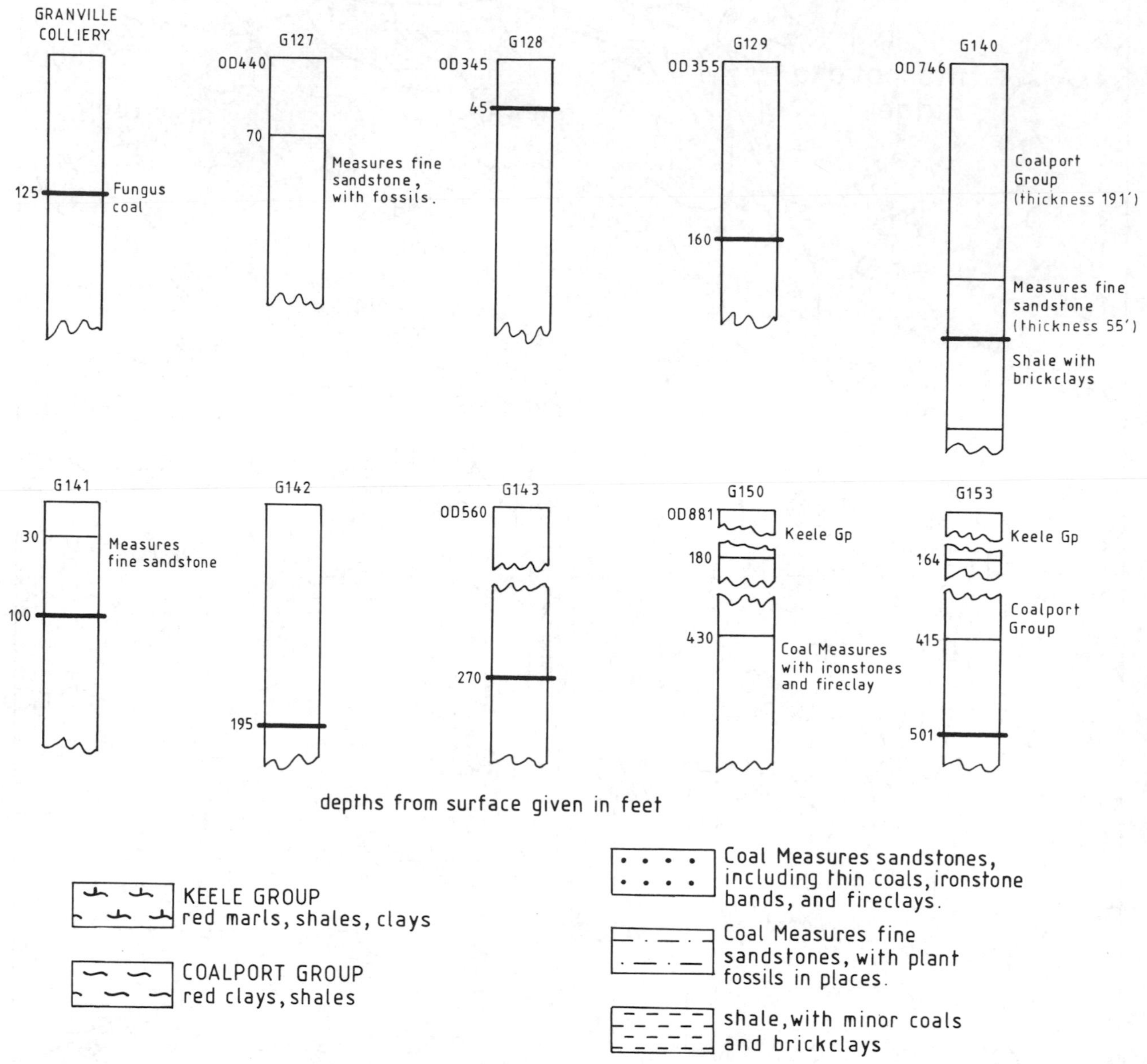

GRANVILLE COLLIERY
125
Fungus coal
G127
OD440
70
Measures fine sandstone, with fossils.
G128
OD345
45
G129
OD355
160
G140
OD746
Coalport Group (thickness 191')
Measures fine sandstone (thickness 55')
Shale with brickclays
G141
30
Measures fine sandstone
100
G142
195
G143
OD560
270
G150
OD881
Keele Gp
180
430
Coal Measures with ironstones and fireclay
G153
Keele Gp
164
Coalport Group
415
501
depths from surface given in feet
KEELE GROUP red marls, shales, clays
COALPORT GROUP red clays, shales
Coal Measures sandstones, including thin coals, ironstone bands, and fireclays.
Coal Measures fine sandstones, with plant fossils in places.
shale, with minor coals and brickclays

The Coalbrookdale Coalfield lies between Shrewsbury and Wolverhampton. It is small, but because of the nearby ironstone, is one of the places where the Industrial Revolution began. Like almost all other UK coalfields, the rocks are of Carboniferous age. Locate it on the part of the Ten Mile map reproduced here as Plate 1. What is the oldest unit that the coal-bearing rocks (Lower Westphalian) are in contact with?

Opposite is a map of the kind of geology found in the Granville Colliery area. What is the overall structure of the Fungus Coal in this area?

A new mine-shaft is being constructed in the area where borehole G130 has been sunk. Make a vertical column (like those in the key) of what you predict this borehole should contain. In particular, state the depth at which you predict the Fungus Coal will be reached. (Note that all these problems are best tackled by first drawing structure contours for the Fungus Coal. This is done most accurately by combining the topographic and the borehole information on its elevations.)

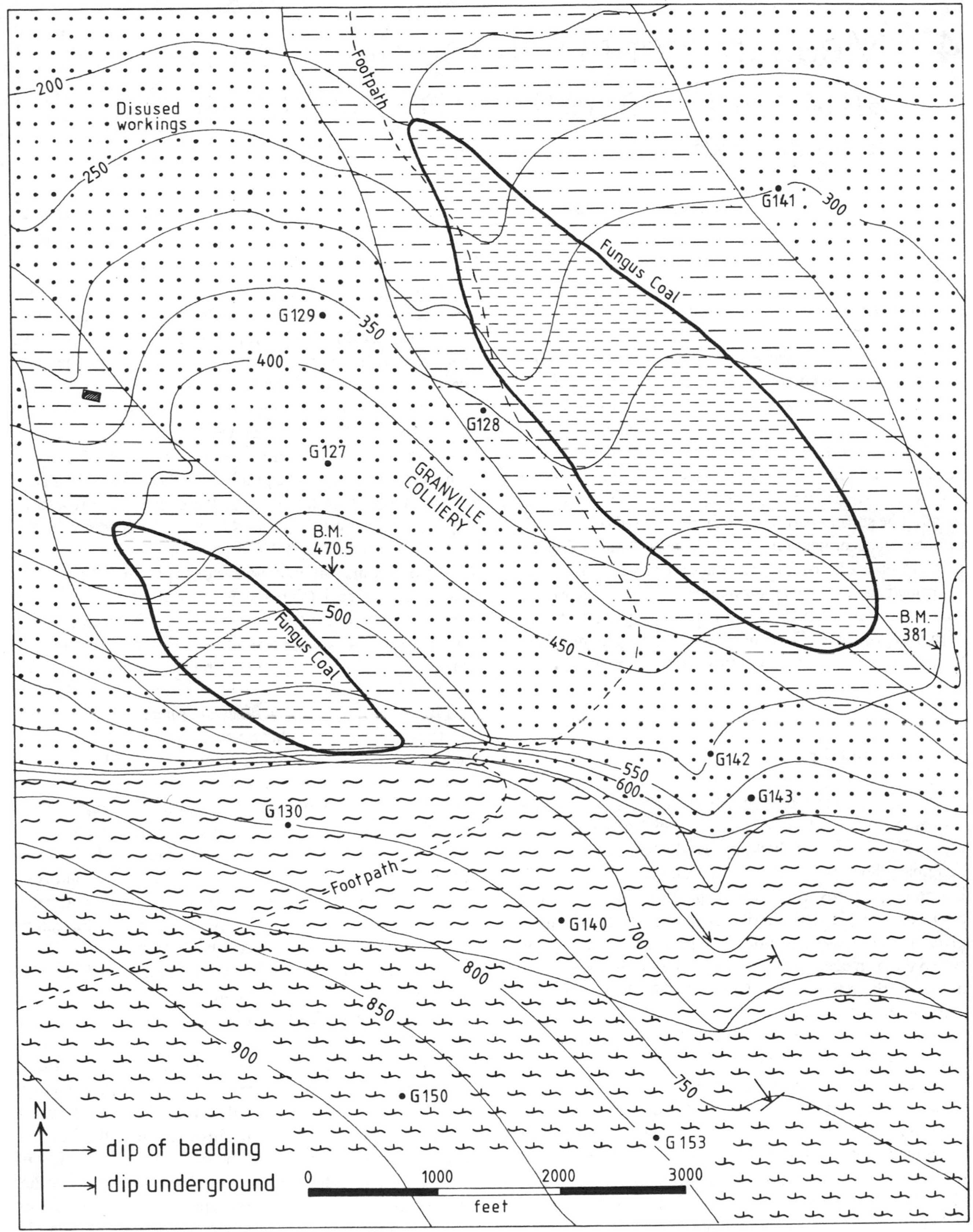
200
Disused workings
250
Footpath
G141
300
Fungus Coal
G129
350
400
G128
G127
GRANVILLE COLLIERY
B.M. 470.5
500
Fungus Coal
450
B.M. 381
G142
550
600
G143
G130
Footpath
G140
700
800
850
900
750
G150
G153
N
dip of bedding
dip underground
0
1000
2000
3000
feet

4 Measurements in three dimensions: strike and dip, formation thickness and depth

4.1 Introduction

We are beginning to see why geological maps are such a powerful and convenient means of conveying information about the three-dimensional configuration of rocks. Nevertheless, it is often necessary to specify the arrangement in words or numbers. Geologists do this by using the concept of strike and dip. The general idea was introduced in section 2.3.1; the first part of this chapter explains it in detail. The second part of the chapter expands on methods of subsurface projection and some useful measurements that can be made from maps. These techniques are of use in applied geology where, for many purposes, the work will have to be done as accurately as possible, especially if sums of money are at risk. Some of the corrections that may have to be borne in mind for this kind of mapwork are introduced.

4.2 Strike and dip

Strike and dip are used to specify the orientation of a geological surface, such as the top of a bed of sedimentary rock. The **strike** of bedding is the direction of any imaginary horizontal line running along a planar bed. It has no *position*, just direction. It therefore does not matter *where* on the plane the strike is measured. It is usually given as a compass direction, either loosely in words, say, NE–SW, or in degrees measured clockwise from north and quoted as three figures, say 045°. The **angle of dip** is the maximum inclination of the bed in degrees from the horizontal. To avoid confusion with strike it is quoted as two figures, say 08° or 30°, and is always given after the strike value. In addition to the angle of dip, there is the direction towards which the surface is inclined, called the **dip direction**. This will always be at right angles to the strike.

Notice that it is not some arbitrary decision by geologists to define the dip direction as perpendicular to strike, or vice versa. It is a property of any tilted plane that the line at right angles to the maximum inclination will be horizontal. Consider the sloping roof of a house (Fig. 4.1a) and imagine rain falling on it. The water will trickle down the steepest slope, that is, in the dip direction. The line at right angles to that direction will be parallel to the ridge of the roof, that is, horizontal. The ridge line of the roof therefore parallels the 'strike' direction. Thus, if the house in Fig. 4.1 is south-facing, in geological terms the front half of the roof is dipping S and striking E–W. If the slope of the roof were 45° we could express its orientation as 090/45° S. This expression conveys precisely and concisely the orientation of that part of the roof. Note that there would be ambiguity without the 'S' at the end. The northern half of the roof is oriented at 090/45° N.

Strike and dip, then, are ways of expressing the orientation of beds of rock (Fig. 4.1b). Any other geological plane can be treated in just the same way. The boundary surfaces of a map unit will have a strike and dip. If the formation comprises bedded sedimentary rocks, its boundaries are likely to be parallel to the beds within it.

The orientation of geological planes is commonly measured in the field during the map survey, and representative values added to the completed map by means of symbols. The map key will explain these. A variety of different symbols have evolved, both for bedding surfaces and for the various other structures to be discussed in later chapters. Some examples are given in Fig. 4.2. If the strike and dip direction of the map unit is not known, an approximate orientation can be judged from the outcrop pattern of the formation (see chapter 6), and an accurate value can be derived by plotting some structure contours.

The strike direction of a formation is paralleled by structure contours. Because the contours are joining points of equal elevation, each contour line itself must be horizontal. Strike direction is horizontal, by definition. There can be only one horizontal direction on an inclined plane, therefore, at any place along a structure contour, the course of the line represents the strike direction. Straight structure contours indicate a consistent direction of strike; curving structure contours show that the strike direction varies. At right angles to structure contours, decreasing in elevation, is the dip direction, and the spacing of the structure contours reflects the amount of dip. The dip value can be found from trigonometry or graphically (Fig. 4.3).

Because strike is horizontal, a horizontal bed cannot have

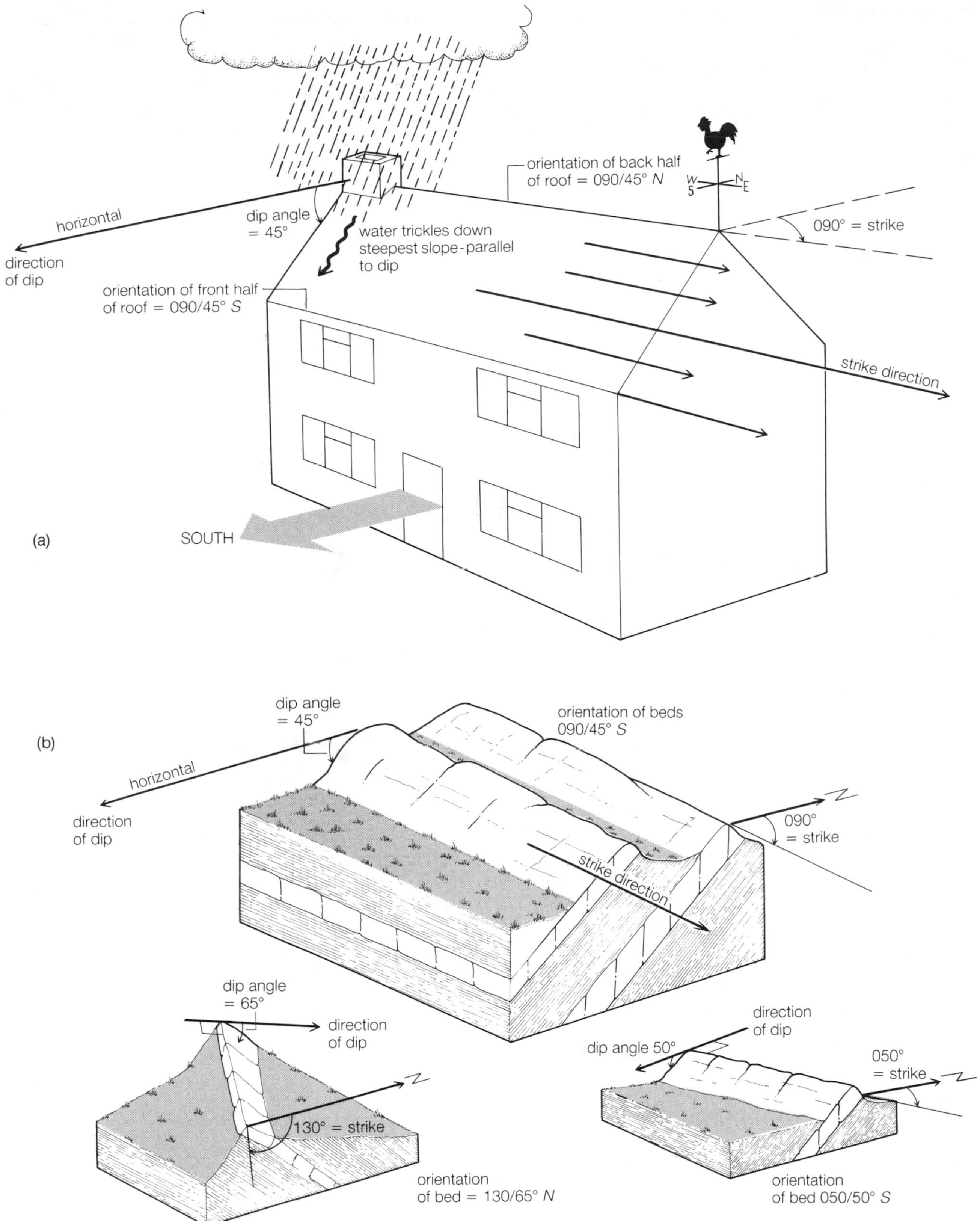

orientation of back half
of roof = 090/45° N
W
S
N
E
horizontal
dip angle
= 45°
direction
of dip
water trickles down
steepest slope-parallel
to dip
090° = strike
orientation of front half
of roof = 090/45° S
strike direction
(a)
SOUTH
dip angle
= 45°
orientation of beds
090/45° S
(b)
horizontal
direction
of dip
090°
= strike
strike direction
dip angle
= 65°
direction
of dip
direction
of dip
dip angle 50°
050°
= strike
130° = strike
orientation
of bed = 130/65° N
orientation
of bed 050/50° S

Fig. 4.1 The concept of strike and dip. (a) Analogy with a house roof. (b) The strike and dip of inclined beds. The front edge of each diagram is oriented N–S. Only in the top diagram does this parallel the dip direction, at right angles to strike; in the bottom two diagrams the beds strike and dip obliquely to the edges of the figures.

GEOLOGICAL CONTACTS:

defined
approximate
conjectural
gradational

BEDDING:

horizontal
90
vertical
40
dipping, dip in degrees
5
dip in degrees, in regions of low dip
younging direction

FOLDS:

axial trace of anticline
10
plunge, in degrees
10
80
strike and dip of axial plane
axial trace of syncline
trace of antiform
trace of synform

FAULTS:

tick on downthrow side
D
U
80
dip in degrees
upthrow side
approximate
thrusts, barbs on hanging wall
extension fault, blocks on hanging wall

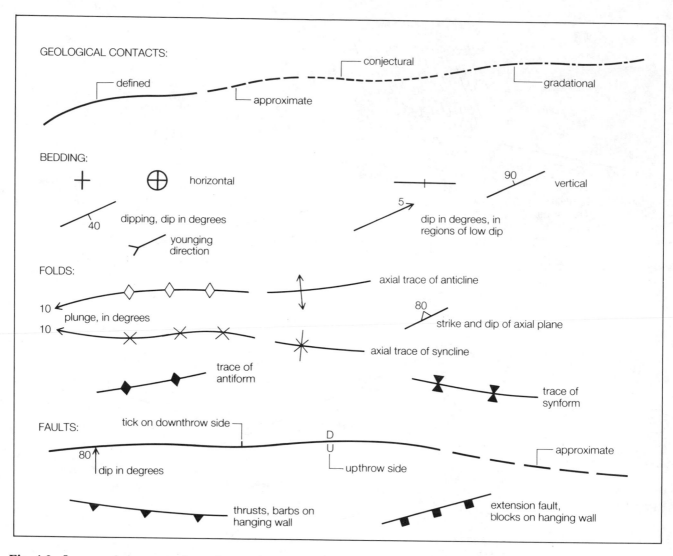

Fig. 4.2 Some symbols commonly used on geological maps. The terms used are explained in the relevant chapters: chapter 8 for folds, and chapters 9 and 10 for faults. Numerous further symbols are given, for example, in Compton (1985, Appendix 7), and the specifications issued by geological surveys and companies.

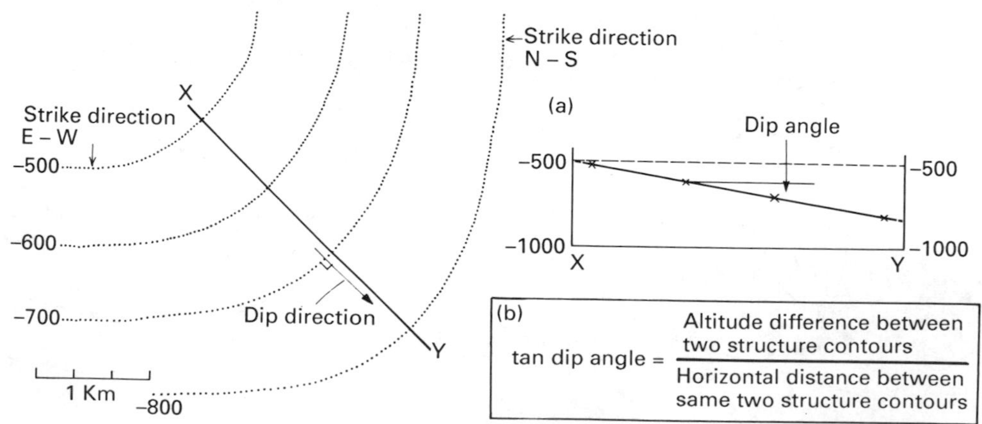

Strike direction
N – S
Strike direction
E – W
X
Y
–500
–600
–700
–800
Dip direction
1 Km
(a)
Dip angle
–500
–500
–1000
–1000
X
Y
(b)
tan dip angle = Altitude difference between two structure contours / Horizontal distance between same two structure contours

Fig. 4.3 Deriving the direction and angle of dip from structure contours. (a) By graphical construction. Note that the section is drawn at right angles to the structure contours, i.e. in the true dip direction, and with a vertical scale equal to the horizontal scale. (b) By trigonometry.

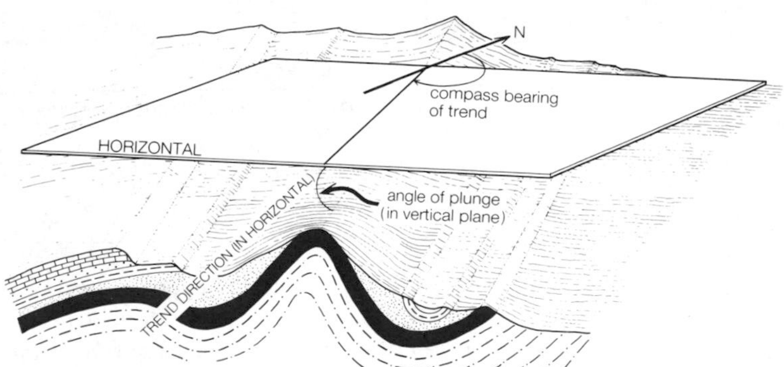
N
compass bearing
of trend
HORIZONTAL
angle of plunge
(in vertical plane)
TREND DIRECTION (IN HORIZONTAL)

Fig. 4.4 Diagram to illustrate the plunge and trend of a line.

a strike direction. Rather it will have an infinite number of horizontal directions. Any slight irregularities in near-horizontal beds will have a great effect on the strike direction. This is why the structure contour map of the Entre-Deux-Mers region (Fig. 3.3) looks so complex. The Calcaire à Astéries has a very low dip, and so its strike direction is highly variable, as indicated by the structure contours. Conversely, steeply dipping beds tend to have well-defined strike directions and, therefore, regular structure contours.

The strike and dip concept will not work for *linear* geological features, for example, the intersections of unconformities or faults with the land surface. Here, plunge and trend are normally used (Fig. 4.4). **Plunge** is the inclination of the line from the horizontal, measured in a vertical plane. **Trend** is the direction of the line, measured in the horizontal as a compass bearing. The two systems of recording orientations exist because it is not possible to find the strike and dip of a line, nor the trend and plunge of a plane. The important practical difference between the two is that the angle of dip is measured at right angles to strike but the plunge is measured in the same direction as the trend.

4.3 Apparent dip

If we draw a geological cross-section in the dip direction, the dip of the beds will be portrayed. On the other hand, a cross-section parallel to the direction of strike will show each bed as horizontal. It has to, because by definition the strike direction is a horizontal line running along the bed. Therefore, a section along a line somewhere in between the dip direction and the strike direction will show the beds inclined somewhere between the dip angle and the horizontal. The closer the section line to the strike direction, the flatter the beds will look. The closer the dip direction, the steeper they will appear. In the actual dip direction the inclination reaches its maximum and is therefore the **true dip**. The intermediate angles of inclination are known as **apparent dips** (Fig. 4.5).

In map work, true dips are used wherever possible.

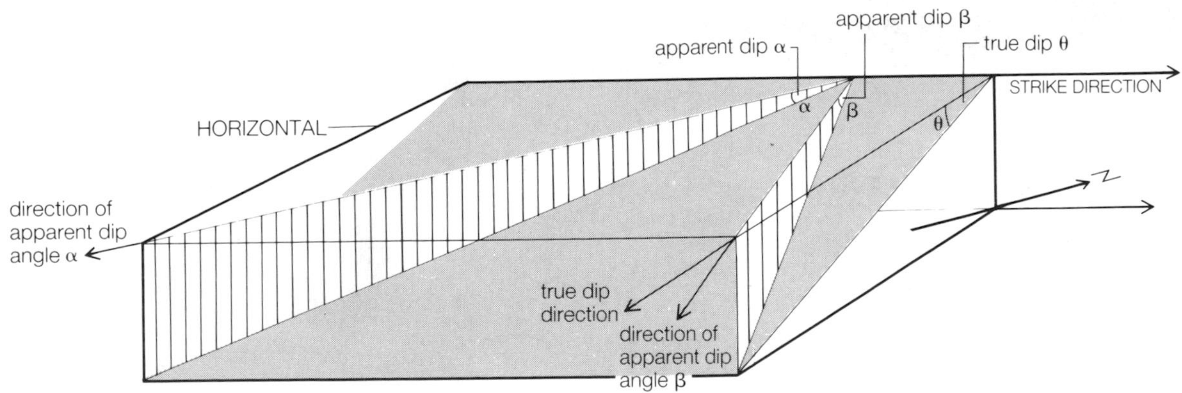
apparent dip β
apparent dip α
true dip θ
STRIKE DIRECTION
HORIZONTAL
α
β
θ
N
direction of
apparent dip
angle α
true dip
direction
direction of
apparent dip
angle β

Fig. 4.5 True and apparent dips. Any horizontal line along the inclined plane, i.e. the strike direction, parallels the front and rear edges of the block. At right angles to this direction is the true dip direction, parallel to the side edges of the block, and showing the true angle of dip. Dip angles in other directions, say α and β, are apparent angles of dip.

Sometimes in practice, however, the surveyor can measure only an apparent dip, and it is this that is recorded on the map. An adjustment will be required to find the true dip. More commonly, the true dip is provided on the map, but for some reason the dip in another direction is required. It may be needed, for example, in engineering work where a road-cut or tunnel is being sited.

The conversion between true and apparent dips can be made in numerous ways, involving various permutations of trigonometry, construction, and cunning predetermined devices. Travis and Lamar (1987) listed over a dozen different methods. Explanations of the more common

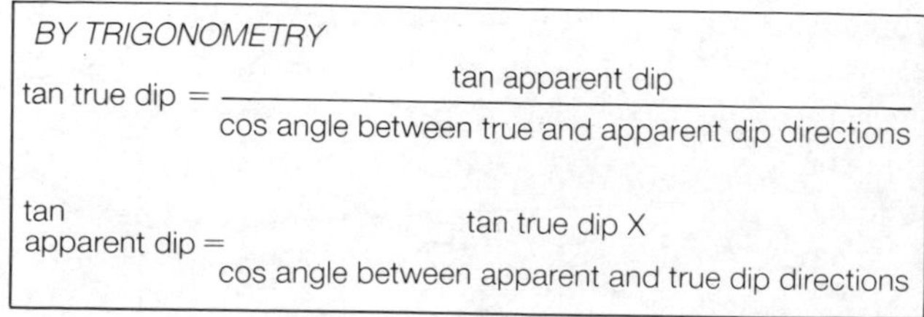

BY TRIGONOMETRY
tan true dip = tan apparent dip / cos angle between true and apparent dip directions
tan apparent dip = tan true dip X cos angle between apparent and true dip directions

Fig. 4.6 Converting between true and apparent dips using trigonometry. Note that the directions of both the true and apparent dips have to be known, and either the true or the apparent dip angle.

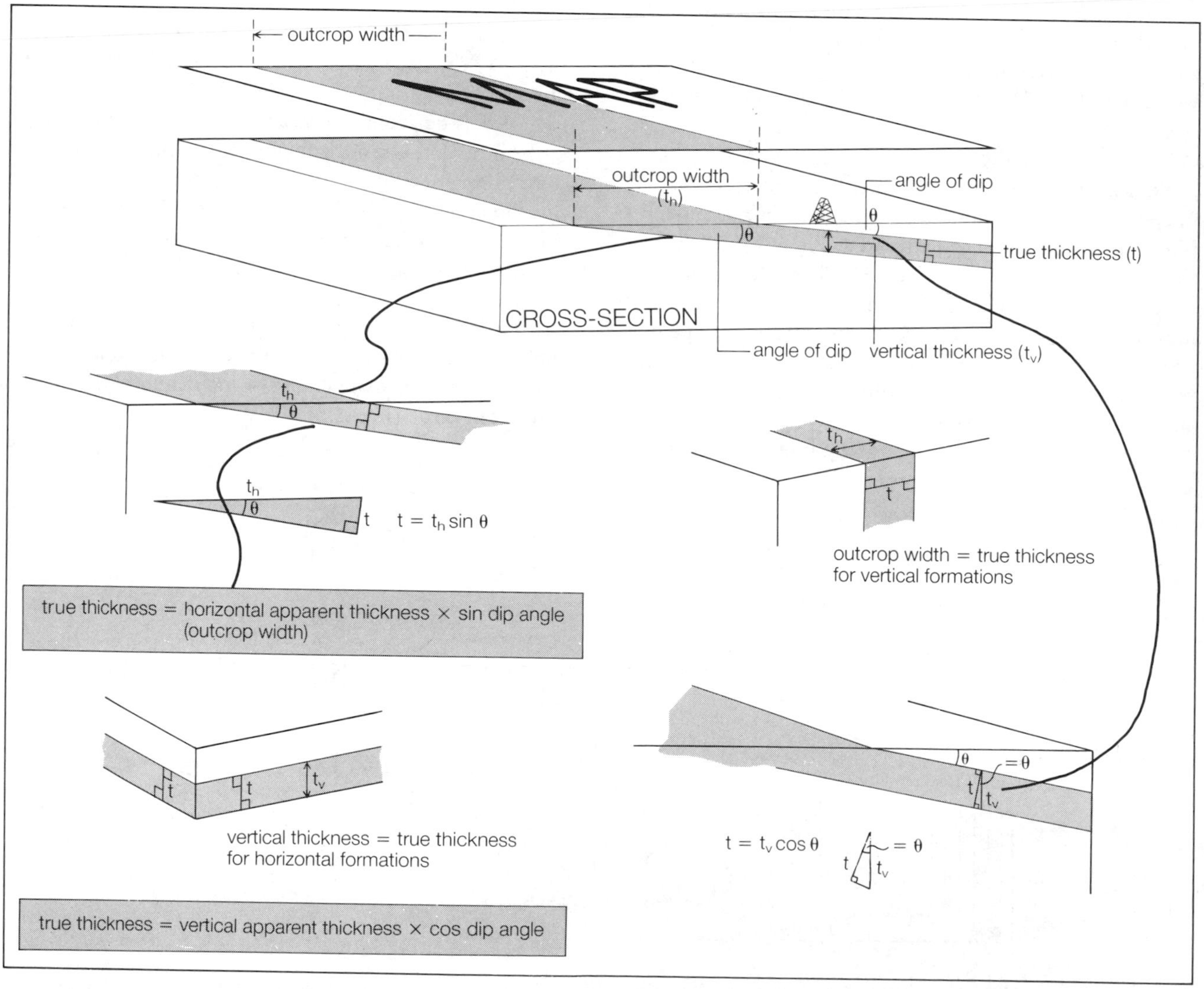

Fig. 4.7 Formation thickness. The diagrams illustrate the trigonometric relationships between outcrop width and true thickness (assuming level ground), and vertical thickness (as observed in a borehole or well) and true thickness.

techniques are given by Rowland (1986), Ragan (1985) and Dennison (1968), and Fig. 4.6 shows the basic trigonometric relations. The important thing, whichever technique you adopt, is to visualise and understand what you are doing.

4.4 Formation thickness

Geologists often need to find from a map the **thickness** of a particular unit. It may be a matter of seeing how the thickness varies from place to place in order to build up a better picture of how the formation was laid down, or the thickness may be required in order to decide whether or not there is sufficient quantity of material of commercial interest for it to be worthwhile extracting. On published maps the thickness of units may be indicated on the key. If the thickness is variable, it may be given as a range. Some newer geological maps show the thickness to scale in a vertical column, sometimes incorporating a depiction of any lateral variations in thickness. Note that the vertical scale of such columns will be specified, and will not necessarily be the same as that of cross-sections or the horizontal scale of the map. Many maps, however, do not state thicknesses, and the geologist has to work them out.

The **true thickness** of a unit is the distance between the top and the base of the unit measured *at right angles* to these bounding surfaces. It is the shortest distance between the top and bottom boundaries. Measurements at any other angle will give a greater value, called the **apparent thickness**. When we look at the units appearing on a geological map, only in the case of the units being tilted to vertical will their outcrop width equal the true thickness (Fig. 4.7). In any other inclination of bedding, the outcrop width as seen on the geological map will be an apparent thickness only. Formation thicknesses encountered in a borehole or well, or derived from the difference in elevation between the top and bottom surfaces, will be vertical apparent values. Only in the case of horizontal beds will these equal the true thickness (Fig. 4.7).

As with apparent dips, there are various approaches to making the necessary conversions; simple trigonometric relationships are shown in Fig. 4.7. Note that the outcrop width/true thickness correction given there assumes that the land surface is horizontal. This is often a reasonable approximation on small-scale maps, unless it is exceptionally rugged terrain, but a thickness value derived from a small-scale map is not going to be very accurate anyway. It is on large-scale maps that thickness determinations are most accurately made, and here, the ground slope may have to be taken into account. If the slope is reasonably uniform and can be approximated in cross-section to a straight line, then the trigonometric methods shown in Fig. 4.8 can be applied. If the map scale is so large that considerable irregularities occur within the outcrop of the unit of interest, then the unit will have to be broken down into sub-units which adequately approximate to a straight line (Fig. 4.8d). An alternative approach, avoiding the problems of the land surface, is to construct an accurate scale drawing in the true dip direction of the unit and simply to measure its scaled true thickness.

If the thickness of a formation is known at a number of places, the values can be plotted on a map and interpolated as a series of contours joining points of equal thickness, called **isopachs**. Where structure contours have been drawn for both the top and bottom surfaces of a formation, the difference between the two elevations at given points readily gives vertical thicknesses, which can also be contoured, as **isochores**. The oil industry makes much use of isopach and isochore maps, both in exploration and the calculation of reserves (see also Badgley (1959) and section 15.2.3).

4.5 Formation depth

The **depth** of a formation is the vertical distance from ground level to the subsurface unit. If the formation has appreciable thickness, it will be necessary to specify whether the depth is being given to its upper or lower surface. Although depth is commonly measured to the top boundary, where the unit would be first encountered by vertical drilling, it is BGS practice to quote depths to the base of a formation. However, provided that the map trace of the upper or lower boundary is employed as appropriate, and that the dip angle as recorded at the land surface can be assumed to continue underground, either way it is a straightforward matter to calculate the depth of the unit, especially where the ground is reasonably flat (Fig. 4.9a). A simple correction can be made if the ground level is sloping (Fig. 4.9b,c). Of course, rarely in nature will the dip of the bed be constant. If there are indications on the map that the dip is variable, the method can only be approximate, and the error margin will grow with increasing distance of projection. In commercial applications where accuracy is imperative, it is common to obtain further information such as borehole/well data or seismic sections with which the map predictions can be compared.

Bear in mind the matter of apparent dip (section 4.3): if the depth measurements on the map are not being made in the true dip direction, adjustments will have to be made. A further value of structure contours emerges here, for if they have been constructed on the map, the numerical difference between their elevation and that of the ground surface gives the bed depth directly, at any point of interest.

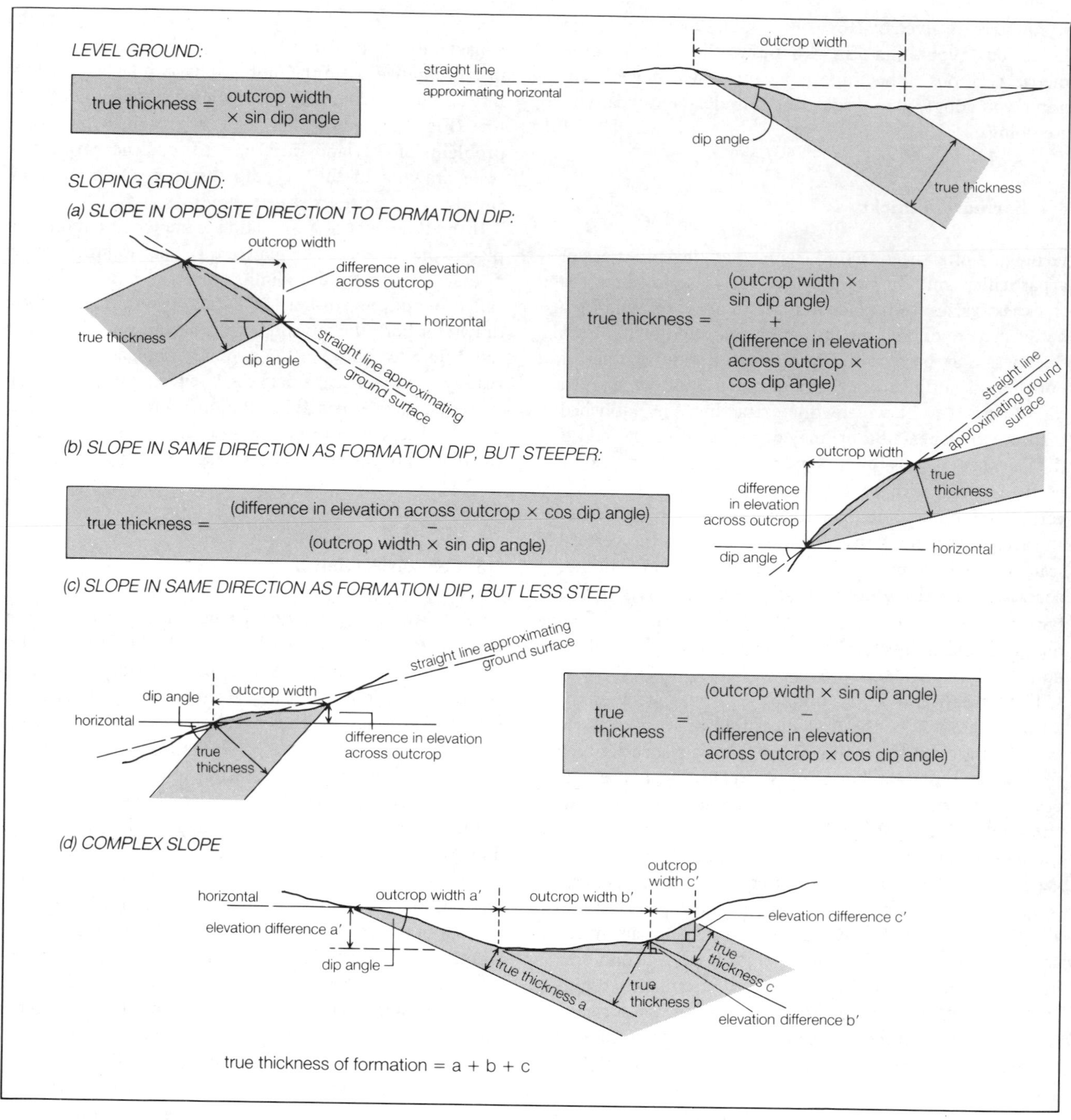

LEVEL GROUND:
true thickness = outcrop width × sin dip angle
outcrop width
straight line
approximating horizontal
dip angle
true thickness
SLOPING GROUND:
(a) SLOPE IN OPPOSITE DIRECTION TO FORMATION DIP:
outcrop width
difference in elevation across outcrop
horizontal
true thickness
dip angle
straight line approximating ground surface
true thickness = (outcrop width × sin dip angle) + (difference in elevation across outcrop × cos dip angle)
(b) SLOPE IN SAME DIRECTION AS FORMATION DIP, BUT STEEPER:
true thickness = (difference in elevation across outcrop × cos dip angle) − (outcrop width × sin dip angle)
straight line approximating ground surface
outcrop width
difference in elevation across outcrop
true thickness
horizontal
dip angle
(c) SLOPE IN SAME DIRECTION AS FORMATION DIP, BUT LESS STEEP
straight line approximating ground surface
dip angle
outcrop width
horizontal
true thickness
difference in elevation across outcrop
true thickness = (outcrop width × sin dip angle) − (difference in elevation across outcrop × cos dip angle)
(d) COMPLEX SLOPE
horizontal
outcrop width a′
outcrop width b′
outcrop width c′
elevation difference a′
elevation difference c′
dip angle
true thickness a
true thickness b
true thickness c
elevation difference b′
true thickness of formation = a + b + c

Fig. 4.8 Diagrams to show trigonometric methods of deriving true thickness from outcrop width on various land surfaces.

4.6 The 'three-point' method

A common situation in applied geological work is the need for information about the underground arrangement of a unit from knowledge of its elevation at only a few places. Assuming the unit is reasonably planar, a minimum of three elevation points is required (Fig. 4.10). Each can be underground or at surface. Simple graphical constructions

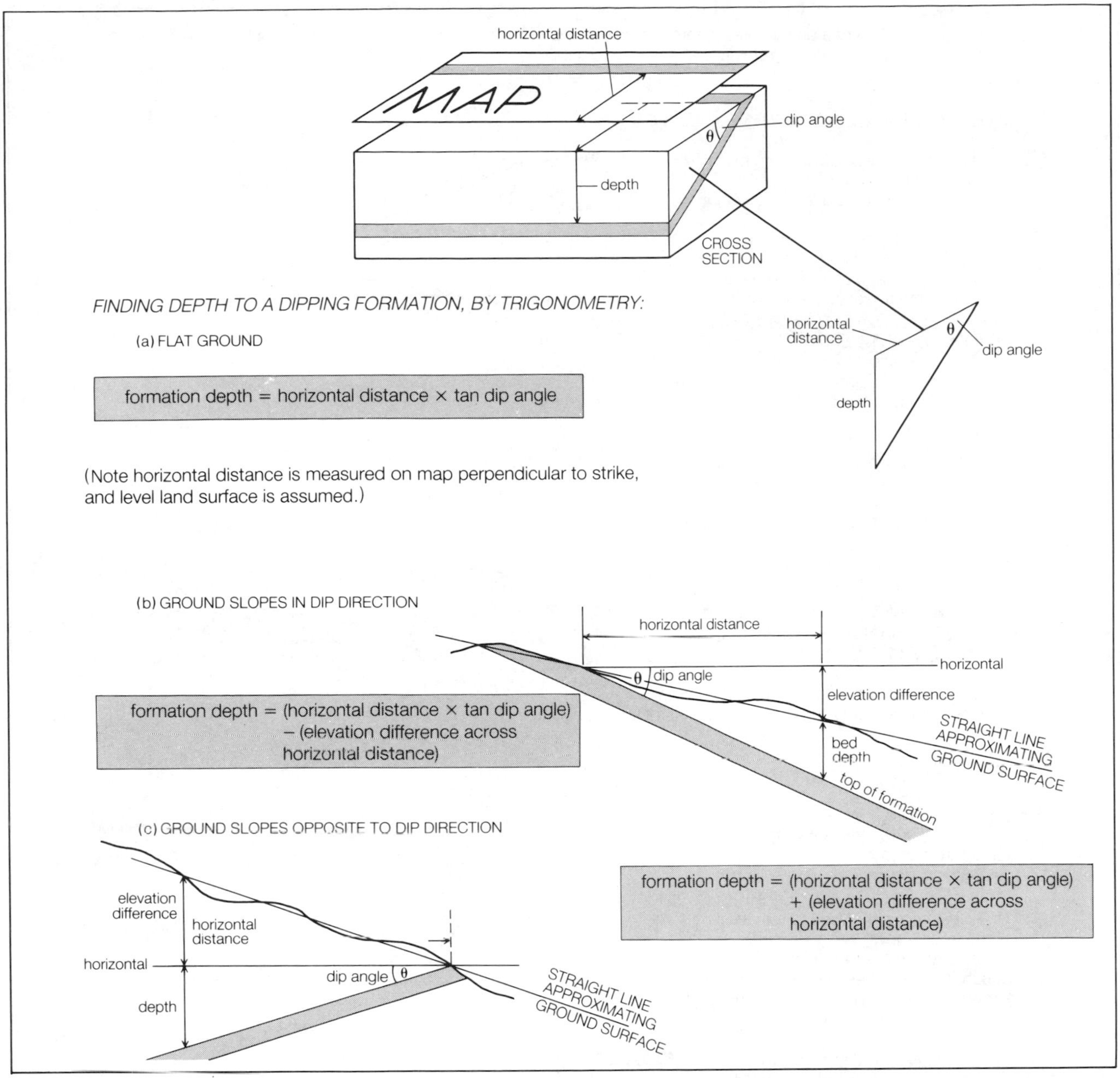

horizontal distance

MAP

dip angle

θ

depth

CROSS SECTION

FINDING DEPTH TO A DIPPING FORMATION, BY TRIGONOMETRY:

(a) FLAT GROUND

formation depth = horizontal distance × tan dip angle

horizontal distance

θ

dip angle

depth

(Note horizontal distance is measured on map perpendicular to strike, and level land surface is assumed.)

(b) GROUND SLOPES IN DIP DIRECTION

horizontal distance

horizontal

θ dip angle

elevation difference

formation depth = (horizontal distance × tan dip angle) − (elevation difference across horizontal distance)

STRAIGHT LINE APPROXIMATING GROUND SURFACE

bed depth

top of formation

(c) GROUND SLOPES OPPOSITE TO DIP DIRECTION

elevation difference

horizontal distance

horizontal

dip angle θ

depth

STRAIGHT LINE APPROXIMATING GROUND SURFACE

formation depth = (horizontal distance × tan dip angle) + (elevation difference across horizontal distance)

Fig. 4.9 Formation depth. Diagrams to show trigonometric methods of finding the depth of a dipping formation.

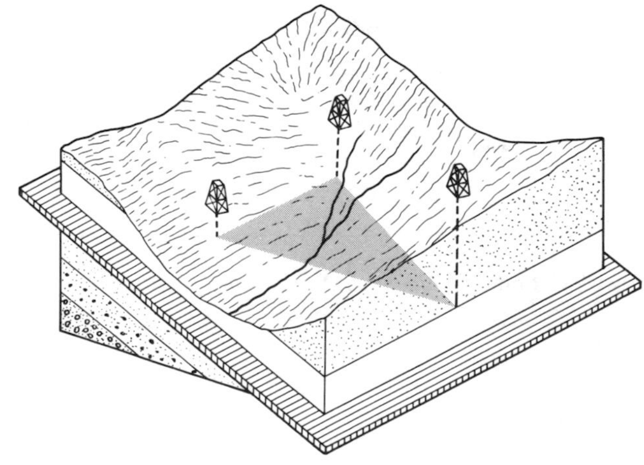

Fig. 4.10 The 'three-point method'. Given a regularly dipping unit and its elevation at three points, various aspects of its orientation can be derived. The first step is to view the three points, here shown as boreholes to a buried unit, as corners of a triangle. The remaining procedures are given in Fig. 4.11.

Knowing the elevation of a unit at three points – from outcrop at a known altitude, elevation in a drill core, etc., or some combination of these, the geologist can:

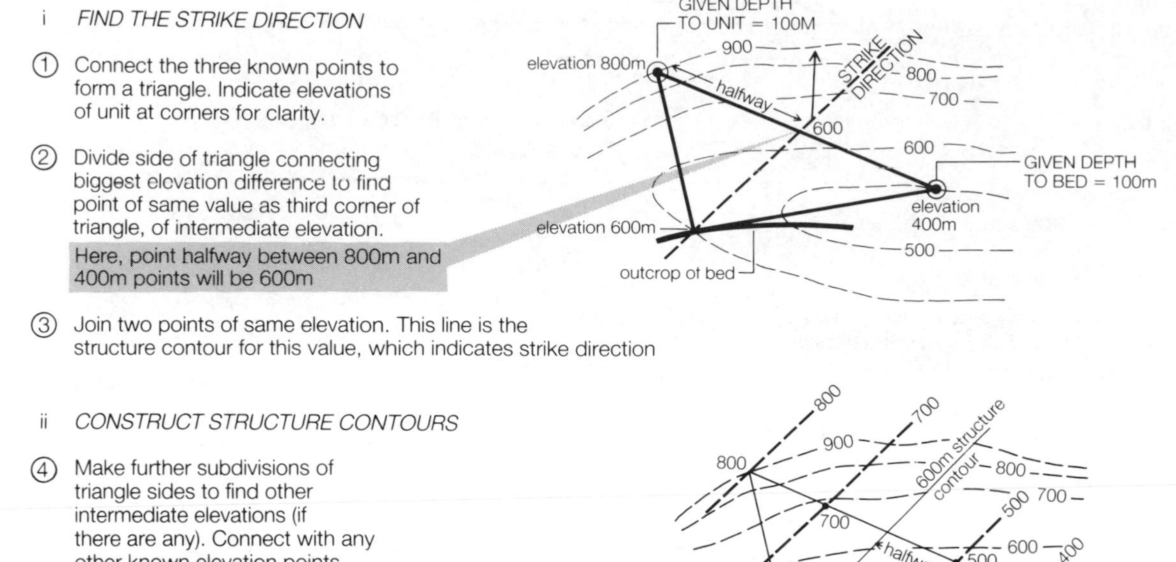
GIVEN DEPTH
TO UNIT = 100M
900
elevation 800m
halfway
STRIKE DIRECTION
800
700
600
600
GIVEN DEPTH
TO BED = 100m
elevation
400m
elevation 600m
500
outcrop of bed

i *FIND THE STRIKE DIRECTION*

① Connect the three known points to form a triangle. Indicate elevations of unit at corners for clarity.

② Divide side of triangle connecting biggest elevation difference to find point of same value as third corner of triangle, of intermediate elevation.

Here, point halfway between 800m and 400m points will be 600m

③ Join two points of same elevation. This line is the structure contour for this value, which indicates strike direction

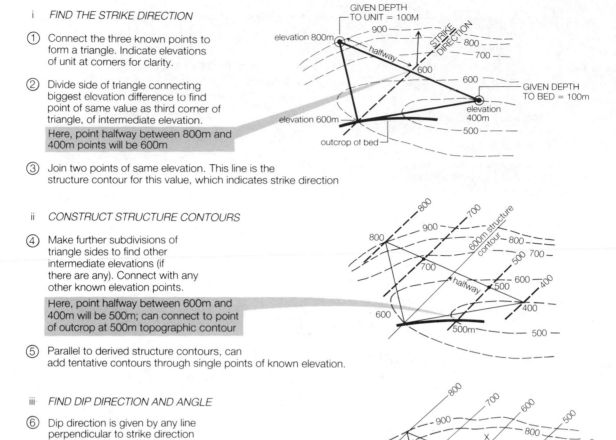

ii *CONSTRUCT STRUCTURE CONTOURS*

④ Make further subdivisions of triangle sides to find other intermediate elevations (if there are any). Connect with any other known elevation points.

Here, point halfway between 600m and 400m will be 500m; can connect to point of outcrop at 500m topographic contour

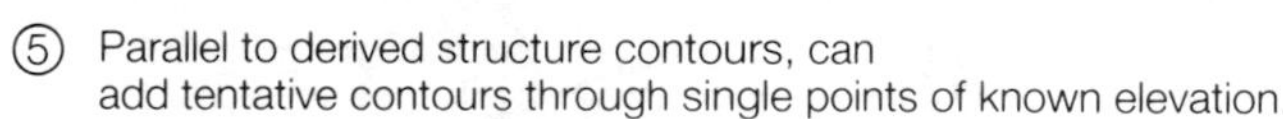

⑤ Parallel to derived structure contours, can add tentative contours through single points of known elevation.

iii *FIND DIP DIRECTION AND ANGLE*

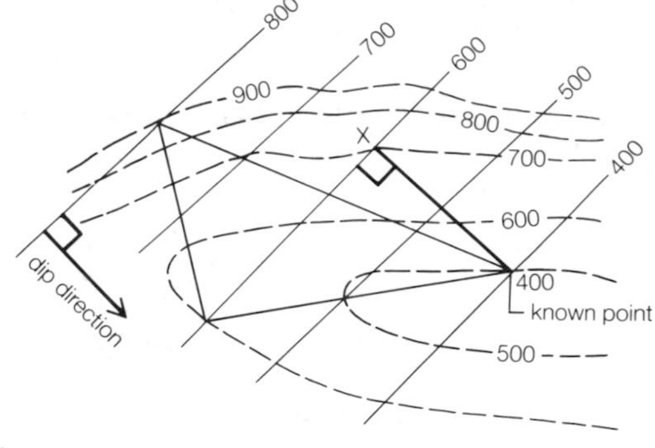
800
700
600
500
400
900
800
X
700
600
dip direction
400
known point
500

⑥ Dip direction is given by any line perpendicular to strike direction (structure contours) towards decreasing elevations.

⑦ Draw line from either greatest or least of the three known elevation points to meet structure contour derived in i, above, at right angles. (These points are the most closely known – should give greatest accuracy). Label intersection with structure contour, say ×.

$$\tan \text{dip angle} = \frac{\text{elevation difference between} \times \text{and known point}}{\text{horizontal distance between} \times \text{and known point}}$$

iv *FIND FORMATION DEPTH*

⑧ Derive strike direction (i, above) and dip angle (iii, above). Measure horizontal distance, at right angles to strike, between point at which depth required and any point where formation elevation is known (structure contour, outcrop, given point) From formation depth = horizontal distance × tan dip angle (fig. 4.9), find depth difference from point of known formation elevation.

Fig. 4.11 Some applications of the 'three-point method'.

can provide different kinds of information on the dipping plane (Fig. 4.11). Of course, the greater the number of elevation points the greater the control, especially if the unit is thought to vary somewhat in dip. Actually, the technique has already been employed here, in section 3.4 and Figs 3.4 and 3.8, for deriving structure contours from borehole data.

An alternative way to derive information from a map on bed dips, thicknesses, and depths is to make a scale graphical construction in the vertical, a kind of cross-section. The accuracy of this approach for measurements depends a lot on drafting precision, but has the advantage of showing the situation pictorially. In fact, fully drawn cross-sections are the most visually effective way of representing the subsurface arrangement of rocks. We turn now to take a closer look at this extremely important facet of mapwork.

4.7 Summary of chapter

1. The orientation of a geological plane is specified by its strike – the compass direction of a horizontal line on the plane, and its dip angle – the maximum inclination from the horizontal. The general dip direction has also to be given.
2. The direction of dip is always at right-angles to the strike direction.
3. In other directions, the dip is a lesser value, called the apparent dip.
4. The thickness of a formation is measured at right-angles to its bounding surfaces. Except for vertical units, the outcrop width is an apparent thickness only.
5. The depth to a formation at a given point can be derived from the dip of the unit at a nearby outcrop.
6. Given the elevation of a plane at three or more points, the orientation of the plane can be derived.

4.8 Selected further reading

Rowland, S. M. (1986). *Structural analysis and synthesis*, Oxford, Blackwell.
(Chapter 1 presents four methods for dealing with apparent dips; chapter 3 discusses thicknesses.)

Ragan, D. M. (1985). *Structural Geology. An introduction to geometrical techniques*, 3rd edn, New York, Wiley.
(Chapters 1 and 2 give methods for working with dips, thicknesses, and depths of formations.)

Dennison, J. M. (1968). *Analysis of geologic structures*. New York, Norton.
(Chapters 1–3 cover true and apparent dips, thickness determinations, and depths, respectively. Derivations of the trigonometric equations are given. Chapter 5 includes three-point problems.)

MAP 6 Boyd Volcanics, New South Wales, Australia

Part of the extreme southern tip of New South Wales appears on the map opposite, enlarged to about 1:14 500 and slightly simplified from Fergusson *et al.* (1979), by permission of the *Australian Journal of Earth Sciences*. The bedding symbol with 'facing determined' indicates that the beds become stratigraphically younger in the direction of the arrow in the normal way, i.e. in this map area there are no inverted successions.

What is the approximate orientation of the Banded rhyolite facies? Quote it as a strike and dip.

The main E–W road in the area crosses the Arkosic facies obliquely, for example, at the point marked α. If there were road-cuts (parallel to the road) in these rocks, at what angle would they be seen to dip? How thick is the unit at the north side of the road?

The base of the Basalt facies is shown to be dipping at 30°. At the point labelled β, at what depth are the phyllites and metaquartzites of the Mallacoota Beds? (The elevation of the stream at β is about 125 m.)

Further exercises on subsurface calculations

Referring to Map 1, of Raton, New Mexico, what is the approximate strike and dip of the Precambrian surface northeast of Las Vegas? Calculate from the structure contours the dip angle of the Precambrian surface a) ESE of Maxwell, and b) SW of Cimarron.

Select three adjacent points on Map 2, say wells 115, 126, and 127, and find the dip direction and angle of the Neocomian in that part of the Lacq Gas Field. What is the strike direction and dip angle of the Neocomian surface in the vicinity of wells 122, 124, and 132?

Consult Map 3, of the Bear Hole area of Montana. Quote, in the conventional way, a representative strike and dip for the Mississippian. Calculate the thickness of the middle and upper Cambrian, bearing in mind the ground slope. At a point 1.5 km north of Long Ridge, at the 8° dip symbol, find the depth of the Upper Devonian using structure contours, and by using trigonometry. Account for any discrepancy between results from the two methods. On the track northwest from Commissary towards Spruce, at what angle would the beds be seen to dip?

On Map 4 of Maccoyella Ridge, New Zealand, what is the true thickness range of the Te Were sandstone? At what depth is the Te Were sandstone below the airstrip?

Vertical thicknesses of some of the units on Map 5 are readily derived from the depths given in the borehole logs. Convert these values to the true thicknesses for the Coal Measures fine sandstones in borehole G141, and for the whole of the Coal Measure sandstones as seen in boreholes G153 and G140.

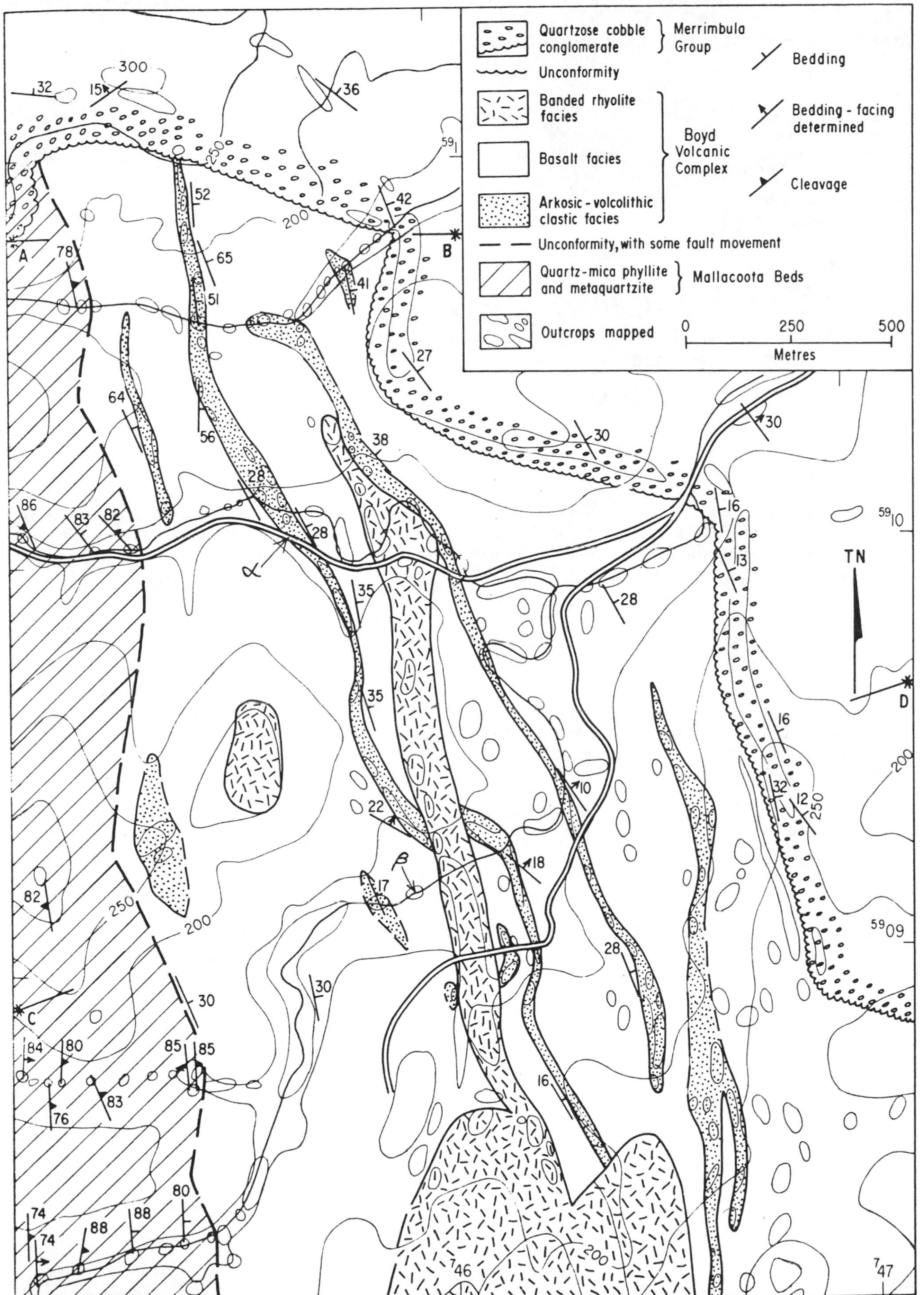
Quartzose cobble conglomerate
Merrimbula Group
Unconformity
Banded rhyolite facies
Basalt facies
Arkosic - volcolithic clastic facies
Boyd Volcanic Complex
Unconformity, with some fault movement
Quartz-mica phyllite and metaquartzite
Mallacoota Beds
Outcrops mapped
Bedding
Bedding - facing determined
Cleavage
0
250
500
Metres
TN
A
B
C
D
α
β

MAP 7 The 'northcrop' of the South Wales Coalfield

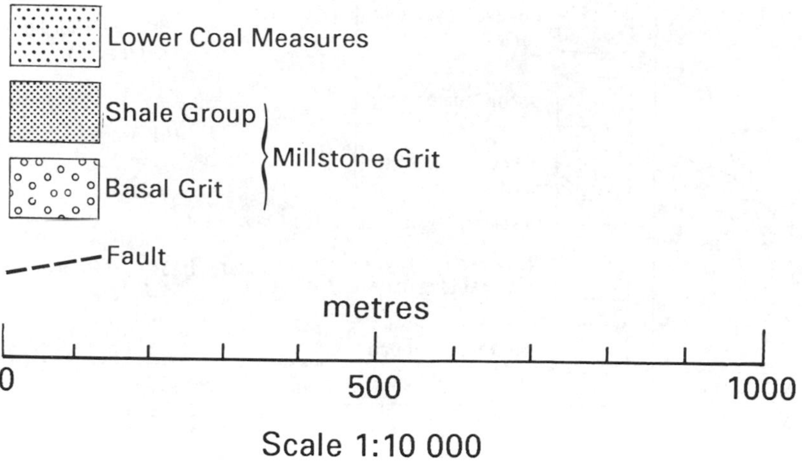
Lower Coal Measures
Shale Group
Basal Grit
Millstone Grit
Fault
metres
0
500
1000
Scale 1:10 000

The map opposite is part of a series of 1:10 000 maps produced during a study of limestone subsidence commissioned by the Welsh Office. It is reproduced here by permission of the Controller of Her Majesty's Stationery Office. The map details part of the Carboniferous succession which comprises the northern flank, or 'northcrop', of the S Wales coalfield. Part of this north crop falls within Plate 1; the area enlarged here is around [SO0911].

Draw structure contours for the top of the shale group of the Millstone Grit. What is the strike and dip of the surface? Comment on its structure.

What is the thickness of the shale group? (If you are solving this question by using outcrop width and dip angle, remember (a) to measure the outcrop width in the true dip direction, and (b) to allow for any topographic slope.)

If a borehole/well was sunk at Pen March, predict what rocks the core would contain. Draw a vertical section for Pen March, showing on the column the stratigraphic succession and, as far as possible, the thicknesses that would be observed in the borehole. (Remember that borehole thicknesses, being vertical, will not be the same as the true thickness of inclined beds.)

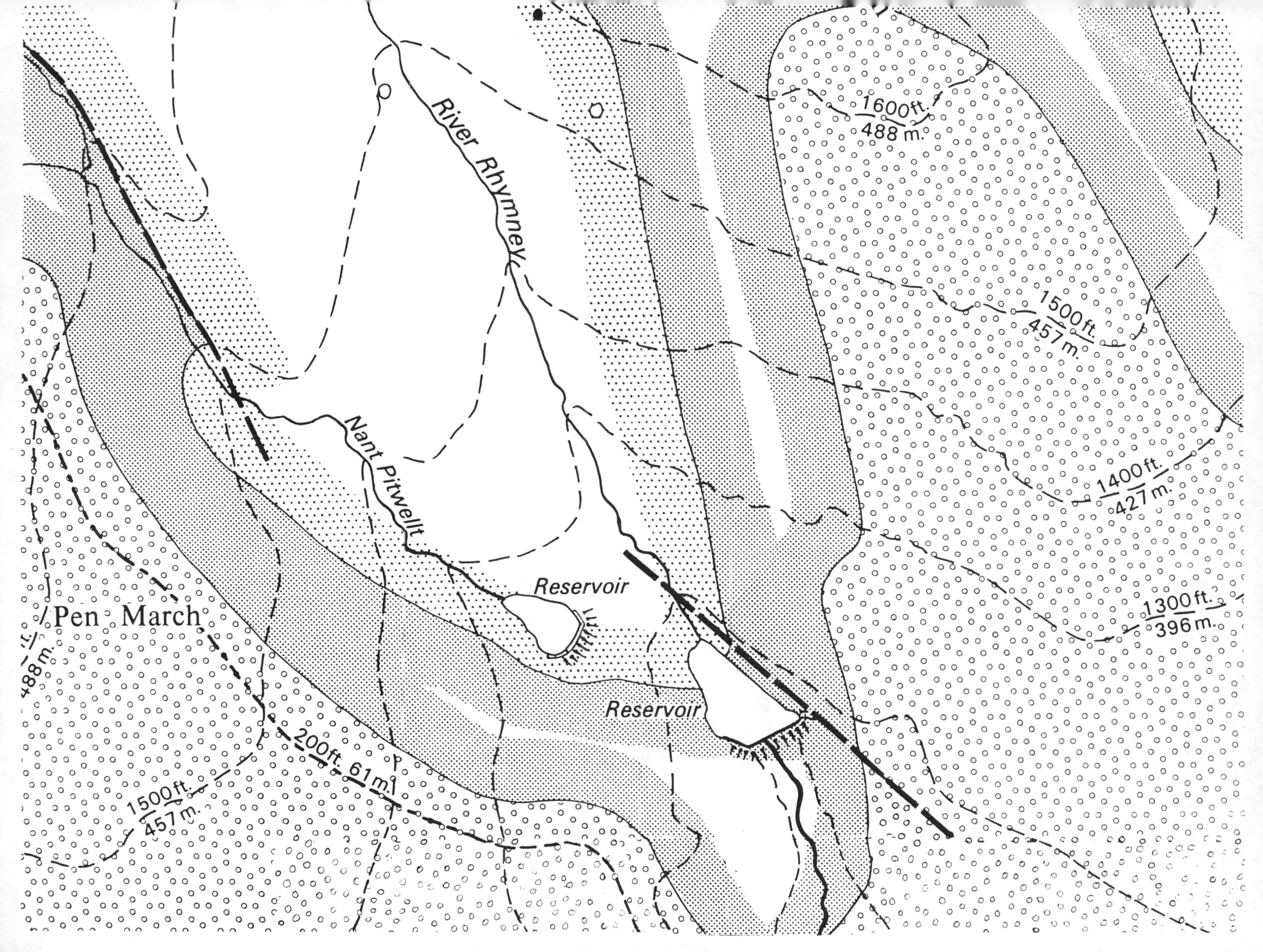

River Rhymney
1600ft.
488 m.
1500ft.
457 m.
Nant Pitwellt
1400ft.
427 m.
Reservoir
1300ft.
396 m.
Pen March
488 m.
Reservoir
200ft. 61 m.
1500ft.
457 m.

MAP 8 Long Mountain, Powys, Wales

Key to letters on map

UL	Upper Ludlow
Ml	*Monograptus leintwardinensis*
Mt	*Monograptus tumescens*
Mn	*Monograptus nilssoni*
Mv	*Monograptus vulgaris*
Cl	*Cyrtograptus lundgrendi*

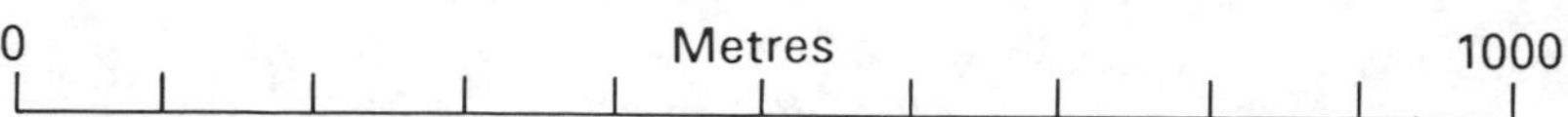
0
Metres
1000

Opposite is a map at 1:10 000 scale of the area south of Long Mountain, near Welshpool, in mid-Wales. The area can be seen on Plate 1 around [SJ2906].

What, from Plate 1, appears to be the overall structure of the rocks forming Long Mountain?

On the area covered by Map 8, the beds are of reasonably consistent in orientation. Structure contours therefore need few control points for their construction. Note, from the map key, that the units on the map are mostly defined on the basis of the fossils they contain. The oldest unit, as always, is at the bottom of the list and the youngest at the top. In which stratigraphic system, according to the BGS Ten Mile map (Plate 1), do these units occur?

Draw sufficient structure contours to be able to specify the strike and dip of the rocks. Quote the strike and dip in the conventional way (e.g. 110/30°N).

Plot the strike and dip on the map using a conventional symbol.

Using this value of strike and dip, calculate the depth to the top of the Cyrtograptus unit at Walton Hall and at Rowley Farm.

Draw some structure contours for this same surface and use them to predict its depth at the same two localities. What might the reasons be for any discrepancy with the depths obtained using trigonometry?

If rocks are exposed along Binweston Lane, at what angle would they be seen to dip?

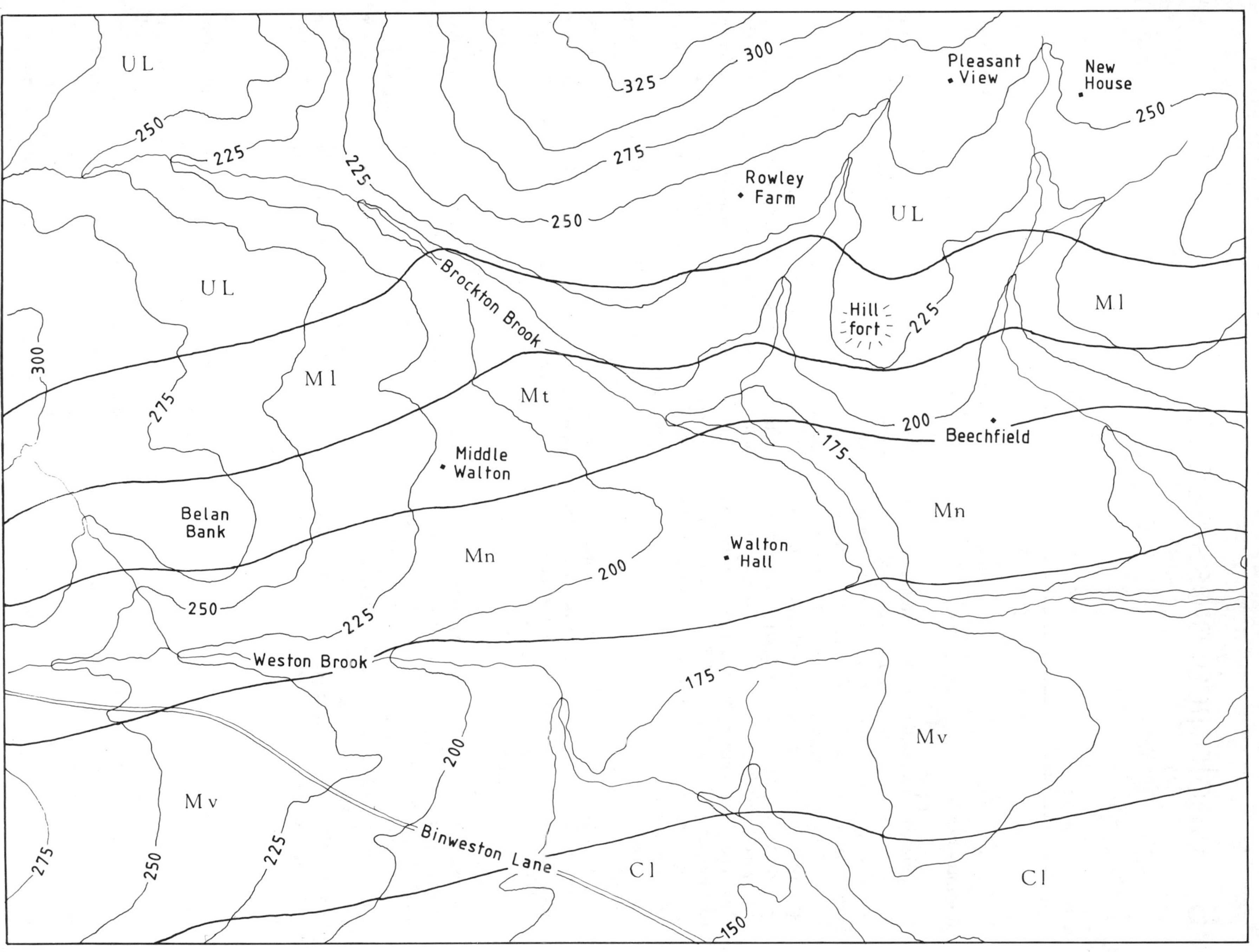
UL
300
325
Pleasant View
New House
250
225
275
Rowley Farm
UL
Brockton Brook
Hill fort
Ml
Mt
Middle Walton
200
Beechfield
175
Belan Bank
Mn
Walton Hall
Mn
Weston Brook
Mv
Mv
Binweston Lane
Cl
Cl
150

5 Geological cross-sections

5.1 Introduction

Rock formations are readily observed in steep faces, such as cliffs, canyons, and mountainsides, in a kind of natural cross-section. It is perhaps for this reason that cross-sections seem more immediately familiar than geological maps, and give a more striking picture of the arrangement of the beds. This is borne out historically, as sections were being drawn long before geological maps. Cross-sections portray the arrangement of the rocks as seen in a vertical plane. They are extremely useful devices but, nevertheless, they are strictly two-dimensional. It is the combination of the vertical cross-sections with horizontal geological maps that forms such an effective means of working with three-dimensional geology on paper.

As with maps, cross-sections can be treated in a reconnaissance way, or they can be constructed accurately to enable measurements to be made. As mentioned in the last chapter, quantities such as bed dip, thickness, and depth can often be arrived at more conveniently from cross-sections than by using trigonometry. These days the more routine aspects of constructing and manipulating cross-sections are being done increasingly by computers. The present chapter is mainly concerned with the understanding of cross-sections, so that any available computer facilities can be used to best advantage.

The first half of the chapter discusses some fundamental aspects of cross-sections and their construction. The second half extends the concepts to three-dimensional devices such as block diagrams. In the present context we are largely concerned with constructing cross-sections from existing geological maps. However, geological surveyors normally develop at least sketch cross-sections as part of their fieldwork, so as to keep in mind the spatial arrangement of the rocks. In some situations, particularly in the oil industry (e.g. see Langstaff and Morrill, 1981), it is common for maps to be derived from geological sections. Wells and seismic lines provide much of the subsurface data, which are compiled onto various kinds of cross-sections from which the geological maps are in turn produced. All this illustrates the importance of cross-sections and the way they complement geological maps.

5.2 Line of section

Normally the line across a map along which the cross-section is drawn should be at right angles to the dominant strike of the rocks. This not only gives the best visual impression of structural relationships but, being in the dip-direction, will allow the direct measurement of the true dip of the beds (provided there is no vertical exaggeration, see section 5.3). If the section is not perpendicular to strike, it will show apparent dip values only, and the trigonometric corrections given in Fig. 4.6 will have to be applied. Strike-parallel sections will show nothing of the dip of the beds, although they do have their uses, such as illustrating thickness changes along strike.

If you are planning to draw a cross-section across an area of variable strike, say with two differently oriented rock sequences, you have several options. If one of the sequences seems more important, then the section line could be sited perpendicular to these rocks, with the understanding that the other sequence will have a somewhat illusory appearance on the section. If the section is being constructed by underground projections of dip readings at the surface (section 5.4) rather than from structure contours, the dip amounts for the oblique beds will have to be adjusted to an apparent value (Fig. 4.6). For most purposes, however, corrections to section lines not more than about 15° away from the true dip direction are negligible. An alternative procedure would be to draw two sections, each perpendicular to one of the sequences. In fact, a typical geological map needs several cross-sections to illustrate adequately the subsurface structure of the area. A third possibility is to bend the section line.

The problem of section line arises particularly where a section is being drawn from a map but is utilising some subsurface data. Such added information will probably greatly improve the reliability of the cross-section, but it is unlikely that seismic lines, boreholes, mine adits, etc., will lie exactly on the ideal line of section. Here, it may be better to deflect the section to incorporate directly the subsurface information. Cross-sections used in oil exploration typically have highly zigzag paths, passing through the greatest practicable number of wells. However, where

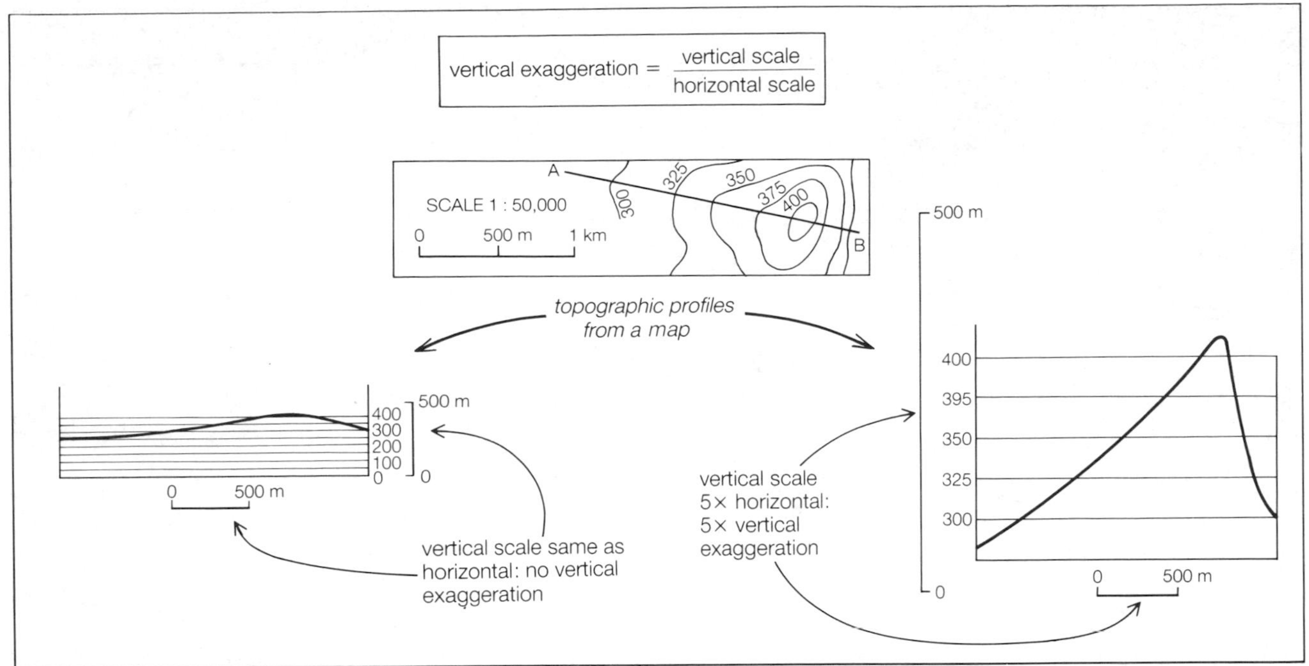
vertical exaggeration = vertical scale / horizontal scale
A
B
SCALE 1 : 50,000
0
500 m
1 km
300
325
350
375
400
topographic profiles from a map
500 m
400
300
200
100
0
0
500 m
vertical scale same as horizontal: no vertical exaggeration
vertical scale 5× horizontal: 5× vertical exaggeration
500 m
400
395
350
325
300
0
0
500 m

Fig. 5.1 Vertical exaggeration and its effect on topographic slope.

the section is being drawn from a map but it is desired to incorporate some information not far from the strike-perpendicular section line, it may be better to project the data to the section rather than bend the line (see Fig.5.6).

5.3 Scale and vertical exaggeration

In the great majority of cases in which a cross-section is being drawn from a map, the horizontal scales of map and section should be the same. It is with the vertical scale that an element of choice arises. Essentially, using a vertical scale greater than the horizontal one allows greater detail to be included on the section but introduces distortion. In general, it is best to use the same horizontal and vertical scales unless there is a strong reason for doing otherwise. If a larger vertical scale is employed it leads to **vertical exaggeration** (Fig. 5.1). This should be quoted on the section. Many published sections are clearly exaggerated, but leave it to the reader to divine by what amount.

If a cross-section is used for carrying out the kinds of measurements discussed in chapter 4, then any vertical exaggeration has to be allowed for. An important effect arising from vertical exaggeration is the steepening of sloping lines on the section. By expanding the vertical scale on topographic sections subtle changes in landslopes can be magnified, say for geomorphological purposes (Fig. 5.1). But the disadvantage is obvious – realism is lost. Gently undulating land can look like alpine mountains!

In the same way, dips on geological cross-sections are increased by vertical exaggeration (Fig. 5.2). All dips, except perfectly horizontal and vertical features, are steepened. The shallower the dip the more it is affected (Fig. 5.3). As a result, two faults, for example, one of steeper inclination than the other, could appear misleadingly similar on a highly exaggerated section (Fig. 5.2). On the other hand, vertical exaggeration can be useful in bringing out small but potentially significant differences between shallow-dipping beds. This could be important, for example, in stratigraphical and sedimentological studies.

The thickness of beds is distorted on sections which employ vertical exaggeration (Fig. 5.4). The overall effect is to expand the thicknesses. Thickness *differences* will also be increased, so that exaggerated sections can be used to show small variations more clearly. However, there is a complication to enhancing thickness differences in this way. The amount of thickness increase depends on the dip of the bed. The thickness of horizontal beds increases most in the same ratio as the vertical exaggeration; vertical beds are not affected at all; and intermediate dips are influenced by various amounts. Dips in the range 1–20° are most susceptible. Two beds of the same real thickness but of different shallow dips will appear of differing thickness on an exaggerated section. A folded bed of constant thickness can take on an attenuated appearance (Fig. 5.4). Folded beds can look like this in nature, but here it is a purely artificial consequence of the vertical exaggeration. As long as you are aware of these effects, they can usually be allowed for when looking at exaggerated sections. The difficulties are that small real variations in thickness can be

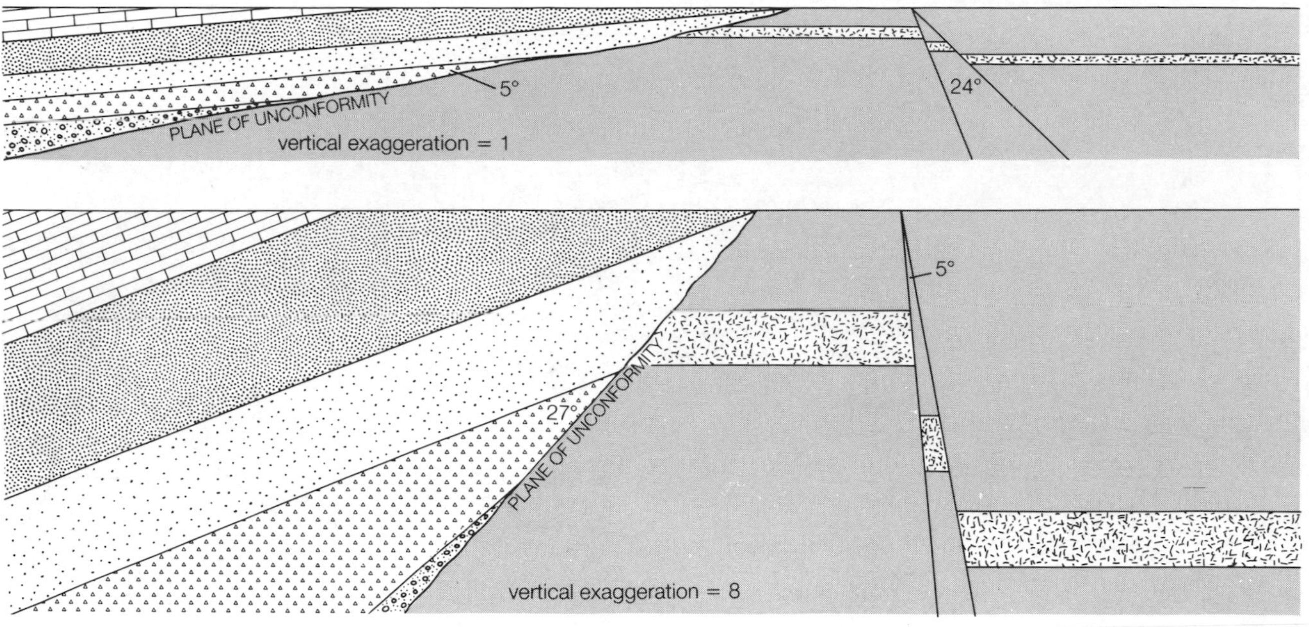
5°
24°
PLANE OF UNCONFORMITY
vertical exaggeration = 1
5°
27°
PLANE OF UNCONFORMITY
vertical exaggeration = 8

Fig. 5.2 The effects of vertical exaggeration on geological surfaces. Note that, because vertical exaggeration affects shallow-dipping surfaces more than steep ones, angular differences *between* shallow-dipping surfaces are increased whereas angles between steep planes are reduced.

(a) trigonometric relation:

TAN EXAGGERATED DIP = VERTICAL EXAG. × TAN UNEXAG. DIP

(b) graphical relation:

curves for d, unexaggerated dip.

Vertical exaggeration

Angle of exaggerated dip

e.g *to find exag. dip:* select curve of unexag. dip (interpolation between curves necessary at high values). From intersection with horizontal line of appropriate vertical exag., project down to find amount of exag. dip

to find unexag. dip: project upwards from point on horizontal axis of known exag. dip to meet horizontal line of known vertical exag. Interpolate to nearest dip curve to find unexag. dip

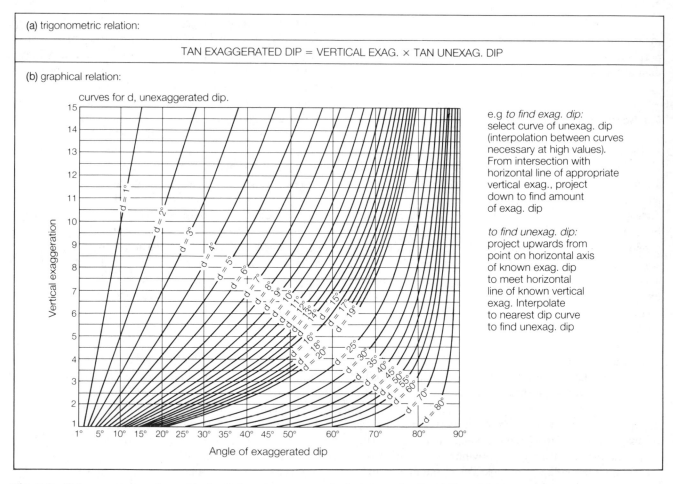

Fig. 5.3 Trigonometric and graphical relations between vertical exaggerations and dip angles.

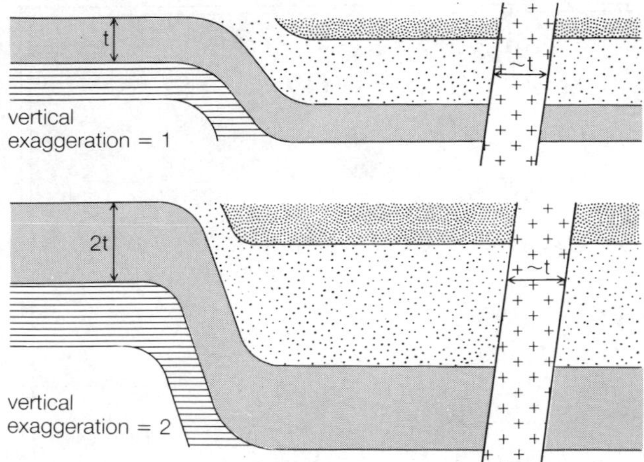

t
~t
vertical
exaggeration = 1
2t
~t
vertical
exaggeration = 2

Fig. 5.4 The effects of vertical exaggeration on formation thickness. Note the large effect on the thickness of horizontal units, the small effect on steep units, and the intermediate effect on moderately dipping beds. If the dip of a unit varies, an apparent attenuation effect can be introduced.

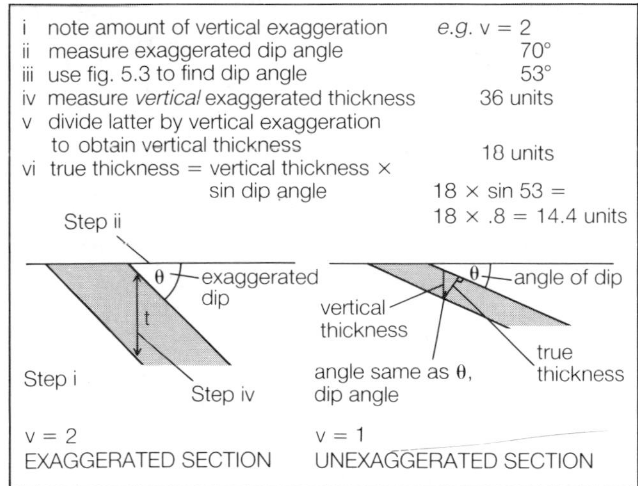

i note amount of vertical exaggeration
e.g. v = 2
ii measure exaggerated dip angle
70°
iii use fig. 5.3 to find dip angle
53°
iv measure *vertical* exaggerated thickness
36 units
v divide latter by vertical exaggeration
to obtain vertical thickness
18 units
vi true thickness = vertical thickness ×
sin dip angle
18 × sin 53 =
18 × .8 = 14.4 units
Step ii
θ
exaggerated
dip
t
Step i
Step iv
θ
angle of dip
vertical
thickness
true
thickness
angle same as θ,
dip angle
v = 2
EXAGGERATED SECTION
v = 1
UNEXAGGERATED SECTION

Fig. 5.5 A simple graphical method for finding the true thickness of a unit shown in a cross-section with vertical exaggeration. Note that the method assumes the section to be drawn at right angles to strike, i.e. in the true dip direction.

masked, and that cumbersome corrections will have to be applied to any thickness measurements (Fig. 5.5).

Where the exaggerated section is used to find depths to subsurface horizons, the necessary correction is less awkward than that for dips and thicknesses. The depth, by virtue of being measured vertically, is greater than the real depth by the same amount as the vertical exaggeration of the section. There may, therefore, be good reasons for expanding the vertical scale of the section, although the fact that the construction can be made with less care is not one of them. If vertical exaggeration is employed for some reason, the results have to be treated with care. It is generally better to have the vertical scale of the section the same as the horizontal.

5.4 Manual drawing of cross-sections

Cross-sections can either be sketched or accurately constructed, depending on the purpose for which they are being produced. When visualising the three-dimensional arrangement of rocks from a map, it is often useful to sketch cross-sections, both to clarify your own mental picture and to communicate it to others. The overall outcrop patterns are paramount in suggesting the arrangement to be sketched on the section. The principles of outcrop assessment were introduced in section 2.3 and are developed further in chapter 6. Any dip values provided on the map allow the subsurface lines to be sketched more realistically. With small-scale maps it is usually not possible to draw anything more precise than a sketch section, simply because more detailed information will not be shown.

On larger scale maps, say around 1:50 000 and larger, it should be possible to construct an accurate cross-section to the same scale as the map. Figure 5.6 shows the method. Good strike and dip information will be necessary to allow judicious location of the section line and sound projection to depth. Ideally, it will be possible to draw some structure contours in the vicinity of the section line. They can then be plotted on the section in the same way as topographic contours.

It is usual to construct the topographic profile first and then project the subsurface geology from it. However, if structure contours are being used to position the geological surfaces, it is more accurate to draw the topography last, as the elevations of the outcrops of those surfaces can be used in addition to the topographic contours to control the course of the topographic profile. Good information on the subsurface form of one formation will help constrain the projections of adjacent surfaces. The greater the control on the cross-section, the more reliable any measurements from it are likely to be. The completed section should provide a basis for confident advice about subsurface conditions.

If the section is drawn in a direction other than that of true dip, dip values given on the map may have to be adjusted (section 5.2). Formations are assumed to retain constant thickness at depth, that is, the lines representing the top and bottom of a unit remain parallel, unless there is evidence on the map of thickness change. Folded beds are extrapolated at depth with curvature, although for more advanced work there is a range of techniques for more refined projection (e.g. see Badgley, 1959, chapter 3; Ramsay and Huber, 1987). Many

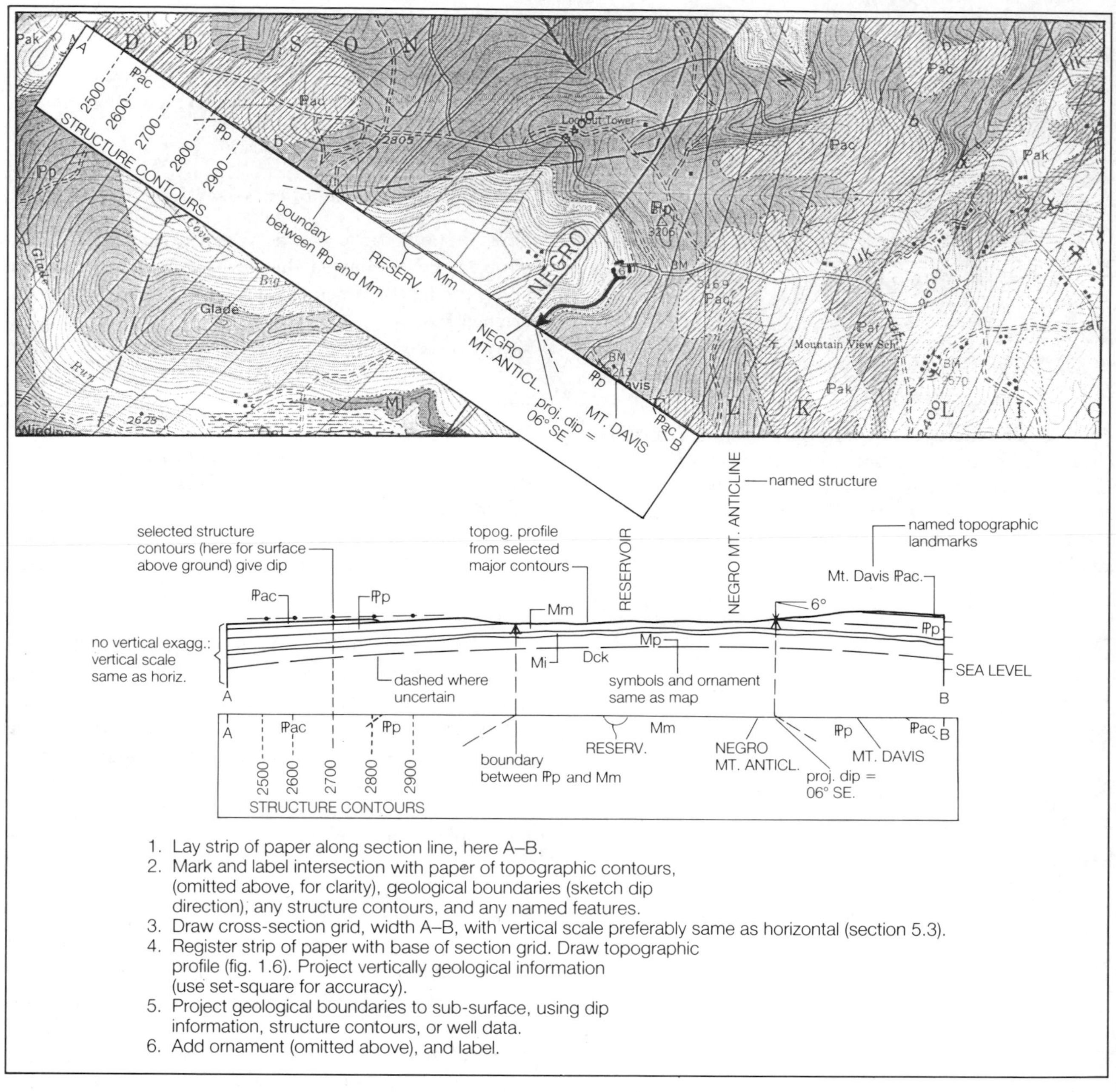

2500
2600
2700
2800
2900
STRUCTURE CONTOURS
boundary between ℙp and Mm
RESERV.
Mm
NEGRO
NEGRO MT. ANTICL.
proj. dip = 06° SE
ℙp
MT. DAVIS
ℙac
A
B
Lookout Tower
2805
Glade
ℙac
ℙp
ℙak
Mountain View Sch.
named structure
NEGRO MT. ANTICLINE
RESERVOIR
named topographic landmarks
Mt. Davis ℙac.
selected structure contours (here for surface above ground) give dip
topog. profile from selected major contours
ℙac
ℙp
Mm
6°
ℙp
no vertical exagg.: vertical scale same as horiz.
Mp
Mi
Dck
SEA LEVEL
dashed where uncertain
symbols and ornament same as map
A
B
A
ℙac
ℙp
2500
2600
2700
2800
2900
STRUCTURE CONTOURS
boundary between ℙp and Mm
Mm
RESERV.
NEGRO MT. ANTICL.
ℙp
ℙac
B
MT. DAVIS
proj. dip = 06° SE.
1. Lay strip of paper along section line, here A–B.
2. Mark and label intersection with paper of topographic contours, (omitted above, for clarity), geological boundaries (sketch dip direction), any structure contours, and any named features.
3. Draw cross-section grid, width A–B, with vertical scale preferably same as horizontal (section 5.3).
4. Register strip of paper with base of section grid. Draw topographic profile (fig. 1.6). Project vertically geological information (use set-square for accuracy).
5. Project geological boundaries to sub-surface, using dip information, structure contours, or well data.
6. Add ornament (omitted above), and label.

Fig. 5.6 Instructions for drawing a geological cross-section from a map. Map reproduced from Pennsylvania Geological Survey Bulletin C56A, S Somerset County, by permission of the Geological Survey of Pennsylvania.

faults dip at about 70°, but it is conventional to show faults as vertical, unless there is direct evidence otherwise. Faults may flatten to give listric geometry (section 10.2.1), but additional subsurface information is usually necessary to support projections beyond shallow levels. Indicate the sense of fault displacement (section 9.3) if it is known.

The same ornament as used on the map should be added to the section; the datum, horizontal and vertical scales are indicated; and any named structures in the rocks and important topographic landmarks are labelled. Make sure that the line of section is indicated on the map. It is not possible to lay down rules on how rocks should be projected underground. Each situation has to be considered on its own merit. In general, aim for the simplest arrangement which is compatible with the known information. Study examples of published cross-sections; a selection is reproduced in Fig. 5.7.

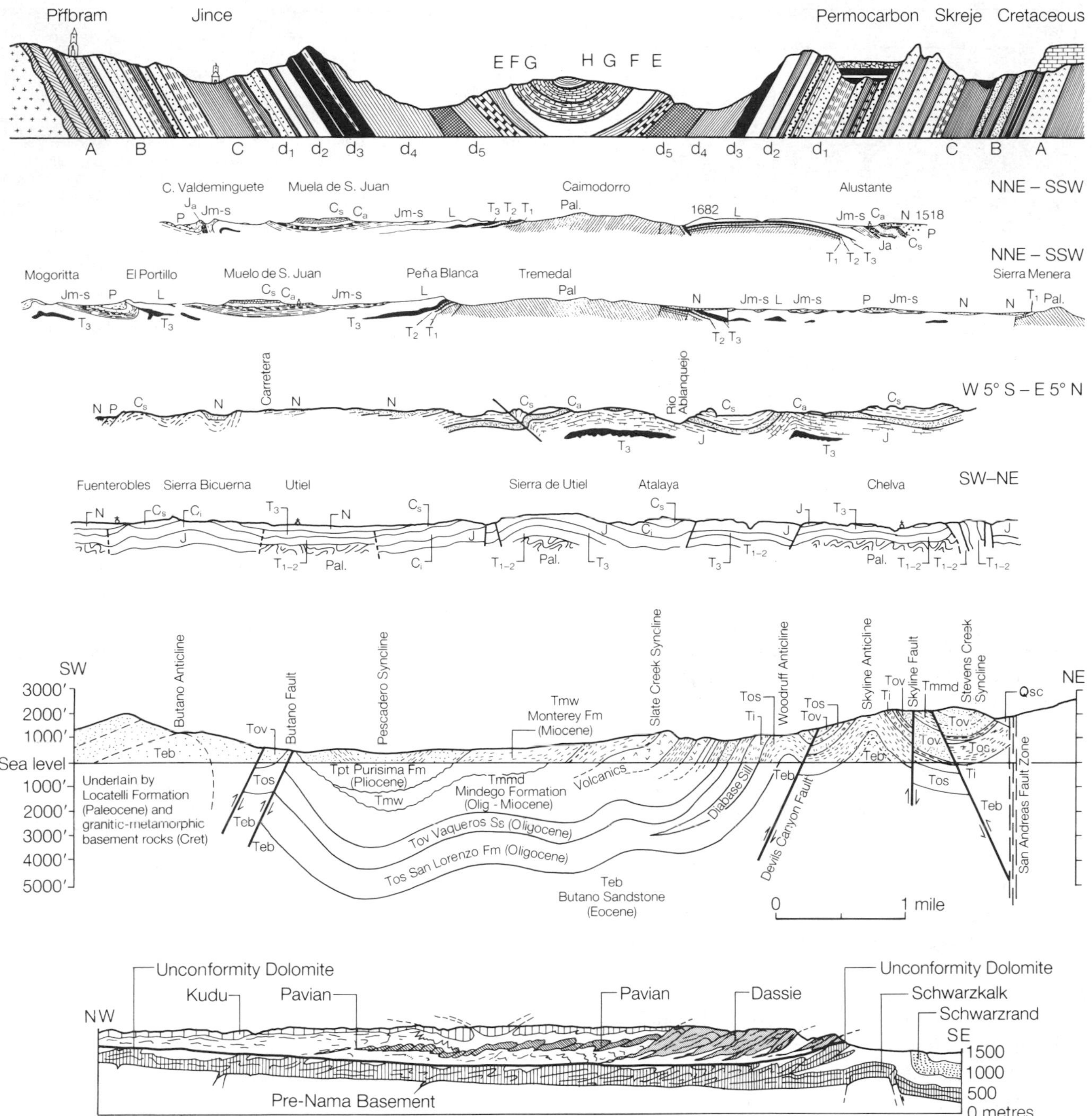
Příbram
Jince
Permocarbon
Skreje
Cretaceous
E F G
H G F E
A B C d1 d2 d3 d4 d5
d5 d4 d3 d2 d1 C B A
C. Valdeminguete
Muela de S. Juan
Caimodorro
Alustante
NNE – SSW
Jm-s
Pal.
1682
N 1518
NNE – SSW
Mogoritta
El Portillo
Muelo de S. Juan
Peña Blanca
Tremedal
Sierra Menera
Carretera
Rio Ablanquejo
W 5° S – E 5° N
Fuenterobles
Sierra Bicuerna
Utiel
Sierra de Utiel
Atalaya
Chelva
SW–NE
SW
NE
3000′
2000′
1000′
Sea level
1000′
2000′
3000′
4000′
5000′
Butano Anticline
Butano Fault
Pescadero Syncline
Slate Creek Syncline
Woodruff Anticline
Skyline Anticline
Skyline Fault
Stevens Creek Syncline
San Andreas Fault Zone
Tmw
Monterey Fm
(Miocene)
Underlain by
Locatelli Formation
(Paleocene) and
granitic-metamorphic
basement rocks (Cret)
Tpt Purisima Fm
(Pliocene)
Tmmd
Mindego Formation
(Olig - Miocene)
Volcanics
Diabase Sill
Tov Vaqueros Ss (Oligocene)
Tos San Lorenzo Fm (Oligocene)
Teb
Butano Sandstone
(Eocene)
Devils Canyon Fault
0
1 mile
Qsc
Unconformity Dolomite
Kudu
Pavian
NW
Pavian
Dassie
Unconformity Dolomite
Schwarzkalk
Schwarzrand
SE
1500
1000
500
0 metres
Pre-Nama Basement

Fig. 5.7 Some examples of published geological cross-sections. (a) An early cross-section, now looking very diagrammatic, across the Bohemian basin, Czechoslovakia, published in 1852 by Joachim Barrande. (b) Four cross-sections of the Iberian fold belt of W Spain. Reproduced from Lemoine (1978), by permission of Elsevier BV. (c) Cross-section of the Coast Ranges, California, USA. Reproduced from Page (1966), by permission of the California Division of Mines and Geology. (d) Cross-section of the Naukluft Mountains, SW Africa. Reproduced from Holmes (1965) after reduction from Korn and Martin (1959), by permission of Thomas Nelson and Sons.

5.5 Structure and stratigraphic sections

All cross-sections are drawn with reference to a particular datum plane, which appears as a horizontal line on the section. Each formation or feature on the section is shown at its scaled elevation with respect to this datum. By far the most common datum is sea-level. Some other marker could be used, and especially on large-scale maps a local datum

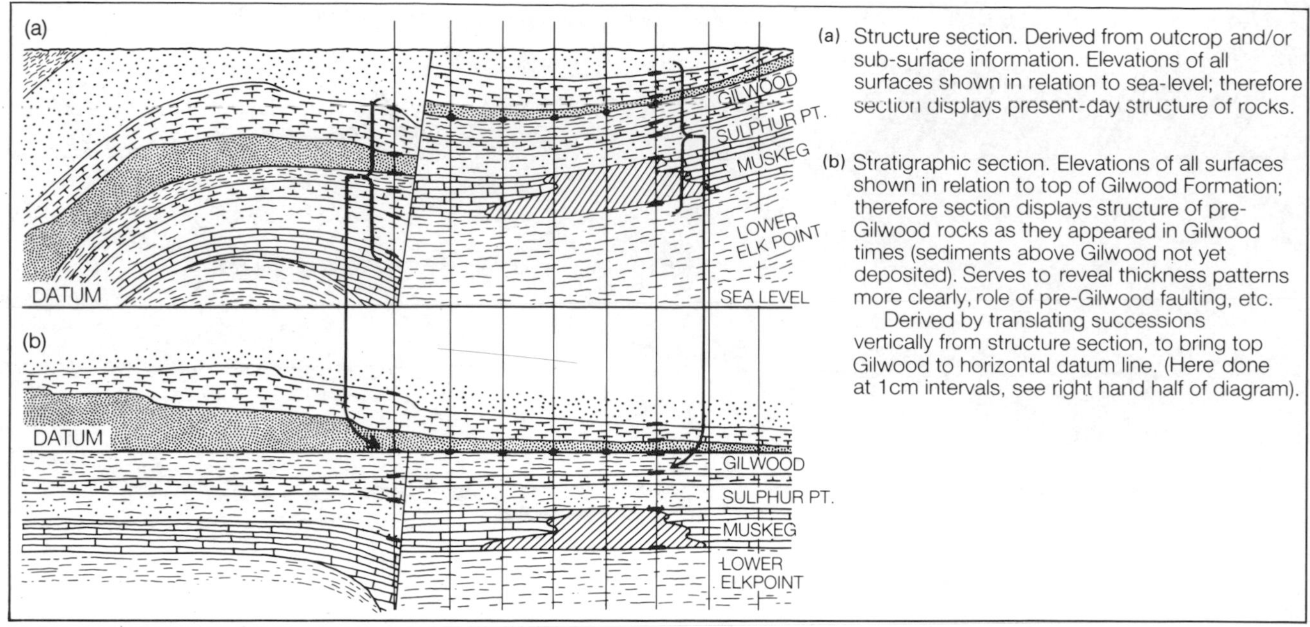
(a)
GILWOOD
SULPHUR PT.
MUSKEG
LOWER ELK POINT
DATUM
SEA LEVEL
(b)
DATUM
GILWOOD
SULPHUR PT.
MUSKEG
LOWER ELKPOINT
(a) Structure section. Derived from outcrop and/or sub-surface information. Elevations of all surfaces shown in relation to sea-level; therefore section displays present-day structure of rocks.
(b) Stratigraphic section. Elevations of all surfaces shown in relation to top of Gilwood Formation; therefore section displays structure of pre-Gilwood rocks as they appeared in Gilwood times (sediments above Gilwood not yet deposited). Serves to reveal thickness patterns more clearly, role of pre-Gilwood faulting, etc.
Derived by translating successions vertically from structure section, to bring top Gilwood to horizontal datum line. (Here done at 1cm intervals, see right hand half of diagram).

Fig. 5.8 Illustrations of structural and stratigraphic sections, and a simple graphical method for converting between them.

may be preferred, perhaps a nearby benchmark if the area is in high terrain or deep in a mine. Irrespective of the elevation of the datum used, the effect of the section is to depict the *structure* of the rock units. Therefore, these cross-sections are properly called **structure sections**. They show the configuration of the rocks, *as they are now*.

For some purposes, however, the present-day arrangement of the rocks is of less interest than the relationships at some past geological time. In this case, a cross-section can be drawn for which the datum is a stratigraphic boundary that formed at the time of interest. Such a construction is called a **stratigraphic section**. The datum horizon normally has to be a reasonably prominent, persistent, stratigraphic unit. It appears on the stratigraphic section as a straight line and the positions of all the other surfaces are referred to it. Rocks below the datum will show the arrangement they had at the time of formation of the datum surface. For example, any intertonguing between units and thickness variations will be highlighted, together with any sedimentary features such as reefs or channels. Any tilting, folding, etc. subsequent to the datum will not appear, otherwise the datum surface would not be horizontal. Such later effects cannot therefore obscure aspects of stratigraphic interest around the time of the datum.

A straightforward way of manually constructing stratigraphic sections from structure sections is shown in Fig. 5.8. It is only approximate because of the implication that the originally horizontal beds got to their present-day form by purely vertical movements – which this construction method simply reverses – and this will not usually be realistic. Any obvious non-vertical displacements, such as low-angle faults (chapter 10), will have to be restored separately.

Stratigraphic sections are much used in the oil industry, partly because the stratigraphic information is important in exploration, and partly because this kind of section is readily constructed from well data. Elaborations of the device are employed too, so it becomes important where different kinds of cross-sections are being employed to specify their nature. This is by no means always done, leaving the reader to work out which datum has been used. However, in most fields of geology, constructions which are called by some combination of 'section', 'cross-section', and 'geological section', will almost certainly be structure sections.

5.6 Three-dimensional diagrams

Although the usual way of representing the geometrical arrangement of rocks is to use sections and maps in conjunction, the role of cross-sections can be extended by giving them a three-dimensional aspect. The two main ways of doing this are to construct either a fence diagram or a block diagram. Each takes two or more conventional cross-sections and converts them into diagrams which look three-dimensional. They are still drawn on a flat surface, but are more strikingly three-dimensional to the eye, and are a highly effective way of visually conveying the spatial arrangement of rocks. The following section avoids detail on manual methods of construction, but outlines the principles behind them.

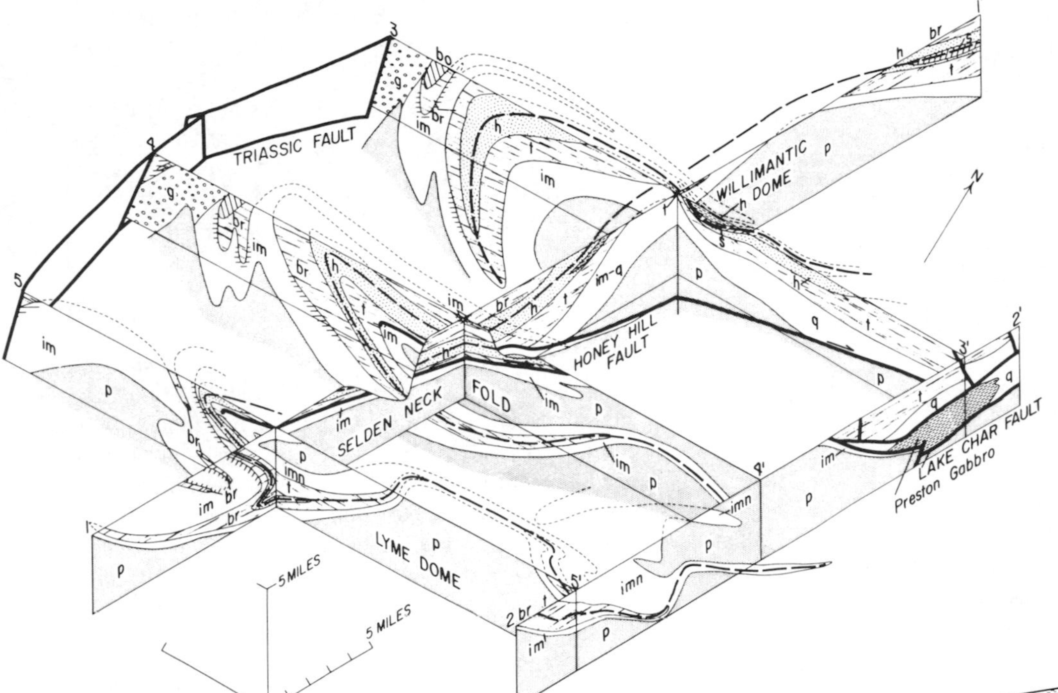
TRIASSIC FAULT
WILLIMANTIC DOME
HONEY HILL FAULT
SELDEN NECK FOLD
LYME DOME
LAKE CHAR FAULT
Preston Gabbro
5 MILES
5 MILES
N

Fig. 5.9 An example of a fence diagram, used here to illustrate complex fold structures in Connecticut, USA. Reproduced from Dixon and Lawrence (1968), by permission of John Wiley and Sons.

5.6.1 *Fence diagrams*

Fence diagrams, sometimes called panel diagrams, are a three-dimensional network of cross-sections drawn in two dimensions (e.g. Fig. 5.9). They have the appearance of interlocking fences, rather like those used in a cattle market. It is useful to draw the diagram on a simplified base map, to show the locations of the sections. The viewing direction is chosen to show the sections to the best advantage. Fences at right-angles to the viewer will appear as conventional cross-sections; any sections close to parallel with the viewing direction will show little information.

Deriving fence diagrams from maps requires the construction of several cross-sections, which will eventually become the panels of the diagram. The various corners of the fences can then be positioned on the base map of the diagram, and the information from the sections transferred to vertical scales extending upwards from the corners. The panels can then be filled in from the cross-sections, if necessary erecting vertical scales within the panels to aid the accurate transfer of the lines from the sections. Lines on rear panels are dashed if they are obscured by part of a forward panel.

If the cross-sections had vertical exaggeration, then this will be translated to the fence diagram. In this case, and if the panel spacing is close, there may be an unacceptable obscuring of the rear panels. A different line of sight may help, but it may be useful to transform the fence diagram and its map base to an isometric projection (Fig. 5.10). The rectangular map base becomes a parallelogram, the sides of which are paralleled by lines that were N–S or E–W on the map. Vertical lines remain vertical. All these lines, which

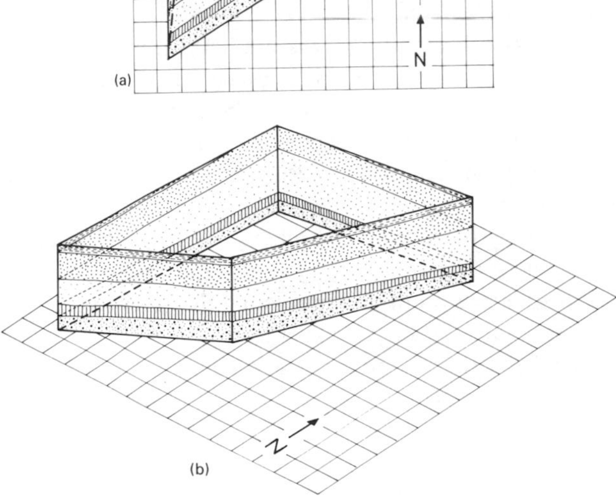
(a)
N
(b)
N

Fig. 5.10 Some aspects of fence diagrams. (a) The orientation of some of the panels, particularly in the west, suppresses the visibility of the information. (b) Greater visibility is gained by transforming (a) into an isometric projection. The gridded base allows this to be done manually. Note, however, that only the vertical lines and those parallel to the N–S and E–W axes preserve their length; in other orientations some distortion is introduced.

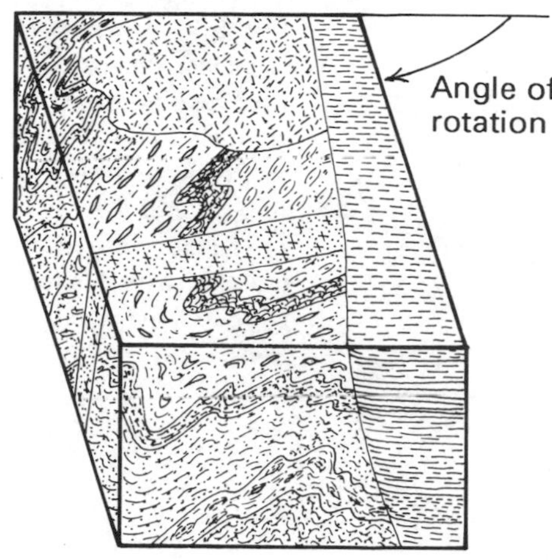
Angle of
rotation

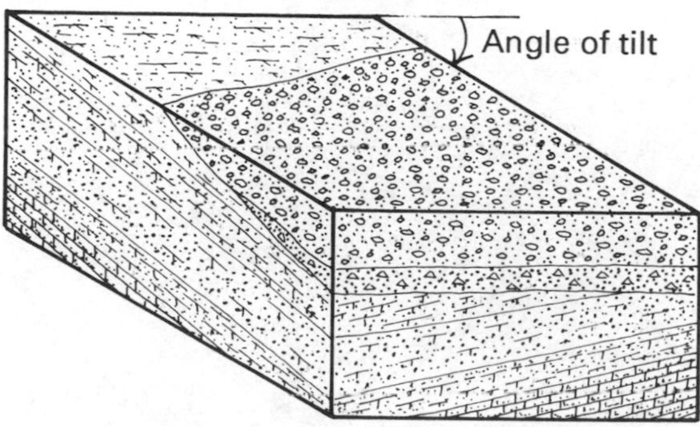
Angle of tilt

Fig. 5.11 Isometric block diagrams. Note that opposing faces of the blocks are parallel. The left-hand block has a high rotation angle (measured in the horizontal plane and indicated by the arrow) giving a good view of the front of the block but not of the sides. It also has a high tilt angle (measured from the horizontal in the vertical plane) to emphasise the top of the block. The right-hand block has a medium tilt, indicated by the arrow, and a medium rotation, giving adequate views of the top and sides of the block.

were originally at right angles, retain the same linear scale in the isometric projection. However, any lines at intermediate angles will change in length, so a grid system such as that shown on the map base in Fig. 5.10 will aid in transferring their locations.

5.6.2 Block diagrams

Block diagrams are two-dimensional drawings of a rectangular block (e.g. Lobeck, 1958). The top of the block is the map plane, and the sides are cross-sections. It is a fairly intuitive way of visualising three-dimensions on paper, and has been used frequently already in this book (e.g. Figs 2.1 and 2.2). However, for quantitative work there are snags, and the kind of projection used to draw the block diagram has to be considered.

Isometric block diagrams are both easy to draw and amenable to direct vertical measurements, because the vertical scales are the same as on cross-sections. However, they have an awkward visual effect (Fig. 5.11). They are constructed in a similar way to isometric fence diagrams, so a horizontal grid is helpful here, too, in manually transferring the information from the starting cross-section to the block diagram.

Perspective block diagrams, on the other hand, give a much more realistic appearance to the block, but introduce further distortion. Block diagrams can be drawn in *one-point perspective*, where the front of the block faces the observer squarely, and all lines not in the plane of the paper meet at one point on the horizon. Sketch versions can achieve the effect by simply making the back of the block narrower than the front.

Block diagrams in *two-point perspective* have their front corner pointing towards the observer, with all non-vertical lines merging to one of two points on the horizon. With both kinds of perspective, the amounts of rotation and tilt of the block can be selected in order to display features to the greatest advantage (Fig. 5.12). However, all the changes in dimensions made in drawing block diagrams interfere with any measurements that are to be made. The manual construction of properly scaled drawings is laborious, and corrections to measurements tedious. Hence, block diagrams are used less for quantitative purposes than for the rapid visual communication of three-dimensional relationships.

Computers are ideally suited to the construction and manipulation of cross-sections and three-dimensional diagrams (section 15.2.3). Trying various lines of section and different amounts of vertical exaggeration; transferring structure sections to stratigraphic sections, and sections to fence and block diagrams; transforming between isometric and perspective projections; varying the amount of rotation and tilt: all these tedious procedures are executed swiftly and effectively by the kinds of computers and graphic capabilities available today. Undoubtedly, these applications will grow. However, the software continues to have built-in limitations, varying according to its complexity and cost. Mistakes can be made in the processing, and any section or diagram can only be as reliable as the geological information on which it is based. Pity the geologist who does not understand what it is that the computer is doing!

5.7 Summary of chapter

1. Cross-sections are drawn in a vertical plane.
2. They therefore closely complement maps, with which they make a powerful way of communicating the three-dimensional arrangement of rock formations.
3. Sections should be drawn at right-angles to the

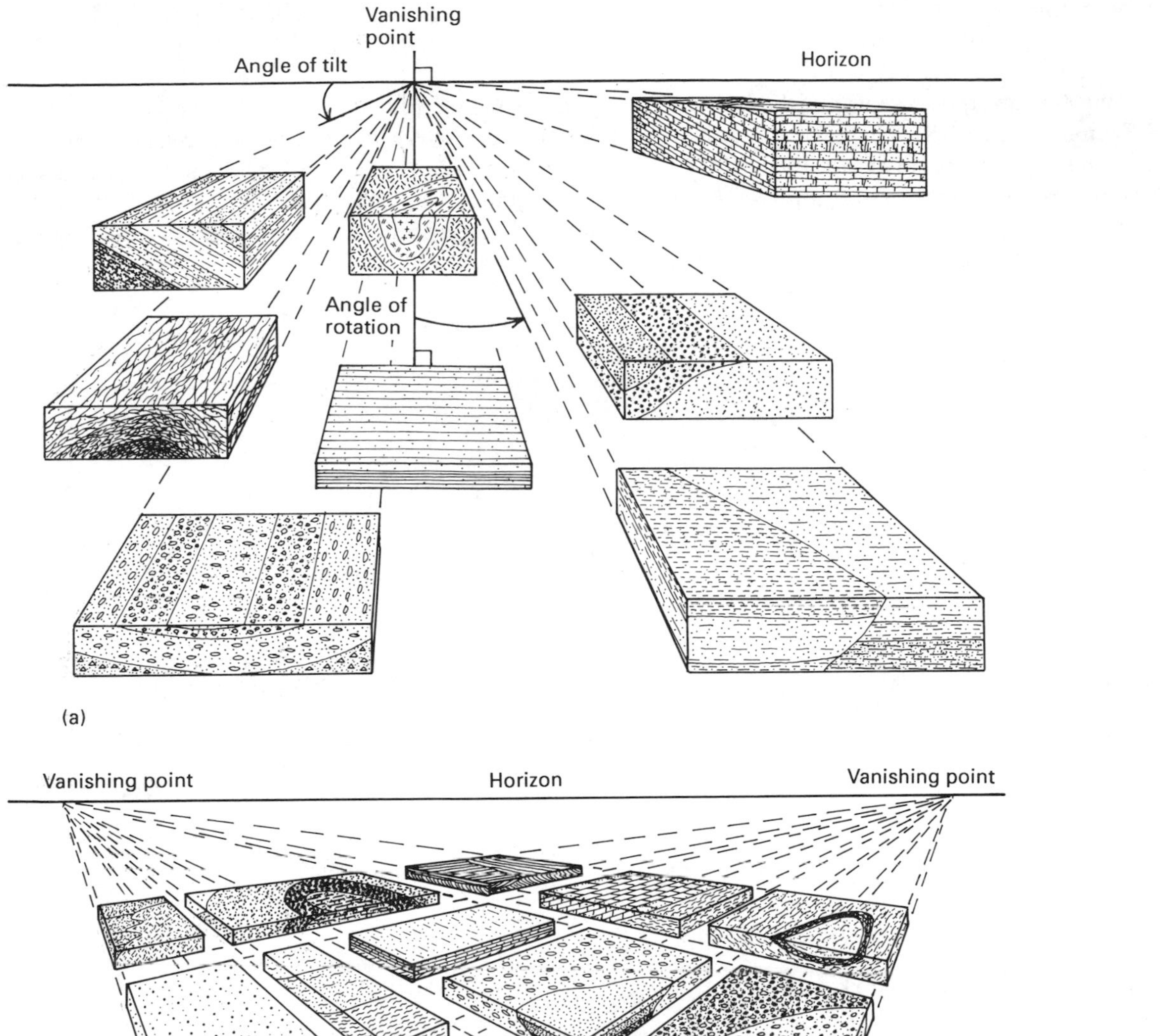
Vanishing point
Angle of tilt
Horizon
Angle of rotation
(a)
Vanishing point
Horizon
Vanishing point
(b)

Fig. 5.12 Perspective block diagrams. (a) Blocks in one-point perspective, with various angles of tilt (measured in the vertical plane) and rotation (measured in the horizontal plane). (b) Blocks in two-point perspective. Note that the amount of distortion in the peripheral blocks, i.e. those with the most tilt and/or rotation, will limit their use.

dominant strike, as far as possible, and should not involve vertical exaggeration unless for good reason.

4. Structure sections are drawn with an altitude such as sea-level as the datum surface; stratigraphic sections have some stratigraphically significant surface as the datum.
5. Accurate fence diagrams, and isometric and perspective block diagrams, are laborious to construct manually. Sketched diagrams are effective at rapidly conveying the overall structure of the rocks.

5.8 Selected further reading

Langstaff, C. S. and Morrill, D. (1981). *Geologic cross sections*, Boston, International Human Resources Development Corporation.
(A straightforward introductory account of the use of sections and three-dimensional diagrams in the oil industry.)

MAP 9 Zambian copper belt

Opposite is a 1:100 000 rcconnaissance map of the region containing the Zambian copper belt. The geological units recognised during this preliminary survey are listed below the map, but *not necessarily in their correct stratigraphic order*.

Make a cross-section to display what appears to be the regional structure. (To do this, it will first be necessary to utilise the principles of cross-cutting relationships and younging directions introduced in chapter 2 to establish the stratigraphic sequence.) List the units in stratigraphic order. Indicate any units which are of unclear stratigraphic age.

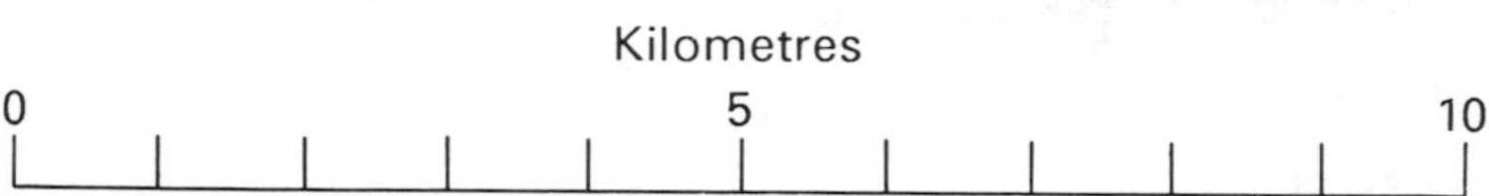
Kilometres
0
5
10

Further exercises in cross-section work

Construct a cross-section at right angles to strike across the Bear Hole, Montana, area in Map 3, and from C–D on Map 6 of the Boyd Volcanics, Australia.

Cross-section work is involved with the questions that accompany Plates 3 and 4, of Epernay, France, and Root River, Canada.

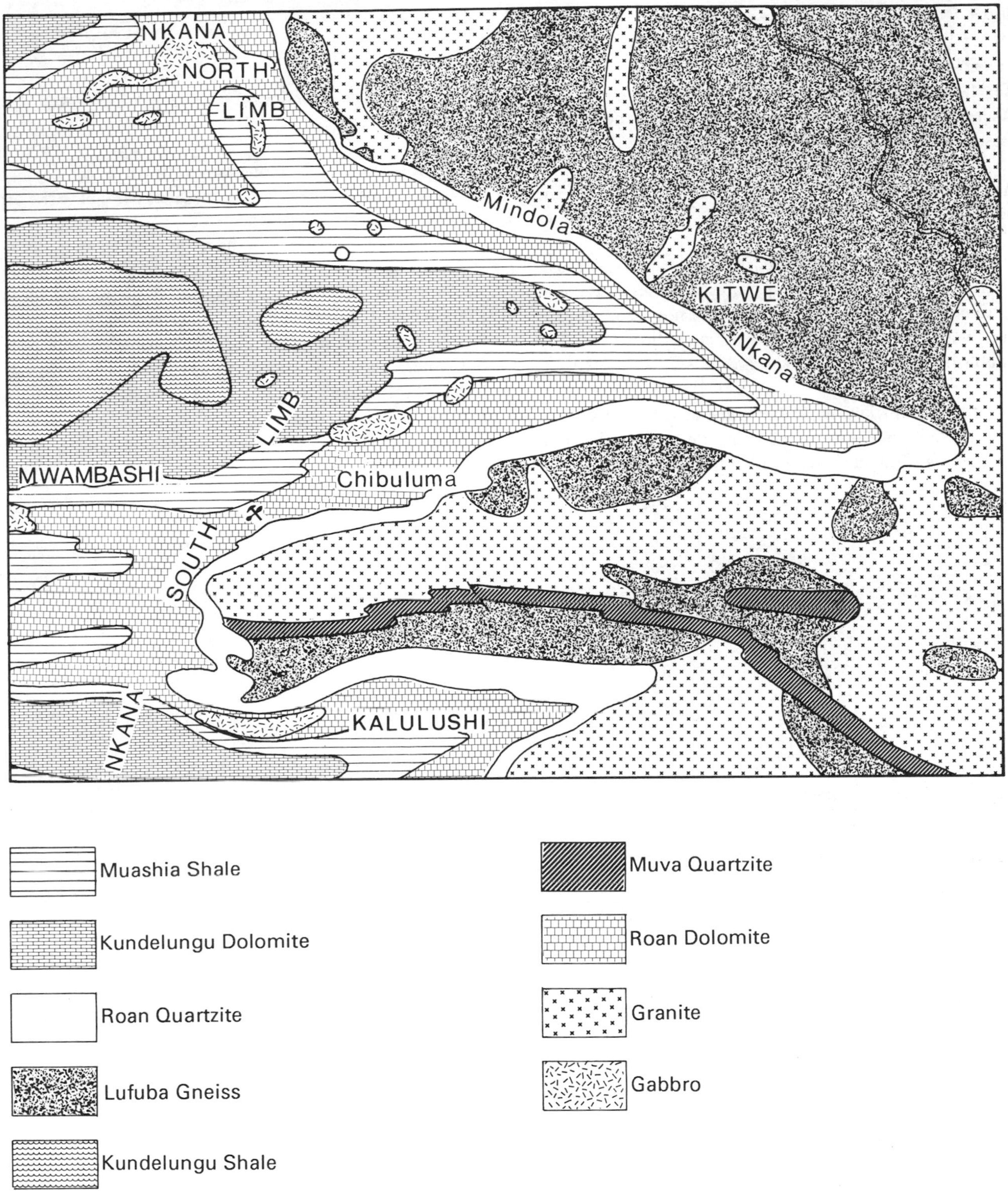

NKANA NORTH LIMB
Mindola
KITWE
Nkana
MWAMBASHI
SOUTH LIMB
Chibuluma
NKANA
KALULUSHI

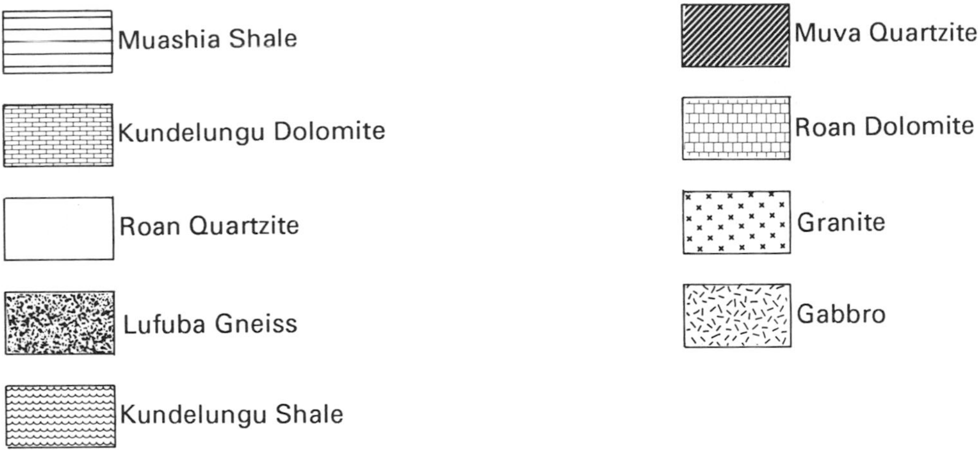

Muashia Shale
Kundelungu Dolomite
Roan Quartzite
Lufuba Gneiss
Kundelungu Shale
Muva Quartzite
Roan Dolomite
Granite
Gabbro

MAP 10 Builth Wells, Powys, Wales

The facing map is of a small area near Builth Wells in mid-Wales. The map units are largely defined on the basis of fossils. The area appears on Plate 1, centred on [SO0950].

According to Plate 1, what is the stratigraphic age of the units?

Construct, as accurately as possible, a geological cross-section. Select carefully the appropriate scales and line of section. (Even if structure contours are not used throughout for the section construction, a few will be needed to establish representative strikes and dips of the units.)

List the true thicknesses of the units, as derived from the cross-section, as closely as you can (i.e. quote minimum thicknesses if the bases or tops are not available).

List the vertical thicknesses as they would be seen in a borehole or well.

Draw an isometric block diagram to illustrate the geological structure of the area. (Make the sides parallel to the dip direction, and the front and back parallel to the strike. Establish the four corners of the diagram at right angles on the map, and trace their positions on to a separate sheet. Erect vertical columns at each corner, draw the skeleton of the block, add altitude scales, and transfer the vertical stratigraphic successions to the three visible corners and a few intermediate locations on the two visible panels. Connect the subsurface units. Add topographic profiles to all four panels, and sketch in the surface geology and drainage.) Comment on the angles of rotation and tilt of the block diagram.

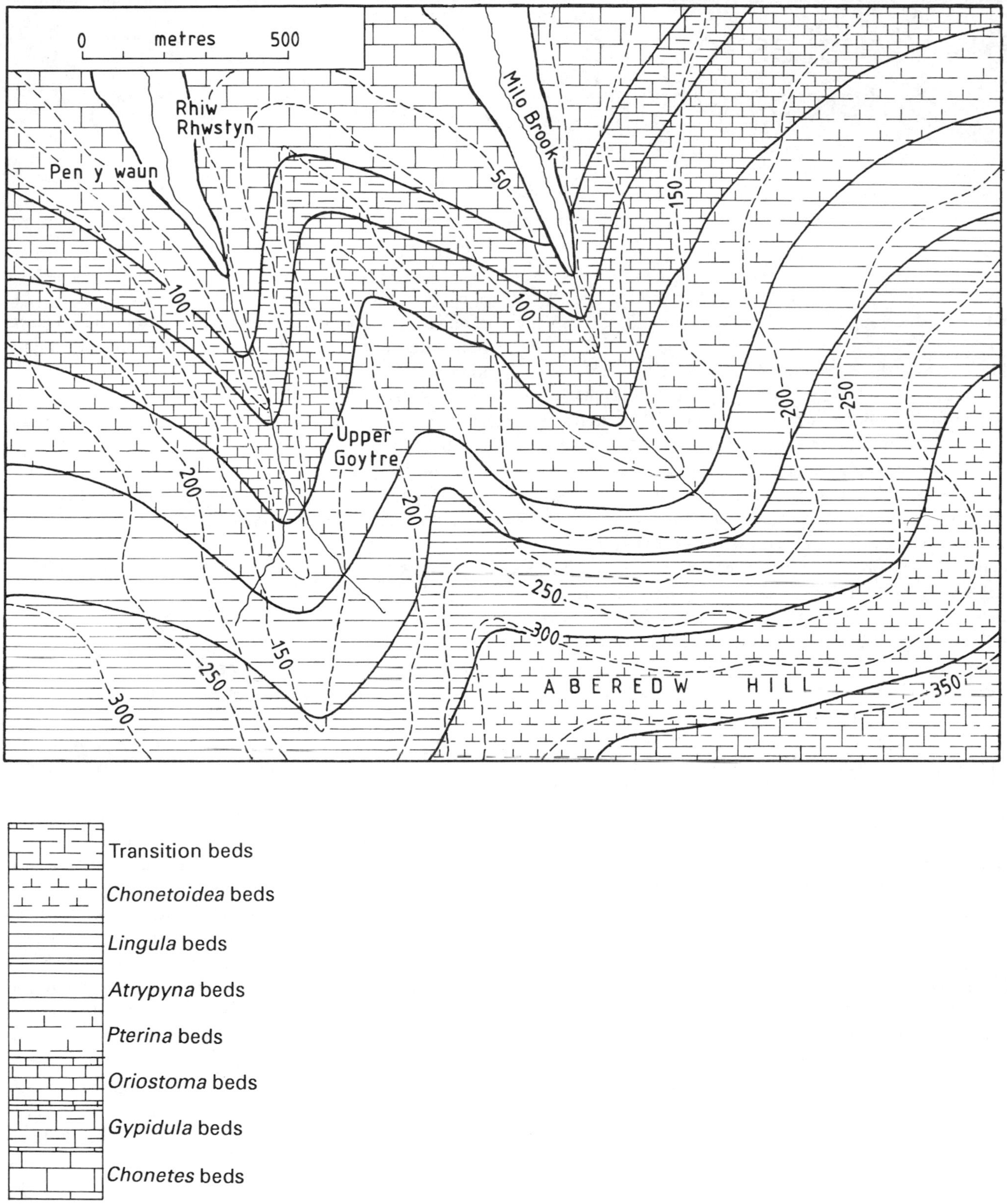

0 metres 500

Rhiw Rhwstyn

Pen y waun

Milo Brook

Upper Goytre

ABEREDW HILL

50 100 150 200 250 300 350

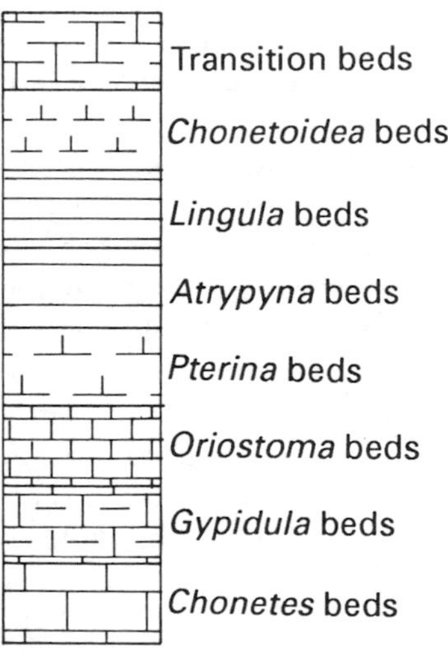

Transition beds
Chonetoidea beds
Lingula beds
Atrypyna beds
Pterina beds
Oriostoma beds
Gypidula beds
Chonetes beds

6 Visual assessment of outcrop patterns

6.1 Introduction

The previous three chapters dealt with using maps in a quantitative way. Methods were discussed of making precise measurements, where in commercial applications small errors could be costly. Now we return to the other approach to geological maps, that of making rapid visual assessments of the geology of an area. Central to this issue is an understanding of the outcrop patterns which appear on maps. Strictly, it is the junctions of outcrops, the trace showing where adjacent units meet, that we look at. The idea was introduced in chapter 2, and even at that stage we deduced from the maps the presence of features such as variably dipping beds, folds, unconformities, and faults. However, we have assumed so far that the land surface is fairly level. This is reasonable on the small-scale maps we worked with in chapter 2, but on large-scale maps the relief can become significant. This can greatly complicate the outcrop patterns and produce misleading effects. On the other hand, much can be deduced by looking at how the map units interact with the land surface. Here, we develop some general points to aid the visual appraisal of outcrop patterns on large-scale maps. We start by looking at horizontal beds, and then the effects produced by successively steeper beds.

6.2 Horizontal formations

Horizontal beds make horizontal outcrops on the ground, irrespective of the gradients and irregularities of the land surface. Steep cliffs or slight incline: the outcrops are still horizontal. Also, because topographic contour lines are horizontal (they must be, connecting as they do points of equal altitude), the outcrops of horizontal units always parallel the topographic contours. In terrains of intricate relief the outcrop patterns can therefore be highly irregular.

A famous example is the Grand Canyon. The deeply dissected canyon walls give very jagged topographic contours and hence a distinctive outcrop style (Fig. 6.1). The outcrops may look complex at first glance but they are simply following the topography. A look at the canyon walls leaves no doubt that the beds are virtually horizontal.

6.3 Dipping formations

6.3.1 Recognition

Section 2.3.1 introduced the appearance of dipping formations on small-scale maps. It was mentioned there that, if the relative ages of the rocks are known, the dip *direction* can be inferred from the direction in which the units become successively younger (providing they are not inverted). On large-scale maps, however, the effect of topography will be more marked, and can be a complicating factor. In fact, the outcrop shapes made by gently dipping beds intersecting with an irregular land surface can be very awkward to assess visually.

Outcrops of units dipping gently in the same direction as the land slope are not too difficult to work with. They *tend* to follow topographic contours in the same way as horizontal beds. The tendency decreases as the dip of the formations increases. It is not realistic to give a dip angle at which the mimicking effect ceases, partly because topographic slopes can be so intricately variable and partly because the beds themselves may be influencing the relief. For example, the tendency for durable beds to form escarpments is well-known (e.g. see the bottom illustration of Fig. 6.5), and the topographic contours of the escarpment

Fig. 6.1 (opposite) Outcrop patterns of horizontal beds: the Grand Canyon, Arizona, USA. The area shown here is Marble Canyon, about 40 km north of the main canyon. Reproduced from the 1:62 500 Preliminary Geologic Map of the Grand Canyon and vicinity, Arizona, by permission of the Grand Canyon Natural History Association. The inset engraving is reproduced from J. W. Powell's account of the surveying of the Grand Canyon (Powell, 1895), described briefly in section 14.3.5.

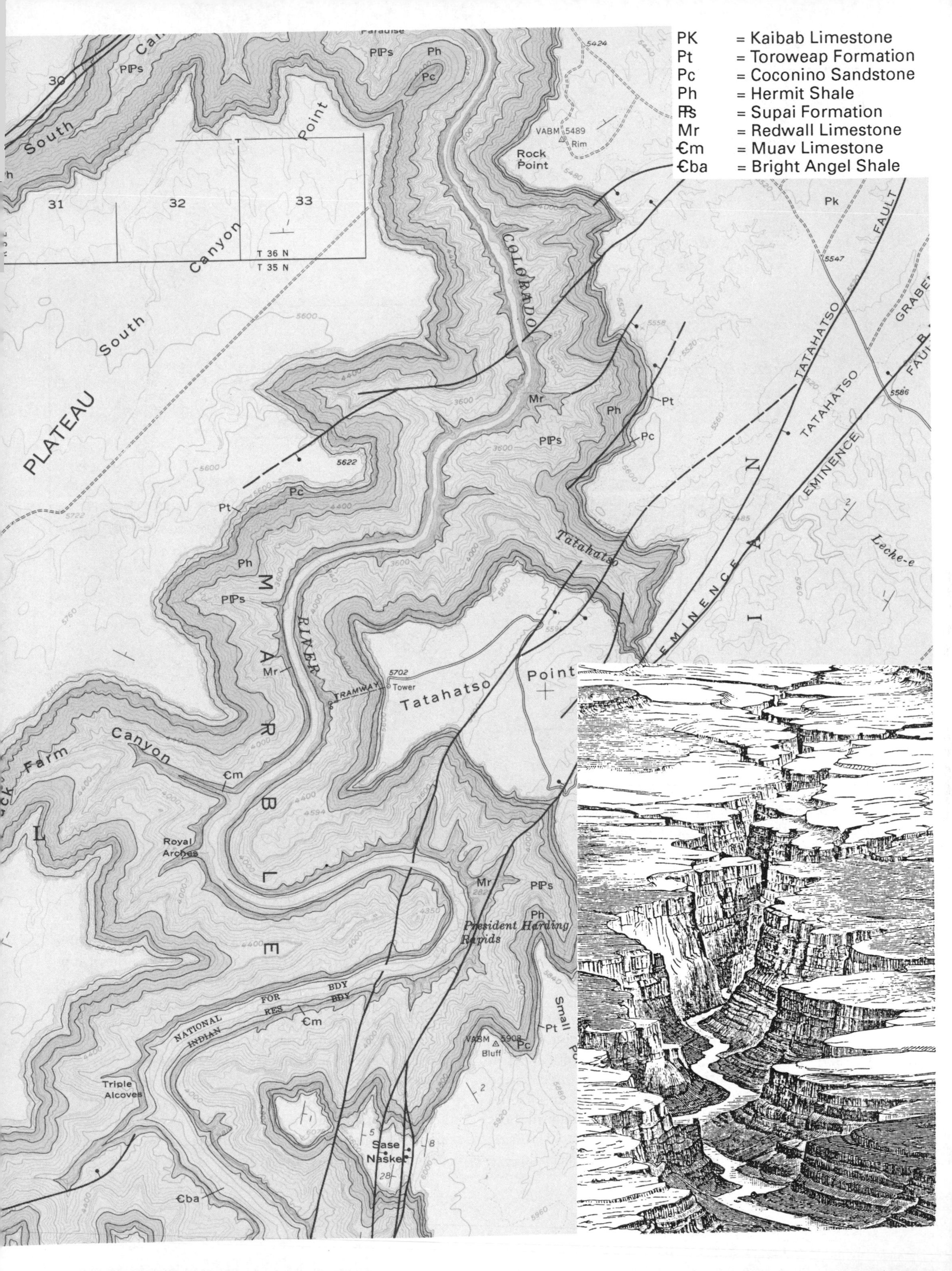

PK = Kaibab Limestone
Pt = Toroweap Formation
Pc = Coconino Sandstone
Ph = Hermit Shale
PPs = Supai Formation
Mr = Redwall Limestone
Єm = Muav Limestone
Єba = Bright Angel Shale
South Canyon Point
South Canyon
PLATEAU
30
31
32
33
T 36 N
T 35 N
Rock Point
VABM 5489
Rim
COLORADO
RIVER
M A R B L E
TATAHATSO FAULT
GRABEN
TATAHATSO
EMINENCE
Tatahatso
Tatahatso Point
TRAMWAY
Tower
5702
5622
Leche-e
Farm Canyon
Royal Arches
President Harding Rapids
NATIONAL FOR BDY
INDIAN RES BDY
Small Po
VABM 5908
Bluff
Triple Alcoves
Sase Nasket
Pk
Pt
Pc
Ph
PPs
Mr
Єm
Єba

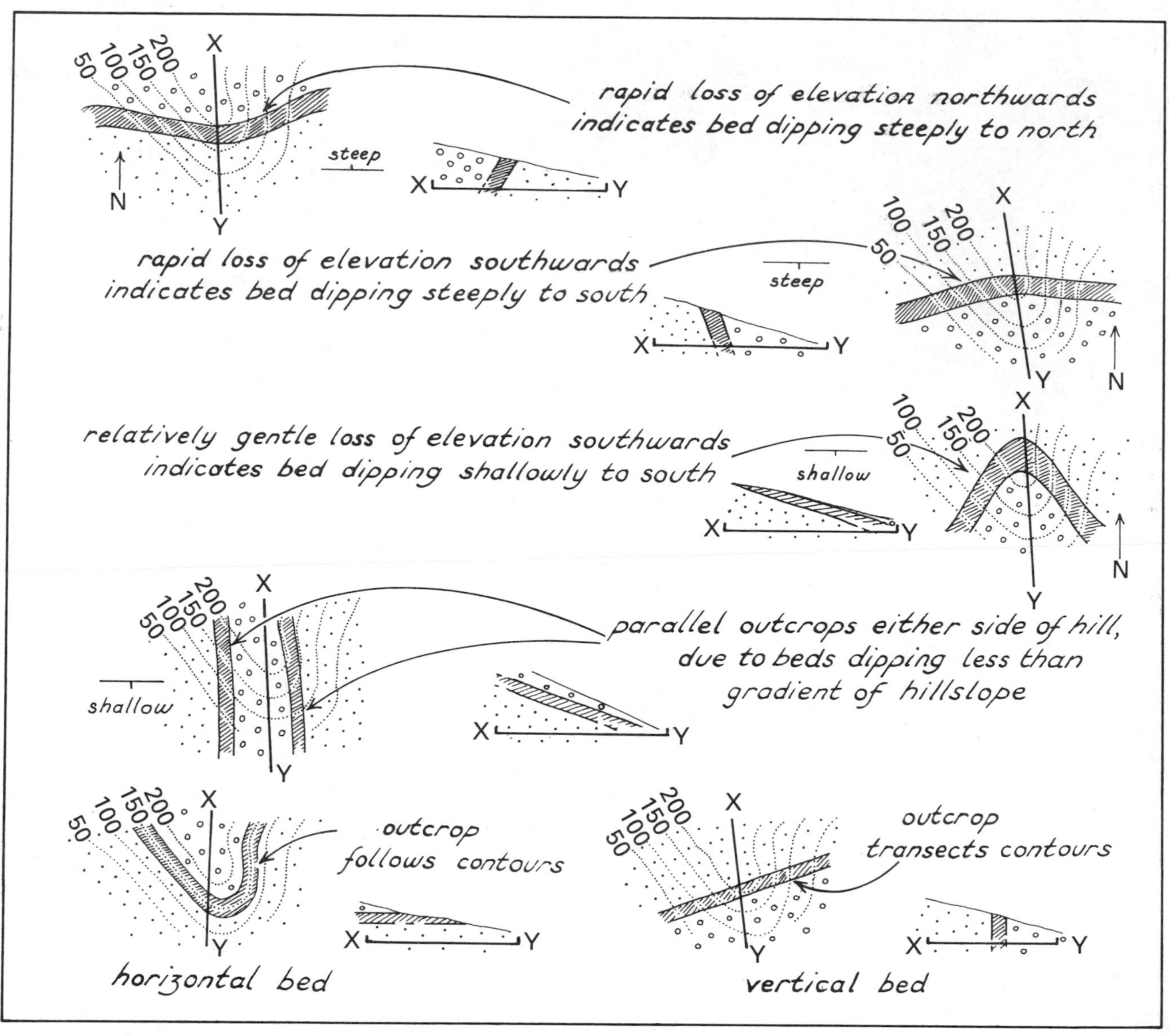
rapid loss of elevation northwards
indicates bed dipping steeply to north
steep
X
Y
N
rapid loss of elevation southwards
indicates bed dipping steeply to south
steep
relatively gentle loss of elevation southwards
indicates bed dipping shallowly to south
shallow
parallel outcrops either side of hill,
due to beds dipping less than
gradient of hillslope
shallow
outcrop
follows contours
horizontal bed
outcrop
transects contours
vertical bed
200
150
100
50

Fig. 6.2 Some examples of the visual assessment of outcrops crossing hills. In each example, the formation is regularly dipping and the hillside of roughly uniform gradient. In practice, less regular outcrops are likely.

tend to parallel the outcrop of the dipping bed. The parallelism does not extend to any irregularities in the escarpment in the way that would happen with horizontal beds, but it does mean that the interpretation of dips from roughly parallel topography and outcrop has to be treated with some care.

Formations dipping gently in the opposite direction to land slopes can, depending on the irregularity of the topography, produce very complex looking outcrop patterns. The safest approach to determining the direction and amount of dip is to look for where the outcrops cross a series of topographic contours, and see in which direction the beds consistently lose overall altitude (Fig. 6.2). Rapid crossing of successive topographic contours implies a steep dip.

Outcrops of formations with moderate dips, in general, cross rounded hills with an arcuate pattern (Fig. 6.3). If the arc curves in the same direction as the topographic contours, the dip direction is opposite to the downslope direction of the hill. If the outcrop arc is in the opposite direction to the curve of the topographic contours, the dip direction is the same as the downslope direction of the hill. In both cases, the openness of the outcrop arc increases as the dip steepens. But hills are so diverse in form that these ideas can be precarious in practice. Visualising the structure contours is a better guide: their direction will be at right angles to the dip direction and their spacing reflects the amount of dip. In desperation you could sketch in a few structure contours temporarily!

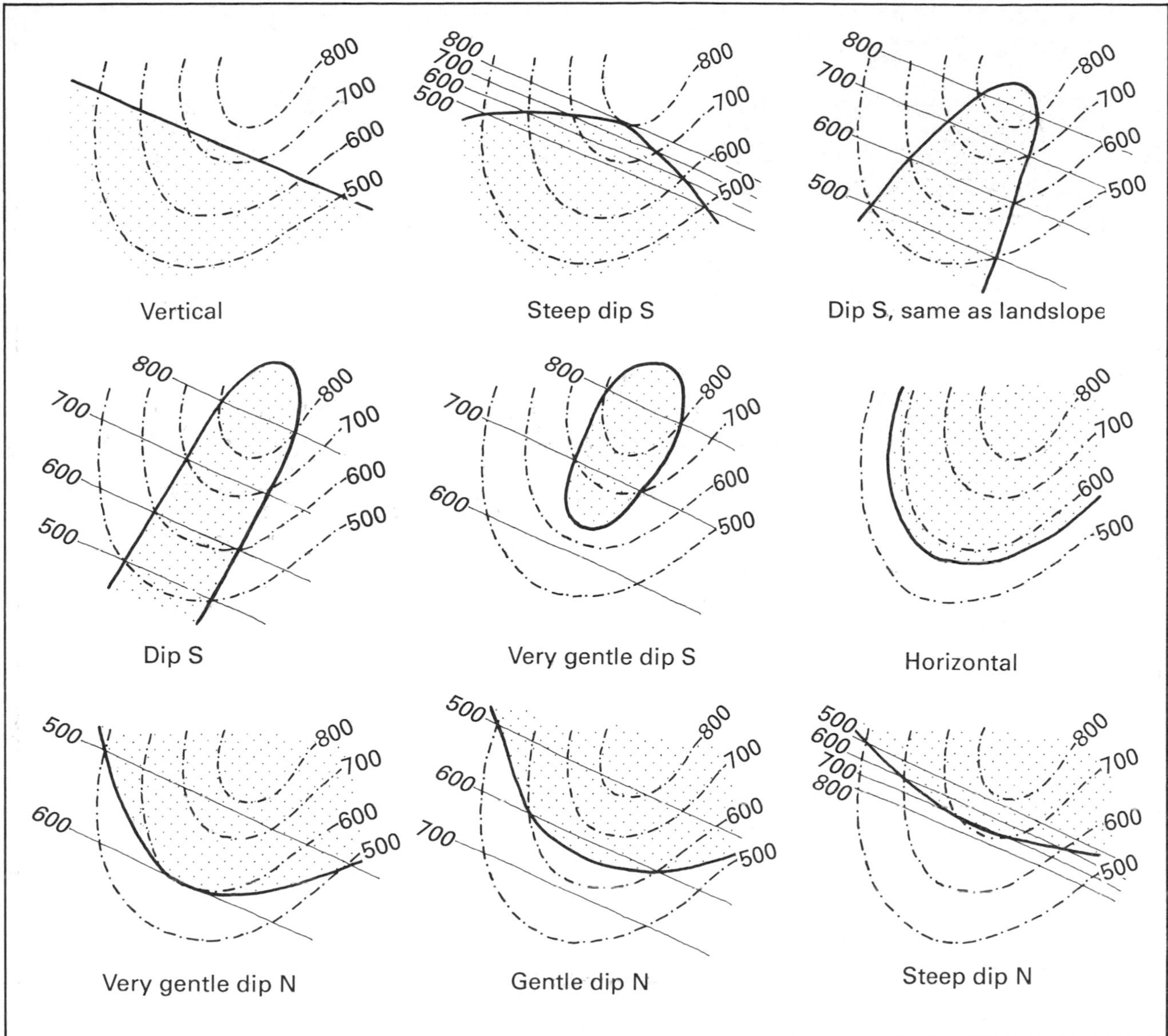

800
700
600
500
Vertical
Steep dip S
Dip S, same as landslope
Dip S
Very gentle dip S
Horizontal
Very gentle dip N
Gentle dip N
Steep dip N

Fig. 6.3 Outcrop shapes made by a uniformly dipping surface crossing a rounded hill. The trace of the boundary between two formations is shown in a heavy line and topographic contours in a dot-dash line. Some structure contours, in light continuous lines, have been added to indicate the differing amounts and directions of dip that produce the different outcrop shapes. North is to the top of the page; south and north below the sketches are approximate directions.

6.3.2 Assessment of formation dip in valleys

The one situation in which rules for visual assessment can be applied with some confidence is where formations cross a valley. Drainage patterns or topographic contours enable any valleys to be identified on a map; the so-called 'V-rules' refer to the *outcrop* shape typically made by formations crossing the valley (Fig. 6.4):

1. the apex of the 'V' points in the direction of bed dip;
2. acute 'V'-shapes reflect shallow dips;
3. open 'V'-shapes indicate steep beds.

These are useful guides for swift outcrop appraisal. However, beware of the exception that proves the rule:

4. beds dipping less steeply than the valley floor give 'V's pointing in the direction *opposite* to bed dip! This uncommon circumstance can be recognised by the topographic contours having an even more acute 'V'-shape than the outcrops.

Regarding very steeply inclined units, their outcrop patterns are normally straightforward to analyse. The 'V-rules' work well. The complicating effect of topography progressively lessens as beds become steeper.

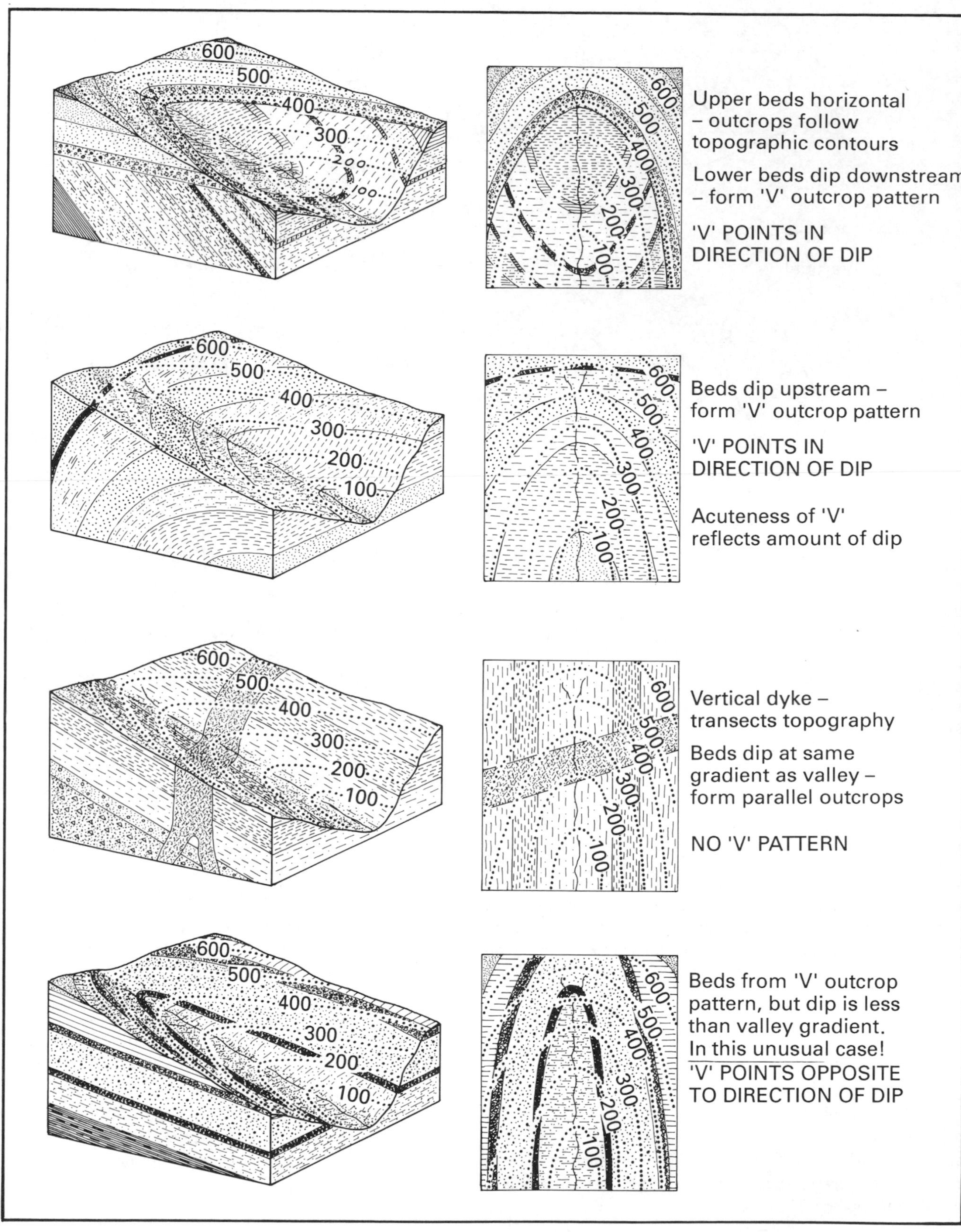
600
500
400
300
200
100
Upper beds horizontal – outcrops follow topographic contours
Lower beds dip downstream – form 'V' outcrop pattern
'V' POINTS IN DIRECTION OF DIP
Beds dip upstream – form 'V' outcrop pattern
'V' POINTS IN DIRECTION OF DIP
Acuteness of 'V' reflects amount of dip
Vertical dyke – transects topography
Beds dip at same gradient as valley – form parallel outcrops
NO 'V' PATTERN
Beds from 'V' outcrop pattern, but dip is less than valley gradient.
In this unusual case!
'V' POINTS OPPOSITE TO DIRECTION OF DIP

Fig. 6.4 Block diagrams and maps to illustrate the 'V-rules' of outcrops crossing valleys.

6.4 Vertical formations

Vertical beds are characterised by straight-looking outcrops. They completely ignore topography (Figs 6.3 and 6.4). With horizontal beds they form two ends of a spectrum of the influence topography has on outcrop shape. Any twists in the outcrops of a vertical unit represent a real change of the strike of the formation.

This behaviour applies to any vertical geological features, not just beds of rock. Igneous dykes commonly appear on maps with straight traces because they are typically vertical. Faults are usually depicted as fairly straight lines. This is no intrinsic property of faults but simply follows from many faults being oriented very steeply or vertically.

6.5 Assessment of formation thickness

It was mentioned in section 2.3.1 that knowing something about the thickness of a map unit allows us to judge, on a small-scale map, the amount of dip from the outcrop width of the unit (Fig. 6.5). Steeper beds make narrower outcrops than shallower beds of the same thickness. Conversely, if

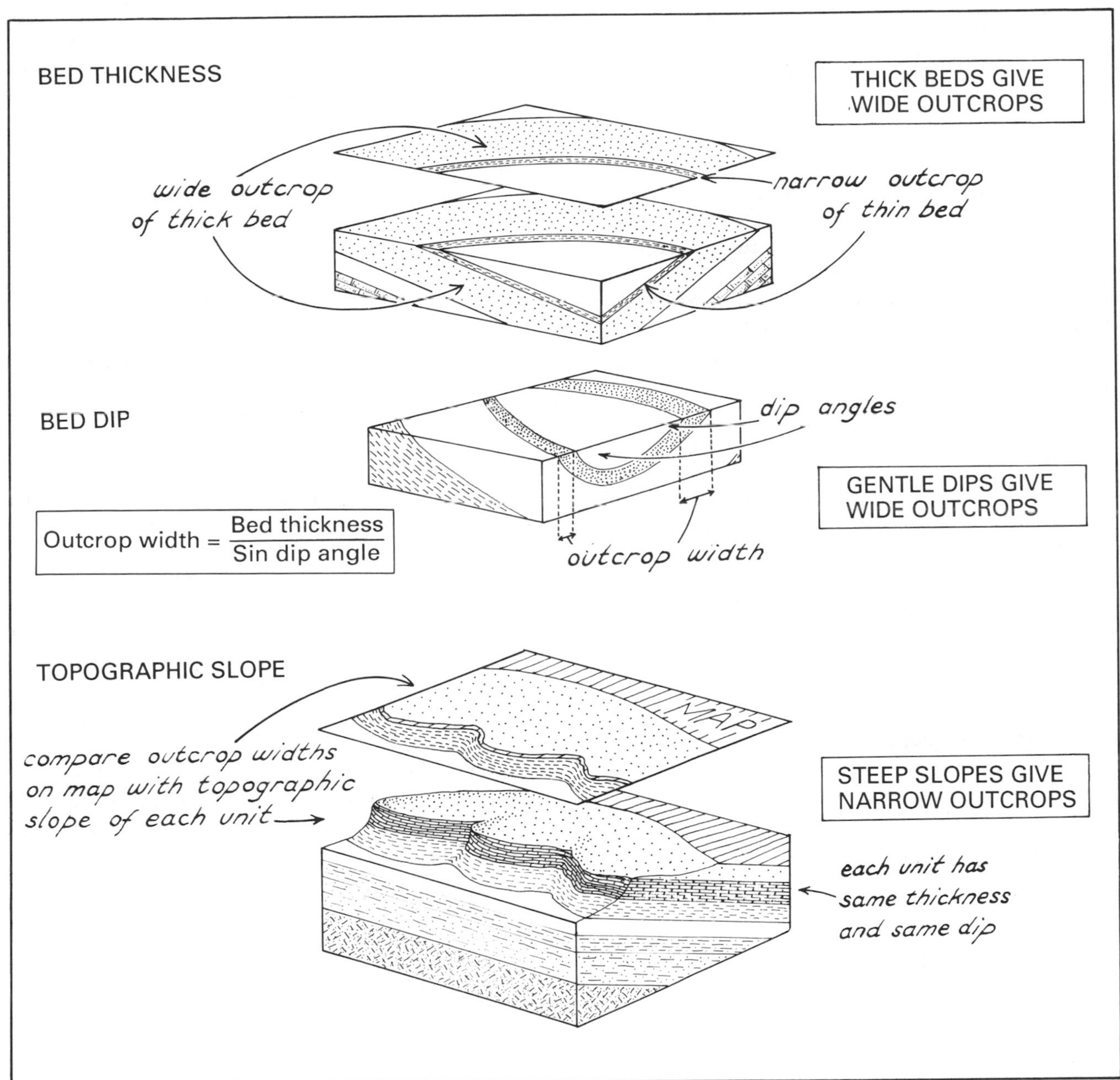

BED THICKNESS
THICK BEDS GIVE WIDE OUTCROPS
wide outcrop of thick bed
narrow outcrop of thin bed
BED DIP
dip angles
GENTLE DIPS GIVE WIDE OUTCROPS
Outcrop width = Bed thickness / Sin dip angle
outcrop width
TOPOGRAPHIC SLOPE
MAP
compare outcrop widths on map with topographic slope of each unit
STEEP SLOPES GIVE NARROW OUTCROPS
each unit has same thickness and same dip

Fig. 6.5 Block diagrams to illustrate the three factors which influence the outcrop width of a formation. The equation relating outcrop width to bed thickness assumes level ground, and is a rearrangement of the equation given in Fig. 4.8.

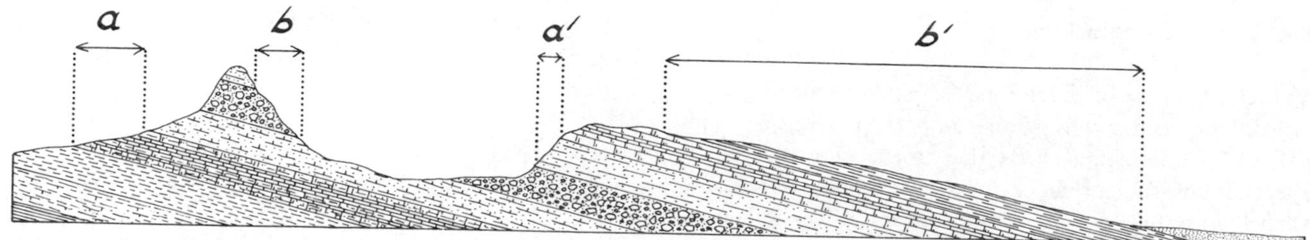
a
b
a′
b′

Fig. 6.6 The relationship between outcrop width and topography. All the formations shown have the same thickness and dip angle. Note that steeper land slopes suppress the outcrop width: compare a with a′, both slopes inclined in the same direction. Slopes inclined in the opposite direction to the formation dip tend to suppress outcrop width relative to slopes in the same direction: compare a with b′, and a′ with b.

we know something about the dip, we should be able to estimate from the outcrop width the approximate thickness of the unit. Thicker beds make wider outcrops than thinner beds of the same dip. However, there is a further factor – the relief of the land surface. On a small-scale map its effect will be diminutive and can be neglected. The ground can be treated as being flat.

On large-scale maps, especially of rugged areas, the effect of topography can be very significant. In general, increasingly steep slopes progressively suppress outcrop width (Fig. 6.6). With horizontal beds, the effect of topography will be at its greatest and the land gradient will have a profound influence on outcrop width. The effect is well illustrated by the Grand Canyon (Fig. 6.1). Shallow-dipping beds, too, give outcrop widths which are highly dependent on topographic slope, but the effect diminishes as beds become steeper. Vertical beds form the other end of the spectrum – their outcrop width equals their thickness irrespective of the topography. So, on large-scale maps the visual assessment of formation thickness knowing the approximate dip, or the estimation of dip knowing the thickness, has to be made with a careful eye on the topographic slope.

6.6 Summary of chapter

1. Outcrops of horizontal formations parallel the topographic contours.
2. The tendency for dipping formations to parallel topographic contours decreases as the angle of dip increases.
3. It is important to visualise mentally in three-dimensions how dipping formations cross landforms, but some generalisations can be made, particularly regarding the 'V'-shapes of outcrops crossing valleys.
4. Outcrops of vertical formations ignore topography and tend to be straight.
5. Outcrop width depends not only on formation thickness and dip, but on the land slope. Increasingly steep slopes progressively suppress outcrop width.

6.7 Exercises on visual assessment

Find areas on Map 3, of Bear Hole, Montana, where the outcrop patterns do not follow the normal 'V'-rules. Indicate an area where the 'V'-rules are obeyed.

On the basis of visual assessment, what is the approximate orientation of the units appearing on Map 8, Long Mountain, and on Map 10, near Builth Wells, Wales?

Using visual assessment alone, deduce the overall orientation of the beds on Plate 3, Epernay, France, and on the eastern half of Plate 8, of Malmesbury, England. Comment on the dip of the andesites and basalts (Ac′) on Plate 5 (Sanquar, Scotland). What is the likely dip of the Southern Upland Fault which appears on Plate 5?

On Plate 6, of the Heart Mountain district, Wyoming, USA, explain why the Carboniferous and Permo-Trias units in the southeast of the area have more pronounced 'V'-shaped outcrops than the Cretaceous formations in the east, yet both sequences have approximately similar dips. What is the approximate orientation of the Carboniferous rocks in Paint Creek (long. 109° 20′, lat. 44° 43′), and of the Cambrian Pilgrim Limestone in Dead Indian Creek (long. 109° 0′, lat. 45° 42′)?

Colour Plates

Plate 1 Part of the 'Ten Mile' map of the UK

Reproduced opposite with a simplified key is a portion of the 1:625 000 map discussed in chapter 2. Some background on how the map was made is mentioned in section 14.2.6. The numbers shown in red on the map refer to BGS. One-Inch and 1:50 000 sheets; the heavy dot-dash lines are faults.

Where on the map area do the oldest rocks occur?

Where are the youngest rocks?

Where are the oldest sedimentary rocks?

Why might the ground making the Longmynd [SO4293] be higher than the land around it?

Following the principles introduced in chapter 2, it should be possible to make interpretations of the outcrop patterns on the map. A journey southwards from Llangynidr [SO1619] would cross rocks dipping in what direction?

Why might the outcrop width of the Carboniferous rocks around Brynamman [SN7214] be greater than the same rocks at Abersychan [SN2604]?

Between Cemınaes [SN8406] and Llanelltyd [SN7219], the overall dip of the rocks is in which direction?

What is (a) the strike direction, and (b) the dip direction of the Silurian rocks around Wenlock Edge [SO5090]?

Comment on the nature of the junction at the base of the Silurian rocks around [SO2694].

What is the nature of the junction of the Permo-Triassic sandstones (unit 89) with older rocks?

Explain the junction of the base of the Lower Old Red Sandstone (unit 75) with older rocks at [SO3505].

Why do the outcrops of Silurian rocks around Leintwardine [SO4173] have a curving pattern?

What geological evidence is there on the map for the existence of a fault running NE–SW from Church Stretton [SO4693]? What can you say about the stratigraphic age of this fault?

If a borehole (well) were sunk at Michaelchurch Escley [SO3332], what is likely to be the first unit to be encountered below the Lower Old Red Sandstone?

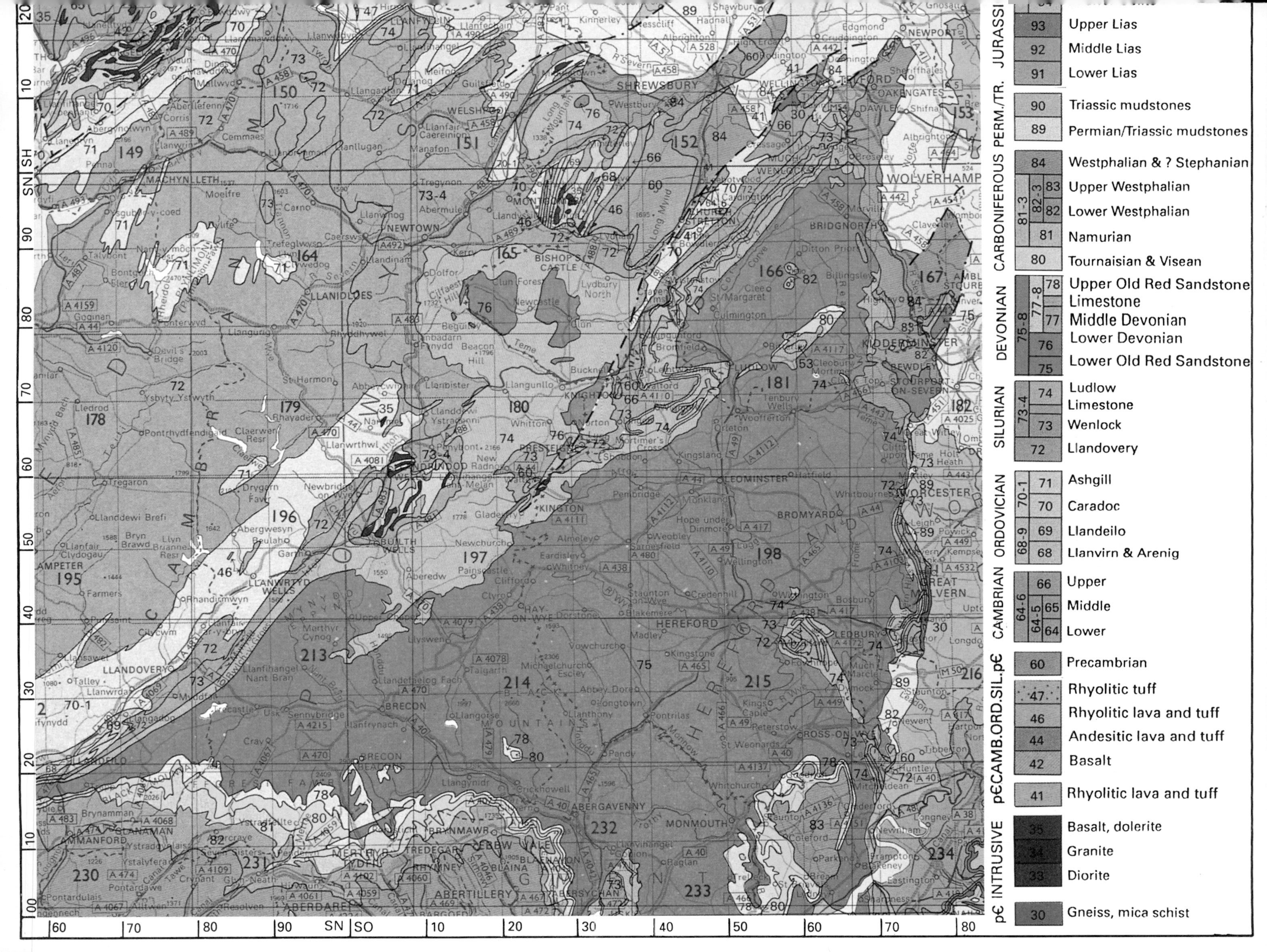
JURASSIC
93 Upper Lias
92 Middle Lias
91 Lower Lias
PERM./TR.
90 Triassic mudstones
89 Permian/Triassic mudstones
CARBONIFEROUS
84 Westphalian & ? Stephanian
83 Upper Westphalian
82 Lower Westphalian
82-3
81 Namurian
81-3
80 Tournaisian & Visean
DEVONIAN
78 Upper Old Red Sandstone
Limestone
77 Middle Devonian
77-8
Lower Devonian
76
75 Lower Old Red Sandstone
75-8
SILURIAN
74 Ludlow
Limestone
73 Wenlock
73-4
72 Llandovery
ORDOVICIAN
71 Ashgill
70 Caradoc
70-1
69 Llandeilo
68 Llanvirn & Arenig
68-9
CAMBRIAN
66 Upper
65 Middle
64 Lower
64-5
64-6
pЄ
60 Precambrian
pЄCAMB.ORD.SIL.pЄ
47 Rhyolitic tuff
46 Rhyolitic lava and tuff
44 Andesitic lava and tuff
42 Basalt
41 Rhyolitic lava and tuff
pЄ INTRUSIVE
35 Basalt, dolerite
34 Granite
33 Diorite
30 Gneiss, mica schist

Plate 2 Part of the 1:2 500 000 map of the US

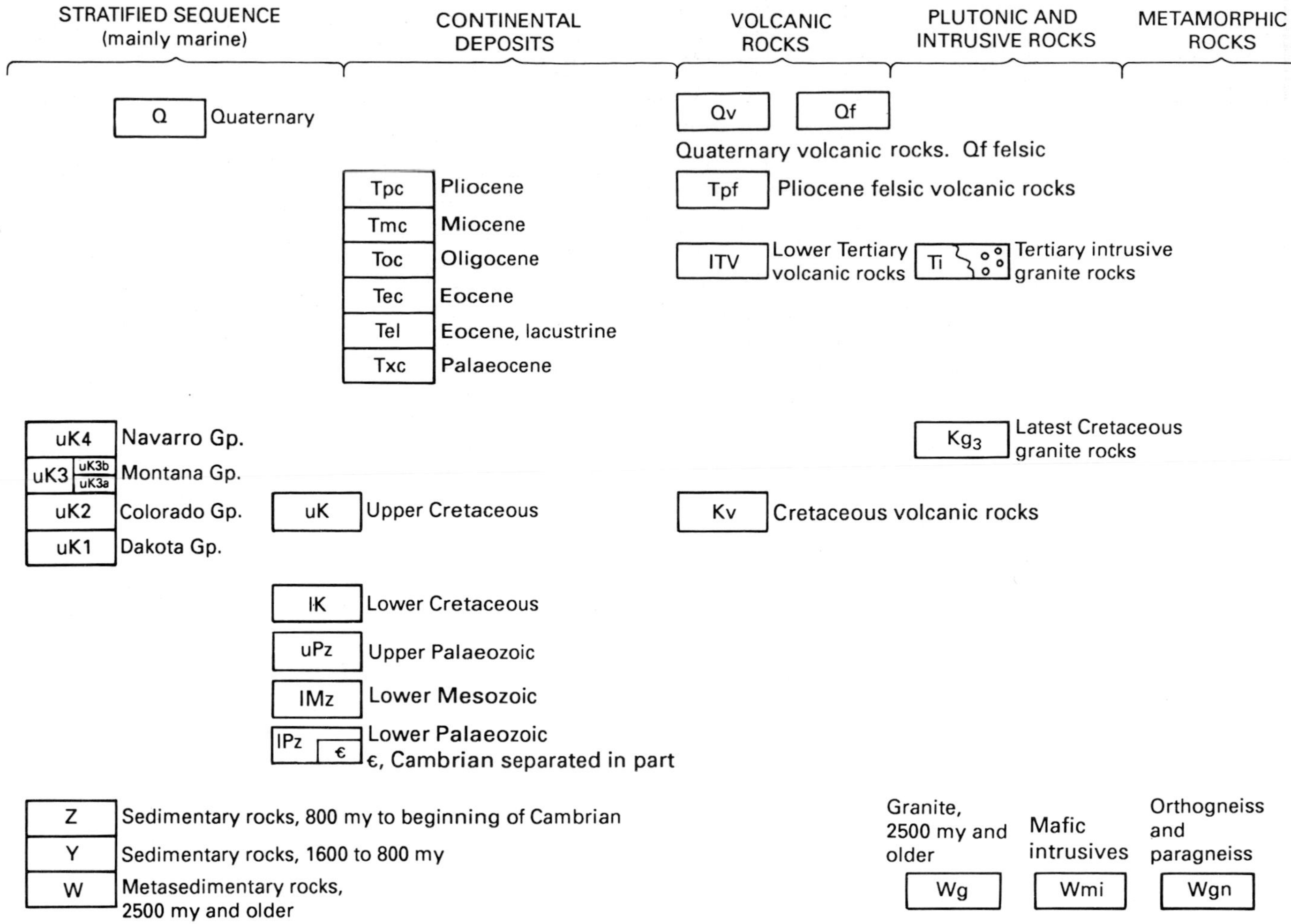

STRATIFIED SEQUENCE (mainly marine)
CONTINENTAL DEPOSITS
VOLCANIC ROCKS
PLUTONIC AND INTRUSIVE ROCKS
METAMORPHIC ROCKS
Q Quaternary
Qv Qf
Quaternary volcanic rocks. Qf felsic
Tpc Pliocene
Tmc Miocene
Toc Oligocene
Tec Eocene
Tel Eocene, lacustrine
Txc Palaeocene
Tpf Pliocene felsic volcanic rocks
ITV Lower Tertiary volcanic rocks
Ti Tertiary intrusive granite rocks
uK4 Navarro Gp.
uK3 uK3b uK3a Montana Gp.
uK2 Colorado Gp.
uK1 Dakota Gp.
uK Upper Cretaceous
Kg3 Latest Cretaceous granite rocks
Kv Cretaceous volcanic rocks
lK Lower Cretaceous
uPz Upper Palaeozoic
lMz Lower Mesozoic
lPz € Lower Palaeozoic
€, Cambrian separated in part
Z Sedimentary rocks, 800 my to beginning of Cambrian
Y Sedimentary rocks, 1600 to 800 my
W Metasedimentary rocks, 2500 my and older
Granite, 2500 my and older
Wg
Mafic intrusives
Wmi
Orthogneiss and paragneiss
Wgn

Reproduced opposite, by permission of the US Geological Survey, is a portion of the map discussed in chapter 2. The legend given above is abstracted from the comprehensive explanation that accompanies the original map.

Towards which direction are the beds around long. 110° 20′, lat. 45° 30′ dipping?

Comment on the nature of the junction at the base of the Miocene continental deposits (Tmc) around long. 111° 30′, lat. 45° 50′.

Describe the structure W of Cody, centred on long. 109° 15′, lat. 44° 30′.

What can be inferred about the fault in Madison County, Montana, centred on long. 111° 30′, lat. 45° 0′? (An earthquake in this vicinity in 1959 caused serious damage and numerous fatalities.)

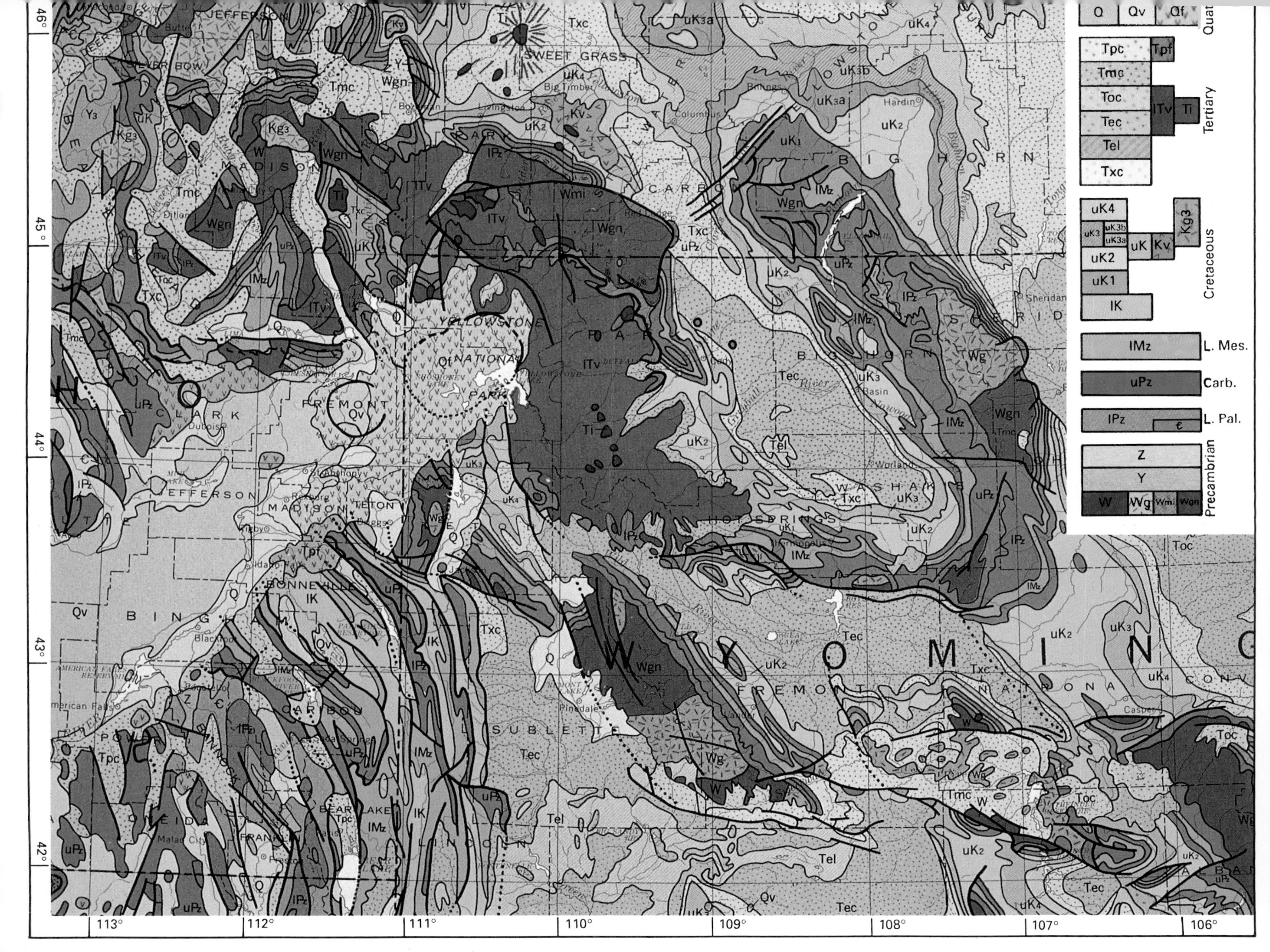

Quat
Q
Qv
Qf
Tertiary
Tpc
Tpf
Tmc
Toc
Tec
Tel
Txc
lTv
Ti
Cretaceous
uK4
uK3
uK3b
uK3a
uK2
uK1
uK
Kv
Kg3
lK
L. Mes.
lMz
Carb.
uPz
L. Pal.
lPz
€
Precambrian
Z
Y
W
Wg
Wmi
Wgn
WYOMING
YELLOWSTONE NATIONAL PARK
BIG HORN
SWEET GRASS
CARBON
MADISON
FREMONT
CLARK
JEFFERSON
TETON
BONNEVILLE
BINGHAM
CARIBOU
BEAR LAKE
FRANKLIN
LINCOLN
SUBLETTE
PARK
HOT SPRINGS
WASHAKIE
SHERIDAN
NATRONA
Billings
Hardin
Columbus
Big Timber
Livingston
Bozeman
Red Lodge
Sheridan
Worland
Basin
Dubois
Rexburg
Rigby
Idaho Falls
Blackfoot
Pocatello
American Falls
Soda Springs
Pinedale
Lander
Casper
Malad City
Preston
46°
45°
44°
43°
42°
113°
112°
111°
110°
109°
108°
107°
106°

Plate 3 Epernay, France

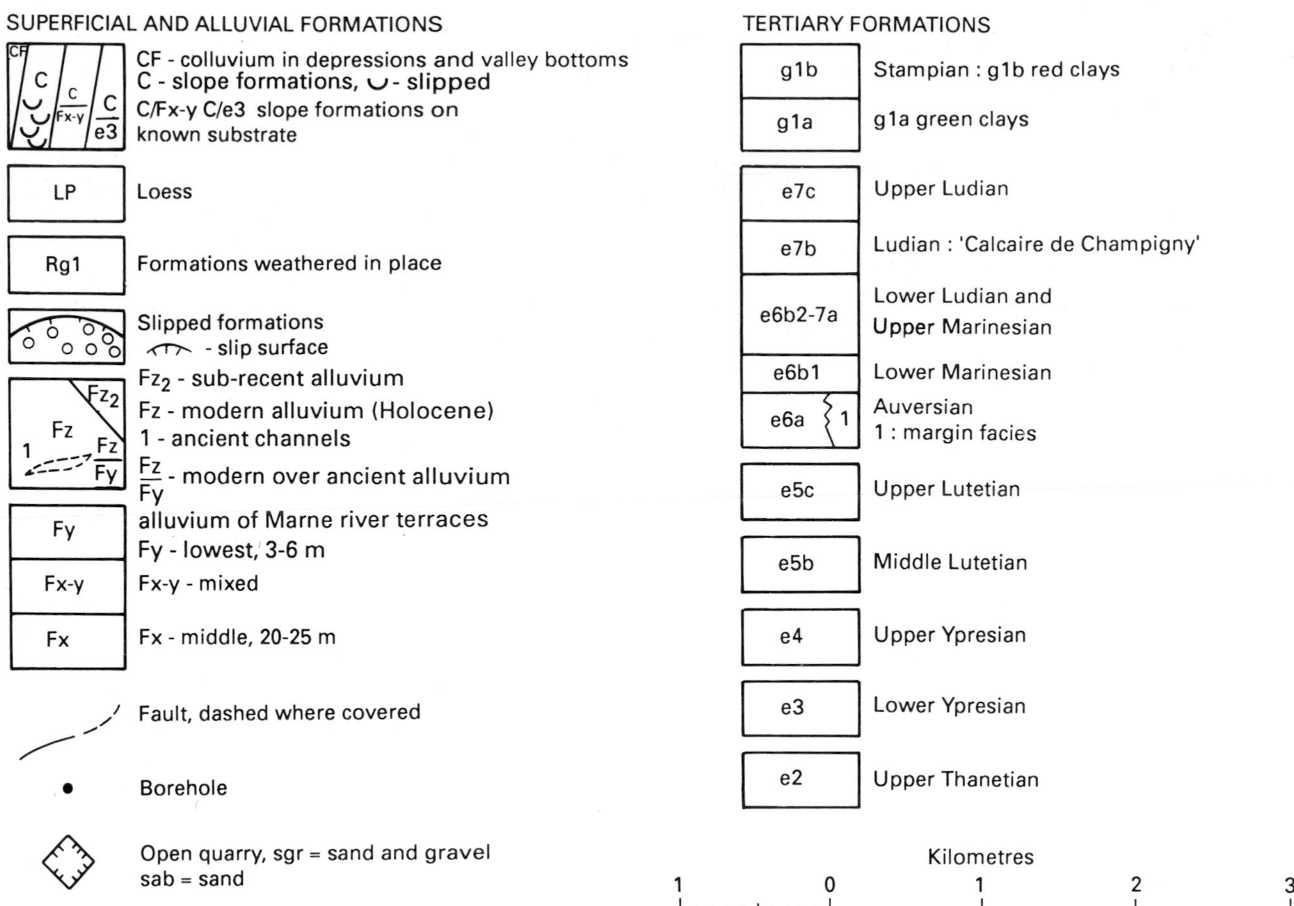
SUPERFICIAL AND ALLUVIAL FORMATIONS
CF - colluvium in depressions and valley bottoms
C - slope formations, ∪ - slipped
C/Fx-y C/e3 slope formations on known substrate
LP Loess
Rg1 Formations weathered in place
Slipped formations
- slip surface
Fz2 - sub-recent alluvium
Fz - modern alluvium (Holocene)
1 - ancient channels
Fz/Fy - modern over ancient alluvium
alluvium of Marne river terraces
Fy - lowest, 3-6 m
Fx-y - mixed
Fx - middle, 20-25 m
Fault, dashed where covered
Borehole
Open quarry, sgr = sand and gravel
sab = sand
TERTIARY FORMATIONS
g1b Stampian : g1b red clays
g1a g1a green clays
e7c Upper Ludian
e7b Ludian : 'Calcaire de Champigny'
e6b2-7a Lower Ludian and Upper Marinesian
e6b1 Lower Marinesian
e6a Auversian
1 : margin facies
e5c Upper Lutetian
e5b Middle Lutetian
e4 Upper Ypresian
e3 Lower Ypresian
e2 Upper Thanetian
Kilometres
1 0 1 2 3

Reproduced opposite is part of the French BRGM 1:50 000 map 157, 'Epernay', published in 1977. It is of the area around the river Marne, in the Champagne region of N-central France. The key given above is translated from the French of the original, and various details have been omitted.

Looking at the topographic contours, printed in brown, and the outcrop patterns, what is the overall orientation of the Tertiary beds? Which of the superficial formations tend to be arranged horizontally and which do not? Where do the Tertiary beds have the steepest dips?

What is the dominant control on which bedrock unit outcrops at a particular place? Which bedrock unit tends to make the steepest topographic slopes? Which units are most prone to landslips? Draw a cross-section to show the relation between relief and bedrock geology. What appears erroneous about the portrayal of the geological succession W of Courthiezy, around [6938 1510]?

The pink lines are structure contours for the top of the chalk (Cretaceous). What do they indicate about the overall arrangement of the chalk? Construct a cross-section to show the structure. In the centre of the village of Chassins [6943 1541], at what depth is the top of the chalk?

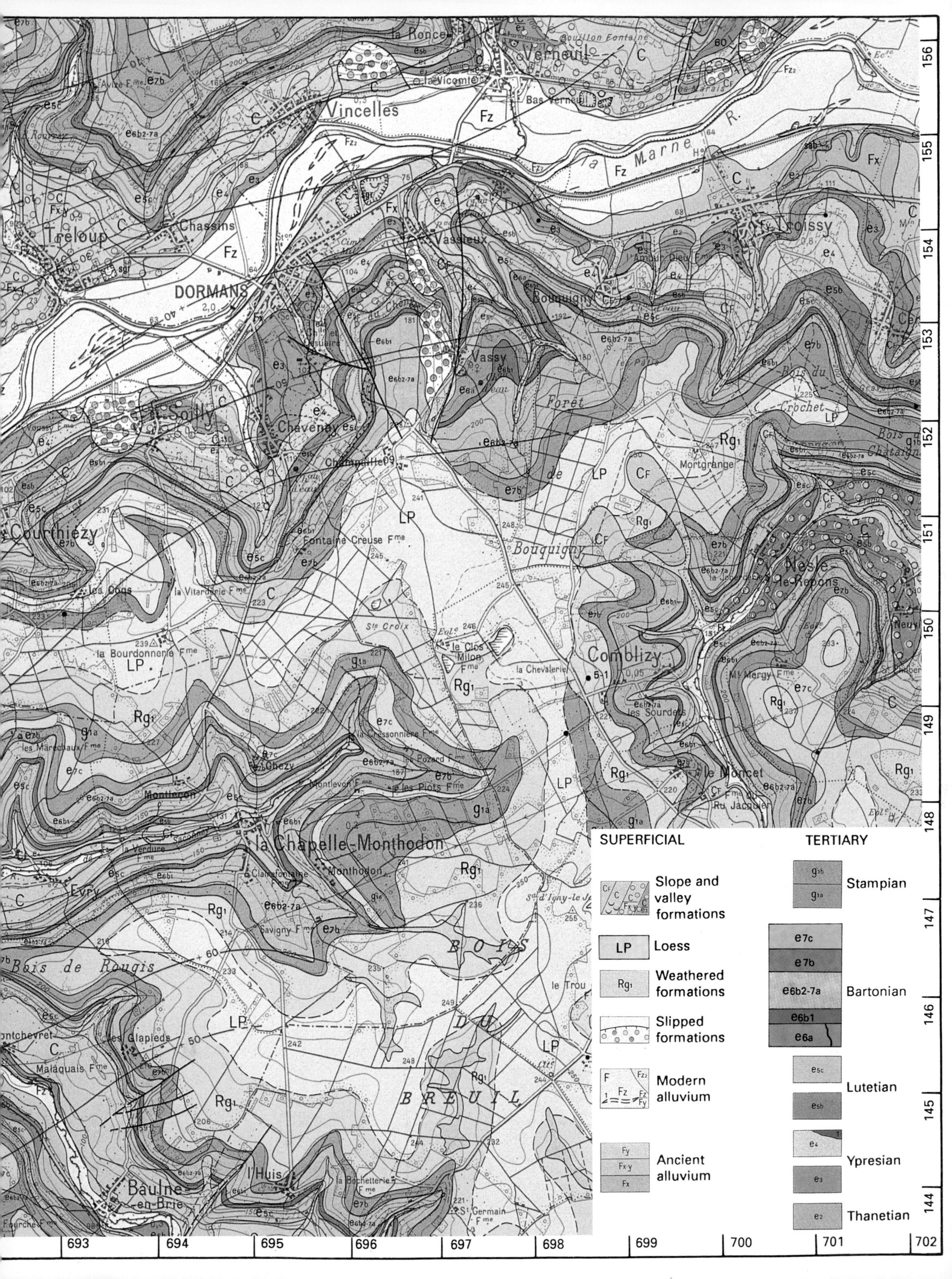

SUPERFICIAL
Slope and valley formations
LP Loess
Rg1 Weathered formations
Slipped formations
Modern alluvium
Ancient alluvium
TERTIARY
Stampian
Bartonian
Lutetian
Ypresian
Thanetian
la Marne R.
DORMANS
Treloup
Chassins
Vincelles
Verneuil
la Ronce
la Vicomte
Bas Verneuil
Troissy
Vassieux
Try
Bouquigny
Vassy
Chavenay
Soilly
Champaille
Courthiezy
Fontaine Creuse Fme
la Vitarderie Fme
les Coqs
la Bourdonnerie Fme
Mortgrange
Forêt de Bouquigny
Nesle le Repons
Comblizy
la Chevalerie
le Clos Milon Fme
Mt Mergy Fme
les Sourdets
le Moncet
Ru Jacquier
la Cressonnière Fme
le Pozard Fme
les Piots Fme
Montlevon Fme
Chezy
Montlecon
les Maréchaux Fme
la Chapelle-Monthodon
Monthodon
Clairefontaine Fme
la Verdure Fme
Evry
Savigny Fme
Bois de Rougis
BOIS DU BREUIL
le Trou
les Glapieds
Malaquais Fme
l'Huis
Baulne-en-Brie
la Bochetterie Fme
St Germain Fme
693
694
695
696
697
698
699
700
701
702

Plate 4 Root River, District of Mackenzie, Canada

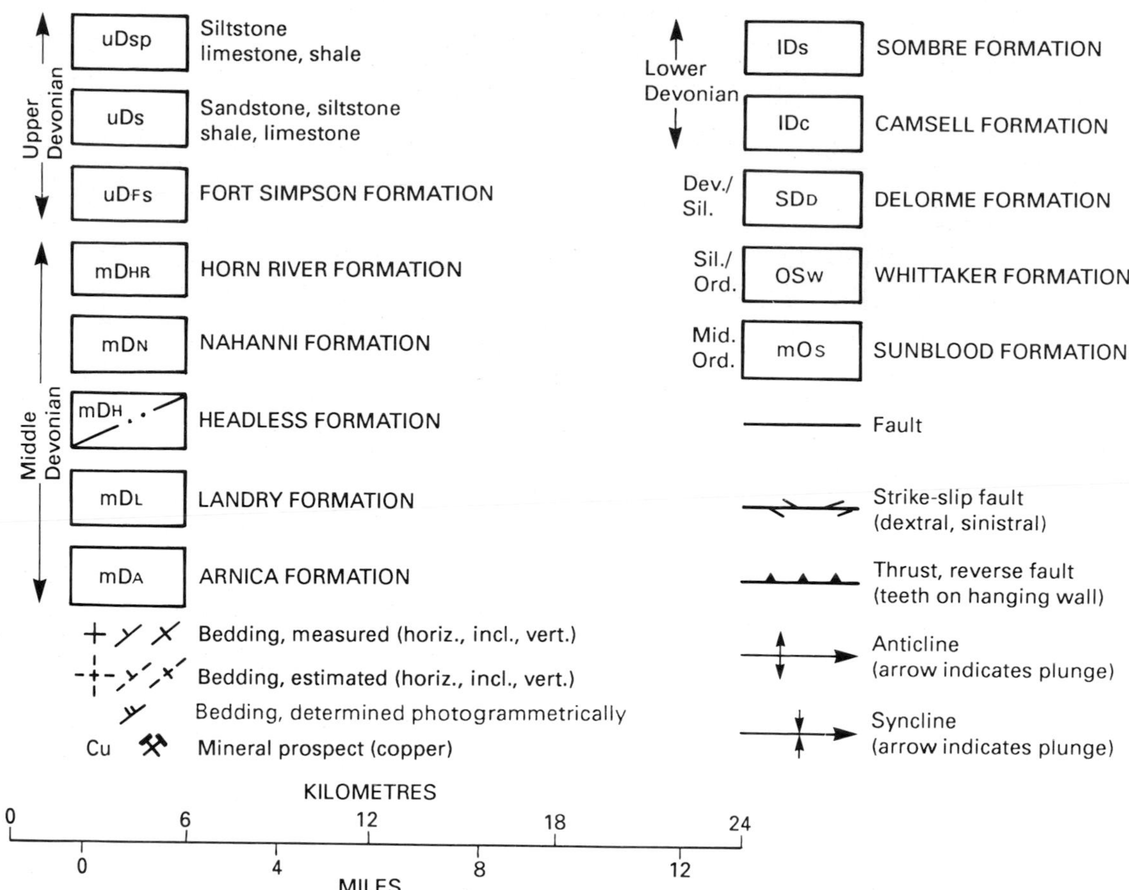

Upper Devonian
uDsp
Siltstone limestone, shale
uDs
Sandstone, siltstone shale, limestone
uDFs
FORT SIMPSON FORMATION
Middle Devonian
mDHR
HORN RIVER FORMATION
mDN
NAHANNI FORMATION
mDH
HEADLESS FORMATION
mDL
LANDRY FORMATION
mDA
ARNICA FORMATION
Bedding, measured (horiz., incl., vert.)
Bedding, estimated (horiz., incl., vert.)
Bedding, determined photogrammetrically
Cu
Mineral prospect (copper)
Lower Devonian
lDs
SOMBRE FORMATION
lDc
CAMSELL FORMATION
Dev./ Sil.
SDD
DELORME FORMATION
Sil./ Ord.
OSw
WHITTAKER FORMATION
Mid. Ord.
mOs
SUNBLOOD FORMATION
Fault
Strike-slip fault (dextral, sinistral)
Thrust, reverse fault (teeth on hanging wall)
Anticline (arrow indicates plunge)
Syncline (arrow indicates plunge)
KILOMETRES
0
6
12
18
24
0
4
8
12
MILES

Opposite is part of the 1:250 000 Geological Survey of Canada map of the Root River district, in the Northwest Territories of Canada. The area falls within an orogenic belt, the Mackenzie Fold Belt, and so the rocks are deformed, particularly by folding.

Are there any folds present for which the axial traces are not marked? Find examples of periclinal synclines and periclinal anticlines. Comment on the plunge direction of the Delorme Syncline. Describe the orientation, attitude, and style of the Delorme Syncline and the Whittaker Anticline. (Assess the limb dips by noting, for example, the 'V'-shape of the outcrops of the Headless Formation in the syncline and the Delorme Formation in the anticline).

Account for the irregular shape of the outcrops of Camsell Formation in the Painted Mountains Anticline.

Draw a cross-section across the map, along the line indicated between lat. 62° 44′ and lat. 62° 46′.

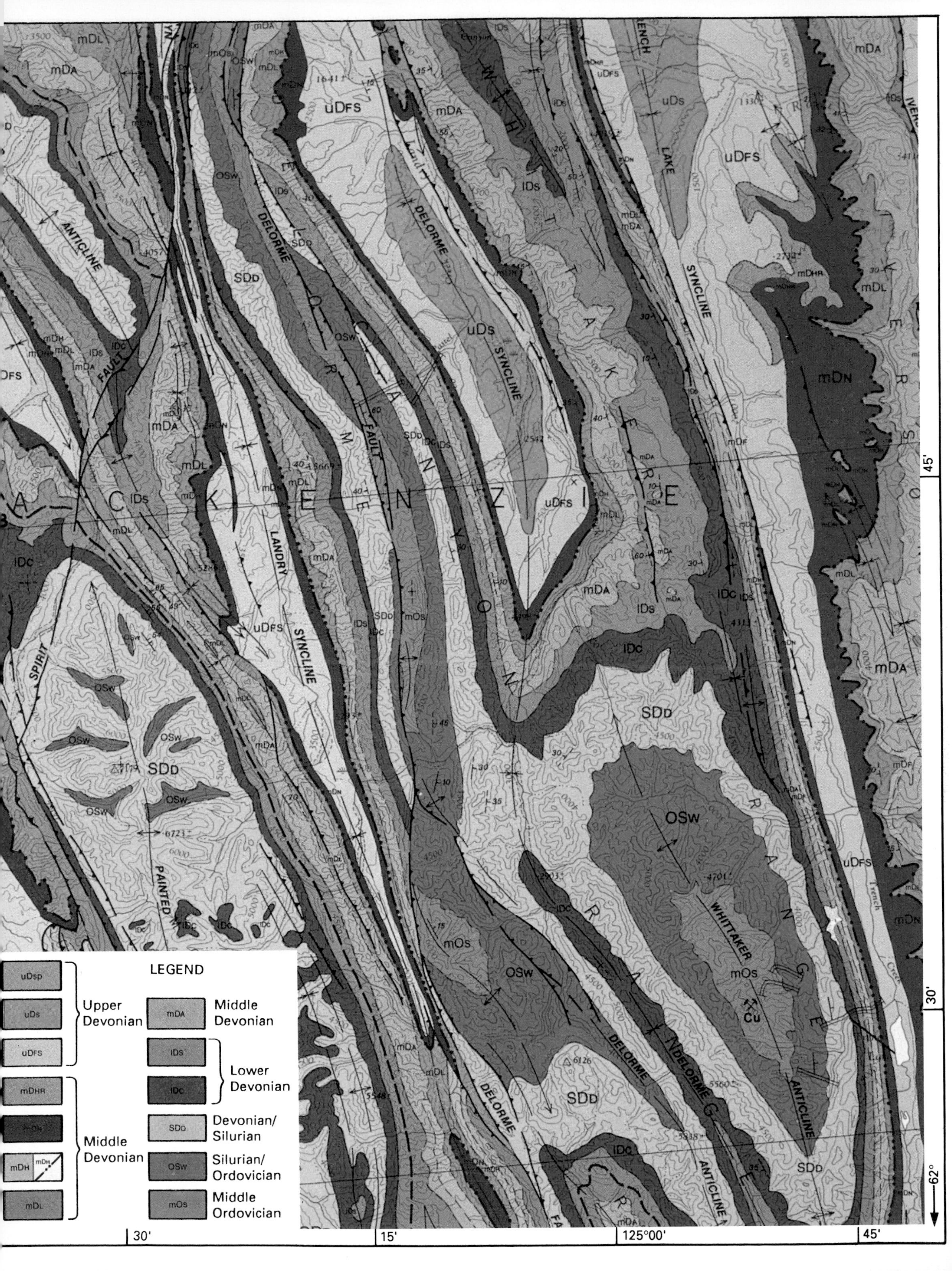

LEGEND
uDsp
uDs
uDFS
Upper Devonian
mDHR
mDN
mDH
mDL
Middle Devonian
mDA
Middle Devonian
lDs
lDc
Lower Devonian
SDD
Devonian/Silurian
OSw
Silurian/Ordovician
mOs
Middle Ordovician
MACKENZIE MOUNTAINS
CANYON RANGES
WHITTAKER RANGE
DELORME FAULT
DELORME SYNCLINE
DELORME ANTICLINE
LANDRY SYNCLINE
PAINTED
SPIRIT
ANTICLINE
FAULT
WHITTAKER ANTICLINE
LAKE SYNCLINE
Cu
30'
15'
125°00'
45'
62°

Plate 5 Sanquar, Southern Scotland

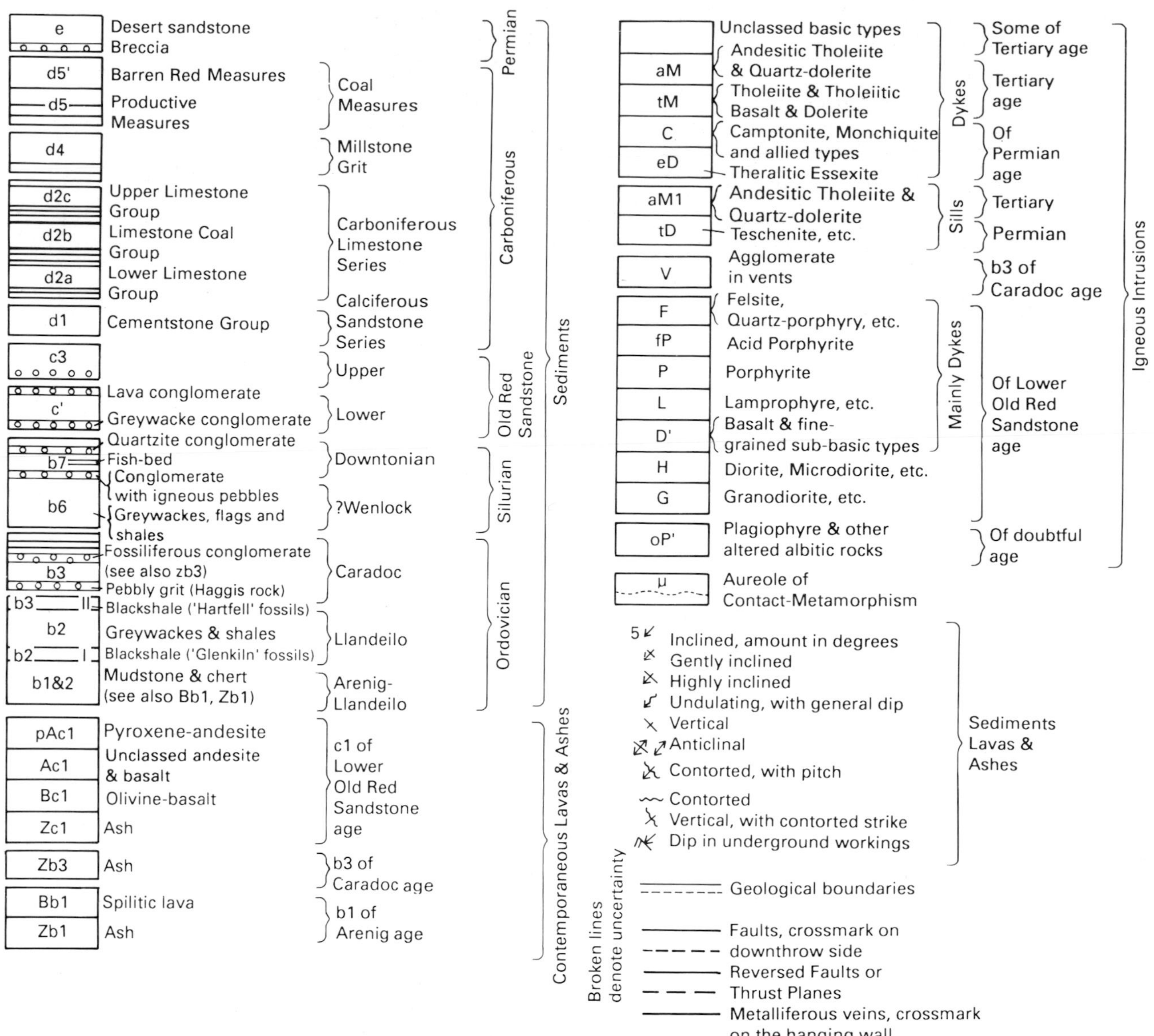

e Desert sandstone
Breccia
d5' Barren Red Measures
d5 Productive Measures
Coal Measures
d4
Millstone Grit
Permian
d2c Upper Limestone Group
d2b Limestone Coal Group
d2a Lower Limestone Group
Carboniferous Limestone Series
d1 Cementstone Group
Calciferous Sandstone Series
Carboniferous
c3
Upper
Lava conglomerate
c' Greywacke conglomerate
Lower
Old Red Sandstone
Quartzite conglomerate
b7 Fish-bed
Conglomerate with igneous pebbles
Downtonian
b6 Greywackes, flags and shales
?Wenlock
Silurian
Fossiliferous conglomerate
b3 (see also zb3)
Pebbly grit (Haggis rock)
Caradoc
b3 Blackshale ('Hartfell' fossils)
b2 Greywackes & shales
b2 Blackshale ('Glenkiln' fossils)
Llandeilo
b1&2 Mudstone & chert (see also Bb1, Zb1)
Arenig-Llandeilo
Ordovician
Sediments
pAc1 Pyroxene-andesite
Ac1 Unclassed andesite & basalt
Bc1 Olivine-basalt
Zc1 Ash
c1 of Lower Old Red Sandstone age
Zb3 Ash
b3 of Caradoc age
Bb1 Spilitic lava
Zb1 Ash
b1 of Arenig age
Contemporaneous Lavas & Ashes
Unclassed basic types
aM Andesitic Tholeiite & Quartz-dolerite
tM Tholeiite & Tholeiitic Basalt & Dolerite
C Camptonite, Monchiquite and allied types
eD Theralitic Essexite
Dykes
Some of Tertiary age
Tertiary age
Of Permian age
aM1 Andesitic Tholeiite & Quartz-dolerite
tD Teschenite, etc.
Sills
Tertiary
Permian
V Agglomerate in vents
b3 of Caradoc age
F Felsite, Quartz-porphyry, etc.
fP Acid Porphyrite
P Porphyrite
L Lamprophyre, etc.
D' Basalt & fine-grained sub-basic types
Mainly Dykes
H Diorite, Microdiorite, etc.
G Granodiorite, etc.
Of Lower Old Red Sandstone age
oP' Plagiophyre & other altered albitic rocks
Of doubtful age
Igneous Intrusions
μ Aureole of Contact-Metamorphism
5 Inclined, amount in degrees
Gently inclined
Highly inclined
Undulating, with general dip
Vertical
Anticlinal
Contorted, with pitch
Contorted
Vertical, with contorted strike
Dip in underground workings
Sediments Lavas & Ashes
Geological boundaries
Faults, crossmark on downthrow side
Reversed Faults or Thrust Planes
Metalliferous veins, crossmark on the hanging wall
Broken lines denote uncertainty

Reproduced opposite is a part of the BGS Sheet 15, Sanquar. It was published in 1937 after a series of revisions, some involving famous BGS geologists such as Ben Peach, John Horne, and Sir Edward Bailey (section 14.2.5). It is reproduced here at its original 'One-Inch' scale (1:63 360), although it is now available as two 1:50 000 sheets. A remarkable amount of the geology of southern Scotland is encapsulated in the portion of the map given here.

Discuss the role of the Southern Upland Fault (the major NE–SW fault in the centre of the area) in influencing sedimentation, volcanism, and structure. Define its age. What else may have influenced the distribution of volcanism?

Judging from the lithologies, how might the environments of deposition have changed from the Silurian to the Old Red Sandstone, from the Old Red Sandstone to the Carboniferous, and from the Carboniferous to the Permian?

What are the main geological trends? Summarise the structural styles seen in the Lower Palaeozoic, the Old Red Sandstone, and the Carboniferous rocks. What evidence is there from the stratigraphic succession that earth movements were active during this period?

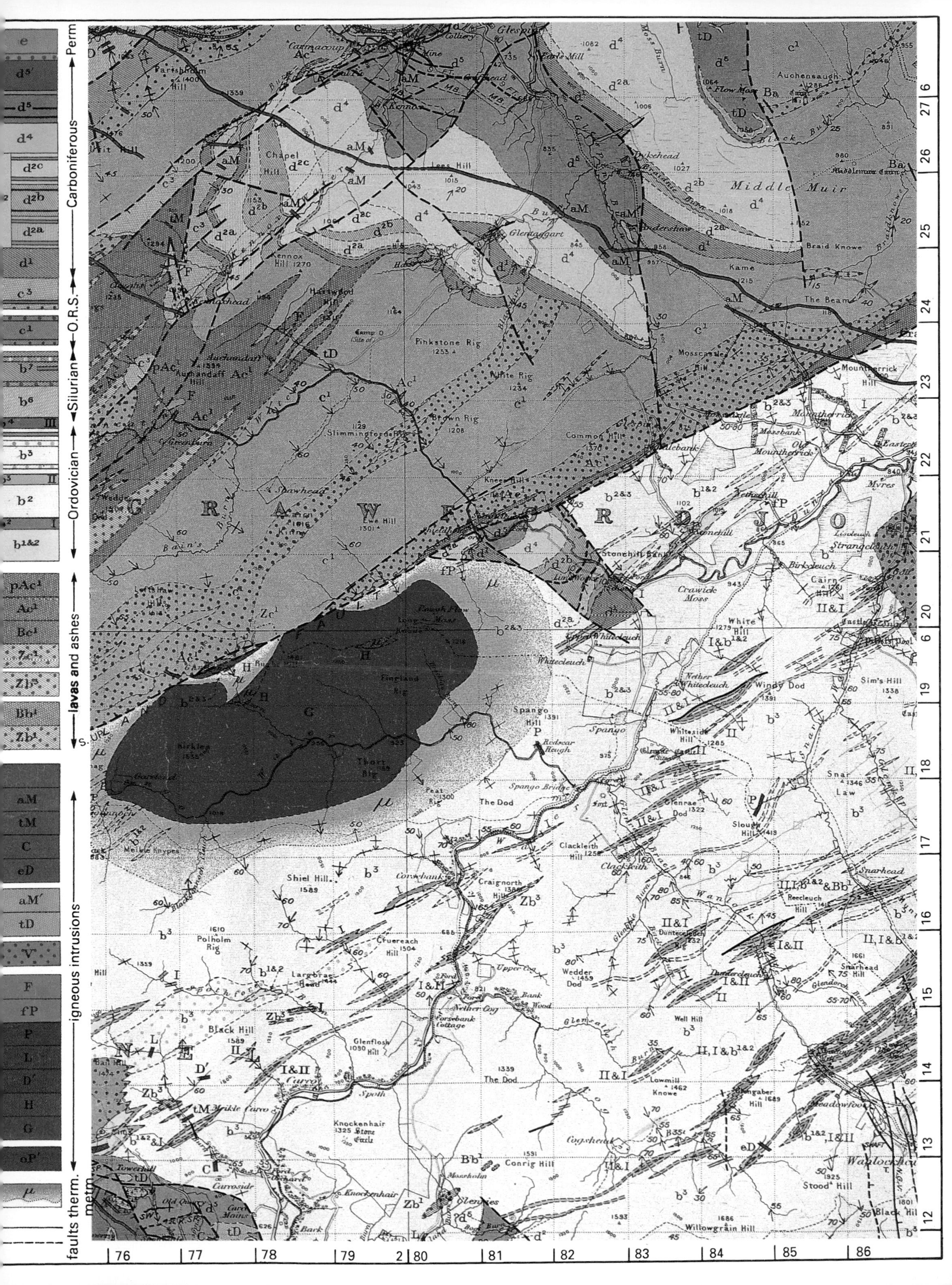

e
d5'
d5
d4
d2c
d2b
d2a
d1
c3
c1
b7
b6
III
b3
II
b2
I
b1&2
pAc1
Ac1
Bc1
Zc1
Zb3
Bb1
Zb1
aM
tM
C
eD
aM'
tD
V'
F
fP
P
L
D'
H
G
oP'
μ
Perm
Carboniferous
O.R.S.
Silurian
Ordovician
lavas and ashes
igneous intrusions
therm.
metm
faults
Glespin
Carmacoup
Parishholm Hill
Auchensaugh
Middle Muir
Braid Knowe
Kame
The Beam
Chapel Hill
Lees Hill
Kennox Hill
Glentaggart
Pinkstone Rig
White Rig
Brown Rig
Slimmingfordeh
Auchendaff Hill
Mosscastle Hill
Common Hill
Ewe Hill
Mountherrick
Crawick Moss
White Hill
Windy Dod
Whiteside Hill
Spango Hill
Redsear Heugh
Spango Bridge
Fingland Rig
Thort Rig
Kirklea
Peat Rig
The Dod
Meikle Knypes
Shiel Hill
Craignorth Hill
Polholm Rig
Cruereach Hill
Largbrae Head
Clackleith Hill
Glenrae Dod
Slough Hill
Snar Law
Reecleuch Hill
Snarhead Hill
Wedder Dod
Well Hill
Glenflosh Hill
Black Hill
Lowmill Knowe
Knockenhair
Conrig Hill
Stood Hill
Willowgrain Hill
Sim's Hill
76
77
78
79
80
81
82
83
84
85
86
12
13
14
15
16
17
18
19
20
21
22
23
24
25
26
27

Plate 6 Heart Mountain, Wyoming

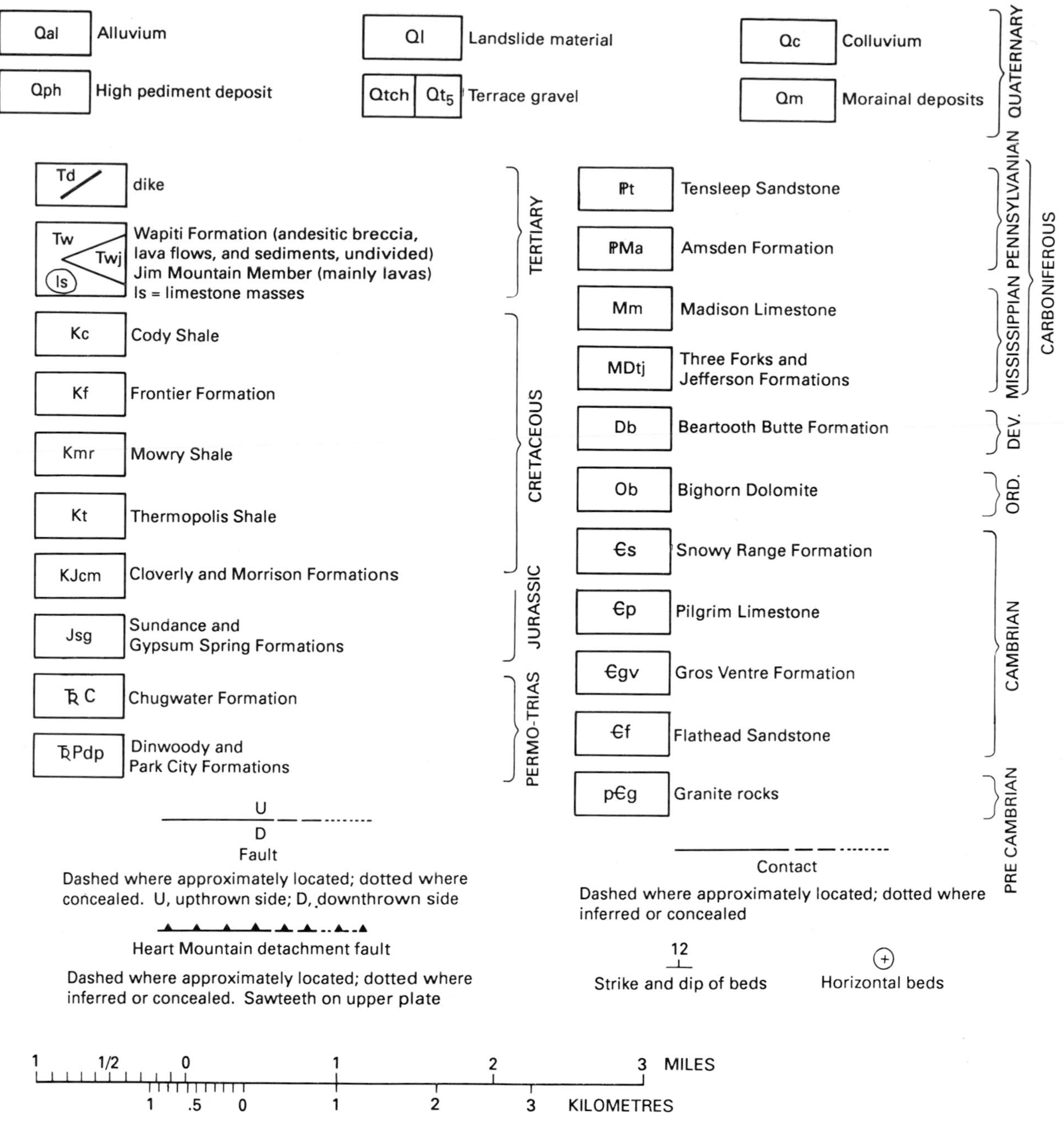

Qal Alluvium
Ql Landslide material
Qc Colluvium
Qph High pediment deposit
Qtch Qt5 Terrace gravel
Qm Morainal deposits
QUATERNARY
Td dike
Tw Twj Is Wapiti Formation (andesitic breccia, lava flows, and sediments, undivided) Jim Mountain Member (mainly lavas) ls = limestone masses
TERTIARY
Kc Cody Shale
Kf Frontier Formation
Kmr Mowry Shale
Kt Thermopolis Shale
KJcm Cloverly and Morrison Formations
CRETACEOUS
Jsg Sundance and Gypsum Spring Formations
JURASSIC
ЋC Chugwater Formation
ЋPdp Dinwoody and Park City Formations
PERMO-TRIAS
Pt Tensleep Sandstone
PMa Amsden Formation
PENNSYLVANIAN
Mm Madison Limestone
MDtj Three Forks and Jefferson Formations
MISSISSIPPIAN
CARBONIFEROUS
Db Beartooth Butte Formation
DEV.
Ob Bighorn Dolomite
ORD.
€s Snowy Range Formation
€p Pilgrim Limestone
€gv Gros Ventre Formation
€f Flathead Sandstone
CAMBRIAN
p€g Granite rocks
PRE CAMBRIAN
U
D
Fault
Dashed where approximately located; dotted where concealed. U, upthrown side; D, downthrown side
Heart Mountain detachment fault
Dashed where approximately located; dotted where inferred or concealed. Sawteeth on upper plate
Contact
Dashed where approximately located; dotted where inferred or concealed
12
Strike and dip of beds
Horizontal beds
1 1/2 0 1 2 3 MILES
1 .5 0 1 2 3 KILOMETRES

The map opposite is reproduced from parts of two USGS 15′ quadrangles in NW Wyoming (Pat O'Hara Mountain, GC-755, and Deep Lake, GQ-478), by permission of the US Geological Survey. It includes a famous structure called the Heart Mountain Fault, described as a 'showpiece' of North American tectonics. Although the geological history of the area was remarkably stable throughout much of the Phanerozoic, at one point huge masses of rock, themselves intact, were dispersed over a vast area along a detachment fault with a puzzlingly low dip angle. How it happened is still the subject of debate.

Discuss the geological history of the area shown, paying particular attention to the nature of the Cambrian – Cretaceous succession, any tectonism before or after the Heart Mountain Fault, and the fault itself, for example, its attitude, any stratigraphic influence on its location, and its timing.

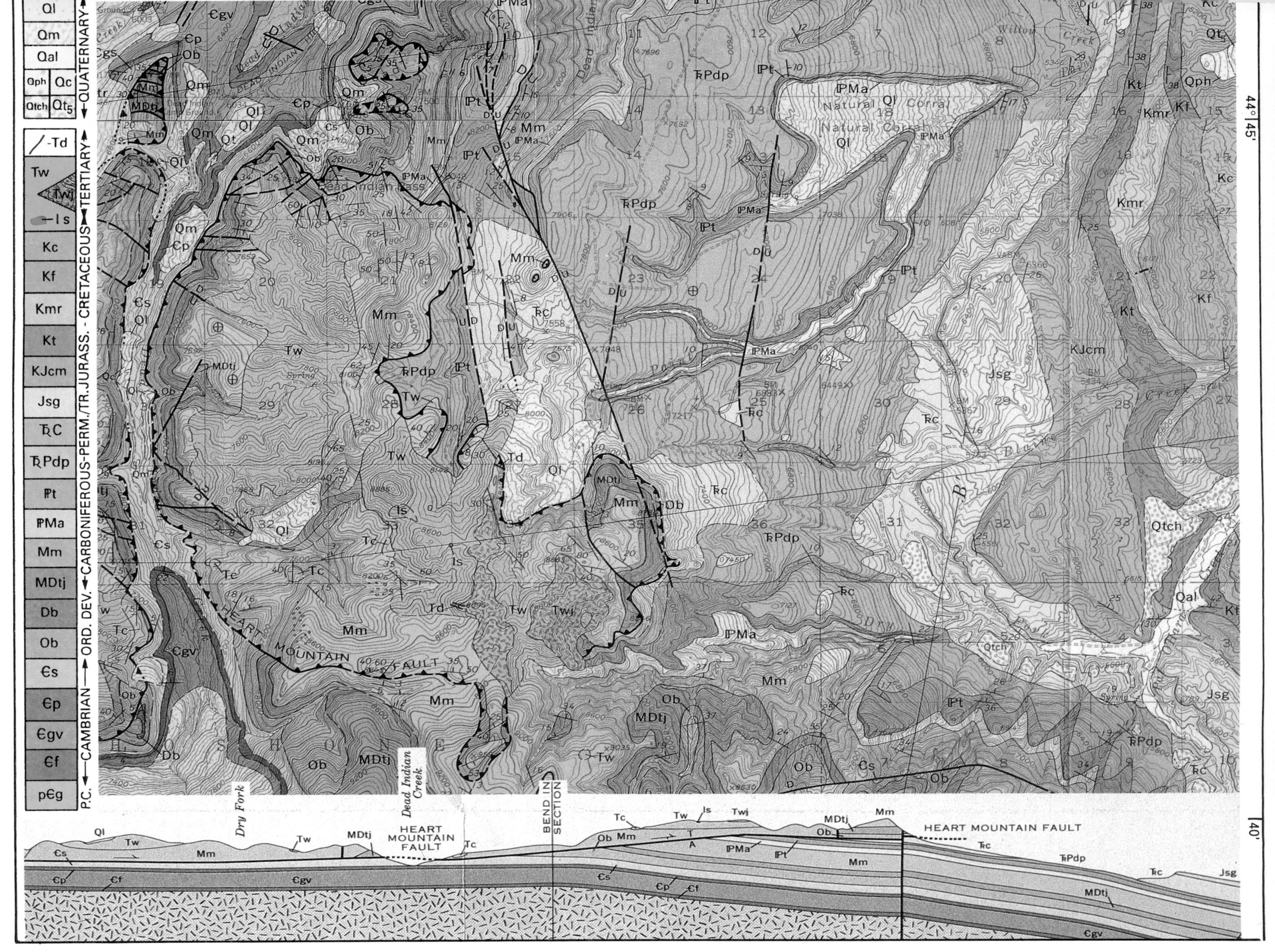
QUATERNARY
TERTIARY
CRETACEOUS
CARBONIFEROUS-PERM./TR.JURASS.
ORD. DEV.
CAMBRIAN
P.C.
Ql
Qm
Qal
Qph
Qc
Qtch
Qt5
-Td
Tw
Twj
Is
Kc
Kf
Kmr
Kt
KJcm
Jsg
TRC
TRPdp
IPt
IPMa
Mm
MDtj
Db
Ob
Cs
Cp
Cgv
Cf
pCg
44° 45'
40'
Natural Corral
Dead Indian Pass
HEART MOUNTAIN FAULT
Dry Fork
Dead Indian Creek
BEND IN SECTION

Plate 7 Marraba, Queensland, Australia

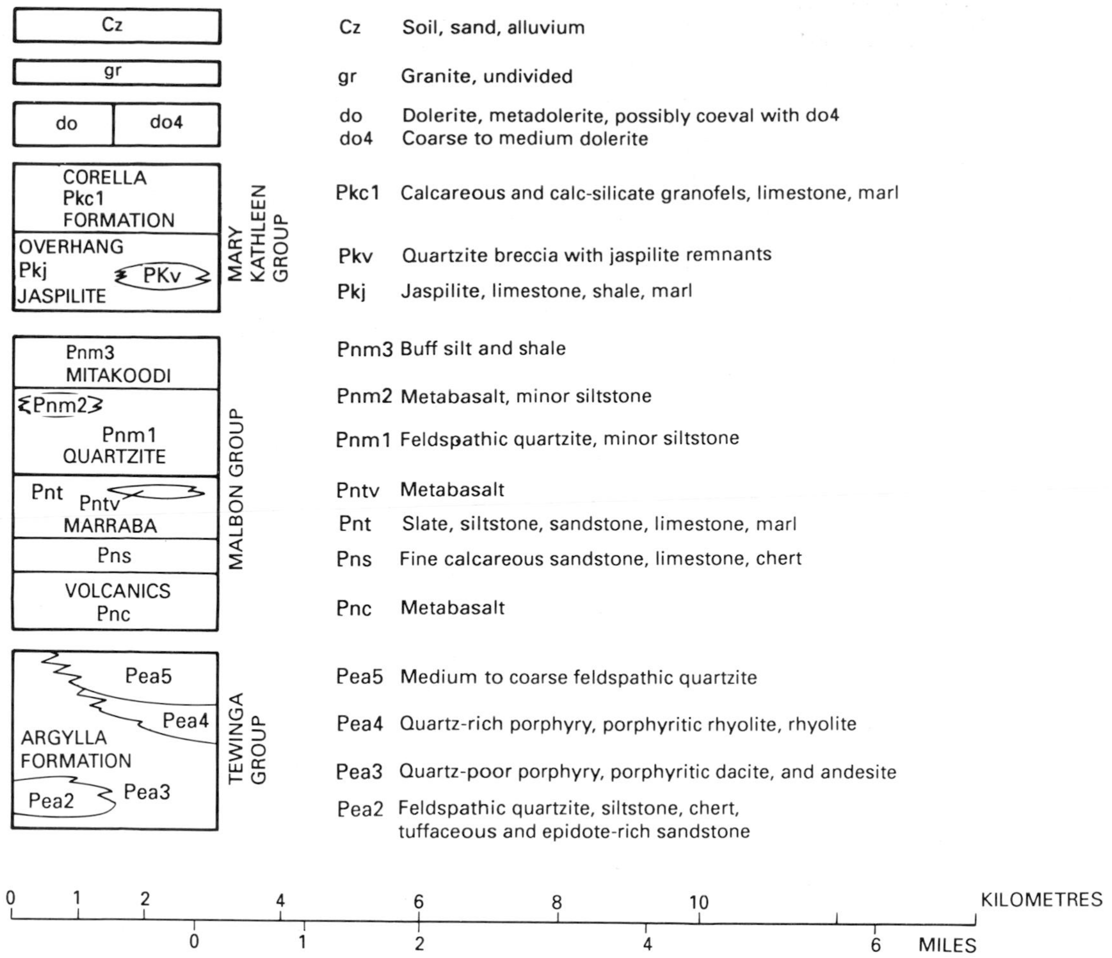

Cz
gr
do
do4
CORELLA
Pkc1
FORMATION
OVERHANG
Pkj
PKv
JASPILITE
MARY KATHLEEN GROUP
Pnm3
MITAKOODI
Pnm2
Pnm1
QUARTZITE
Pnt
Pntv
MARRABA
Pns
VOLCANICS
Pnc
MALBON GROUP
Pea5
Pea4
ARGYLLA
FORMATION
Pea2
Pea3
TEWINGA GROUP
Cz Soil, sand, alluvium
gr Granite, undivided
do Dolerite, metadolerite, possibly coeval with do4
do4 Coarse to medium dolerite
Pkc1 Calcareous and calc-silicate granofels, limestone, marl
Pkv Quartzite breccia with jaspilite remnants
Pkj Jaspilite, limestone, shale, marl
Pnm3 Buff silt and shale
Pnm2 Metabasalt, minor siltstone
Pnm1 Feldspathic quartzite, minor siltstone
Pntv Metabasalt
Pnt Slate, siltstone, sandstone, limestone, marl
Pns Fine calcareous sandstone, limestone, chert
Pnc Metabasalt
Pea5 Medium to coarse feldspathic quartzite
Pea4 Quartz-rich porphyry, porphyritic rhyolite, rhyolite
Pea3 Quartz-poor porphyry, porphyritic dacite, and andesite
Pea2 Feldspathic quartzite, siltstone, chert, tuffaceous and epidote-rich sandstone
0 1 2 4 6 8 10 KILOMETRES
0 1 2 4 6 MILES

Facing is part of the 1:100 000 Marraba Sheet 6956 produced jointly by the Bureau of Mineral Resources in Australia and the Geological Survey of Queensland. The area is immediately W of the town of Cloncurry in W Queensland, one of the hottest parts of Australia, having reached 53° in the shade!

The area reproduced here is just part of the extensive and intricate complex of Proterozoic igneous and metamorphic rocks that is finely portrayed on the full sheet. For simplicity, the numerous structural and other symbols have been omitted from the key above. Also, mining details (the area falls in the important Mount Isa Pb-Zn-Ag region) are here omitted. Note that the cross-section reproduced here does not extend across the width of the map because the section line bends.

On the basis of the map patterns and the cross-section, describe the geological structure of the area, and interpret the successive stages in its geological history.

(Map and section reproduced by permission of the Bureau of Mineral Resources, Canberra, and the Department of Mines, Queensland, Australia.)

Pea5
Pea4
Pea3
Pea2
TEWINGA GROUP
Pnm3
Pnm2
Pnm1
Pnt
Pntv
Pns
Pnc
MALBON GROUP
cz superficial
gr granite
do do4 dolerite
Pkc1
Pkj Pkv
MARY KATHLEEN GROUP
Butcher Bore
Boomerang Waterhole
Slaty Creek
Mitakoodi
MT BROWNIE
Success Bore
SECTION
Scale V/H = 1

Plate 8 Malmesbury, England

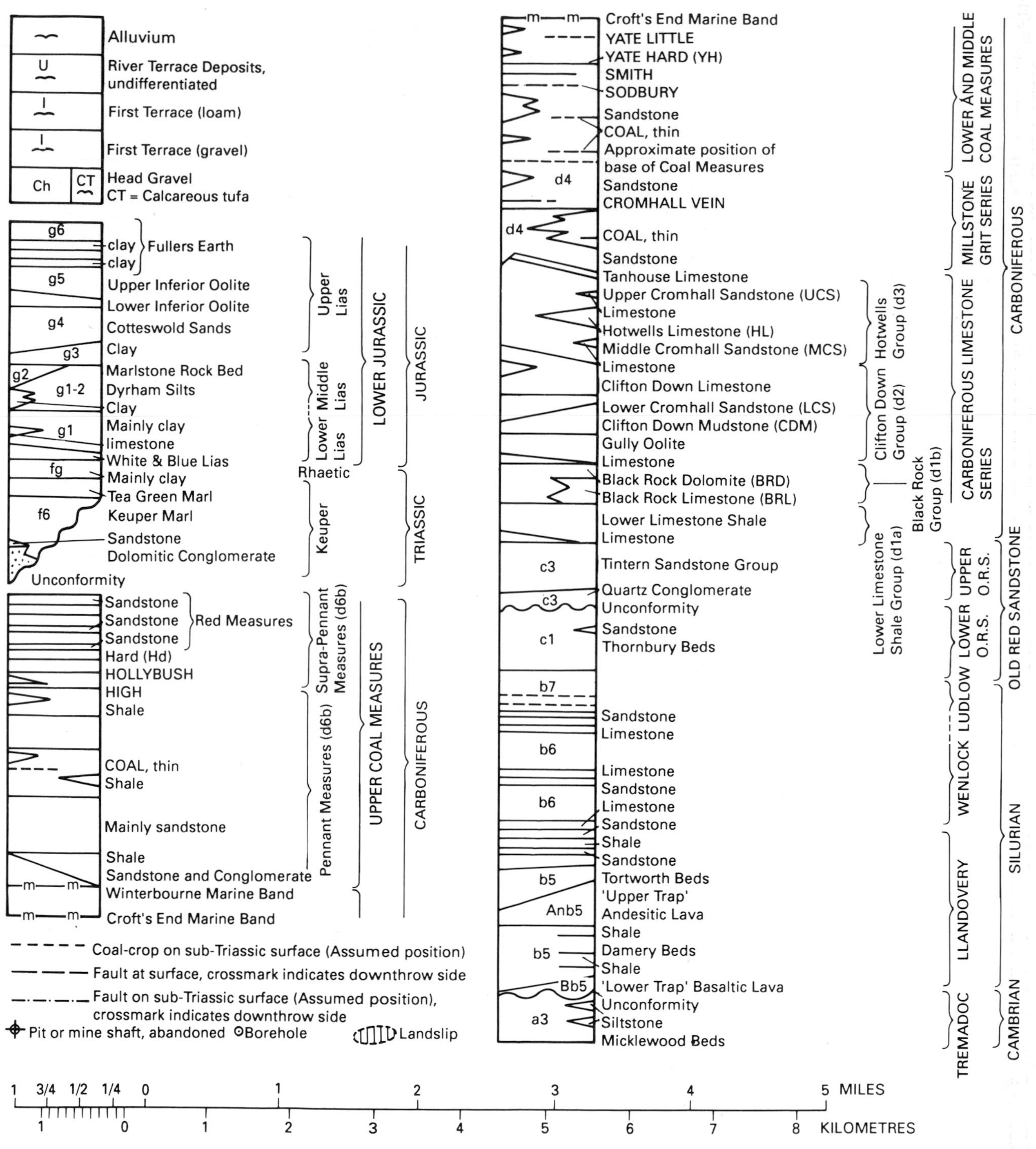

Alluvium
River Terrace Deposits, undifferentiated
First Terrace (loam)
First Terrace (gravel)
Head Gravel
CT = Calcareous tufa
clay
clay
Fullers Earth
Upper Inferior Oolite
Lower Inferior Oolite
Cotteswold Sands
Clay
Marlstone Rock Bed
Dyrham Silts
Clay
Mainly clay
limestone
White & Blue Lias
Mainly clay
Tea Green Marl
Keuper Marl
Sandstone
Dolomitic Conglomerate
Unconformity
Upper Lias
Lower Middle Lias
Lower Lias
Rhaetic
Keuper
LOWER JURASSIC
JURASSIC
TRIASSIC
Sandstone
Sandstone
Sandstone
Red Measures
Hard (Hd)
HOLLYBUSH
HIGH
Shale
COAL, thin
Shale
Mainly sandstone
Shale
Sandstone and Conglomerate
Winterbourne Marine Band
Croft's End Marine Band
Supra-Pennant Measures (d6b)
Pennant Measures (d6b)
UPPER COAL MEASURES
CARBONIFEROUS
Coal-crop on sub-Triassic surface (Assumed position)
Fault at surface, crossmark indicates downthrow side
Fault on sub-Triassic surface (Assumed position), crossmark indicates downthrow side
Pit or mine shaft, abandoned
Borehole
Landslip
Croft's End Marine Band
YATE LITTLE
YATE HARD (YH)
SMITH
SODBURY
Sandstone
COAL, thin
Approximate position of base of Coal Measures
Sandstone
CROMHALL VEIN
COAL, thin
Sandstone
Tanhouse Limestone
Upper Cromhall Sandstone (UCS)
Limestone
Hotwells Limestone (HL)
Middle Cromhall Sandstone (MCS)
Limestone
Clifton Down Limestone
Lower Cromhall Sandstone (LCS)
Clifton Down Mudstone (CDM)
Gully Oolite
Limestone
Black Rock Dolomite (BRD)
Black Rock Limestone (BRL)
Lower Limestone Shale
Limestone
Tintern Sandstone Group
Quartz Conglomerate
Unconformity
Sandstone
Thornbury Beds
Sandstone
Limestone
Limestone
Sandstone
Limestone
Sandstone
Shale
Sandstone
Tortworth Beds
'Upper Trap'
Andesitic Lava
Shale
Damery Beds
Shale
'Lower Trap' Basaltic Lava
Unconformity
Siltstone
Micklewood Beds
Hotwells Group (d3)
Clifton Down Group (d2)
Black Rock Group (d1b)
Lower Limestone Shale Group (d1a)
LOWER AND MIDDLE COAL MEASURES
MILLSTONE GRIT SERIES
CARBONIFEROUS LIMESTONE SERIES
UPPER O.R.S.
LOWER O.R.S.
LUDLOW
WENLOCK
LLANDOVERY
TREMADOC
CARBONIFEROUS
OLD RED SANDSTONE
SILURIAN
CAMBRIAN
MILES
KILOMETRES

Reproduced opposite is part of the BGS 'One-Inch' map (1:63 360) of the Malmesbury district, England. The key given above is simplified from the scaled vertical sections which accompany the original map.

Interpret the geological history of the area shown.

E 7½° S
Priest Wood
Vertical scale one and a half times the horizontal
Cherryrock Farm
Assley Common
W 7½° N
Buckover
FORMATIONS AND STRUCTURES UNKNOWN
Pleistocene & Recent
Jurassic
Triassic
Carboniferous
O.R.S.
Silurian
Camb.
Charfield
Cromhall
Wickwar
Kingswood
Wotton under Edge
Itchington
Latteridge
Iron Acton
Frampton Cotterell
Chipping Sodbury
Little Sodbury
Hawkesbury
Horton
Yate
67
68
69
70
71
72
73
74
75
76
77
82
83
84
85
86
87
88
89
90
91
92
93
94
95
96

7 Unconformities

7.1 Introduction

In the spring of 1788, James Hutton peered from his small boat at the cliffs of Siccar Point in SE Scotland and, seeing horizontal red sandstones lying directly upon vertical beds, became the first to perceive the long time interval implied by this kind of junction. The underlying material had to have been buried, lithified, rotated, and uplifted before the red sandstones were deposited on it.

The concepts of geological time have become central to an understanding of this kind of junction, known as an unconformity. Use of the term has grown in a somewhat complex and confused way, though the details do not concern us here. The first part of this chapter summarises current terminology. The important thing in the present context is the identification and manipulation of unconformities on maps, and the interpretation of what they mean. These aspects are developed in the second part of the chapter.

7.2 Terminology

An **unconformity** is a significant time-break in the stratigraphic succession of an area. It is usually visualised as the junction where the formations of differing stratigraphic age come together, properly called the **surface of unconformity**. The time gap implied by the junction may be relatively small and the unconformity developed only locally, or entire stratigraphic systems may be missing and the unconformity of regional importance.

Most adjacent formations in a stratigraphic succession are probably separated by some time gap to account for the production of the different rock types which define the formations. However, this alone would not be considered enough to call the junction an unconformity. There has to be an indication that part of the known geological record is absent. If the units are discordant at the junction, as at Hutton's Siccar Point locality, then an unconformity is clearly indicated because there has to have been an interval sufficient to allow tilting and erosion of the older rocks before the younger ones were formed. However, if the two units are arranged parallel to each other, their stratigraphic age will have to be known in order to gauge whether or not there is sufficient stratigraphy missing for the junction to rank as an unconformity.

The main kinds of unconformity are depicted in Fig. 7.1. In this scheme, the discordant arrangement originally described by James Hutton would merely be one kind of

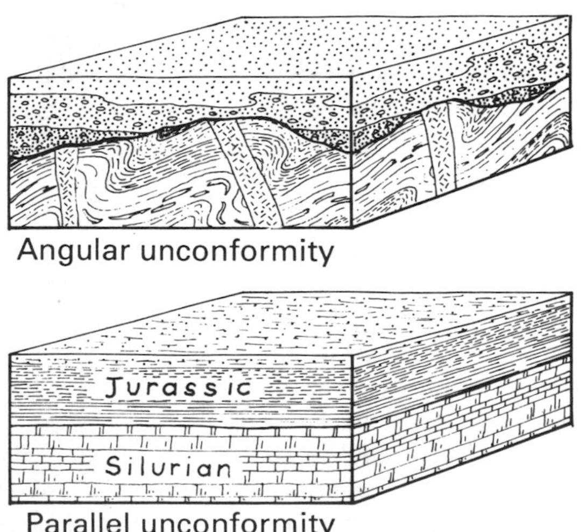
Angular unconformity
Jurassic
Silurian
Parallel unconformity

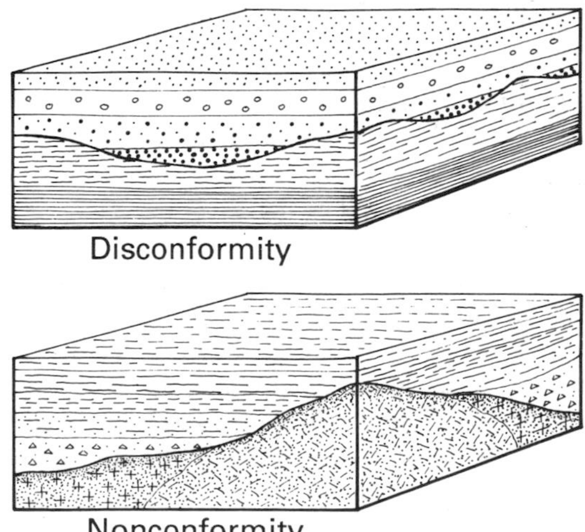
Disconformity
Nonconformity

Fig. 7.1 Diagrams to show the four main kinds of unconformity.

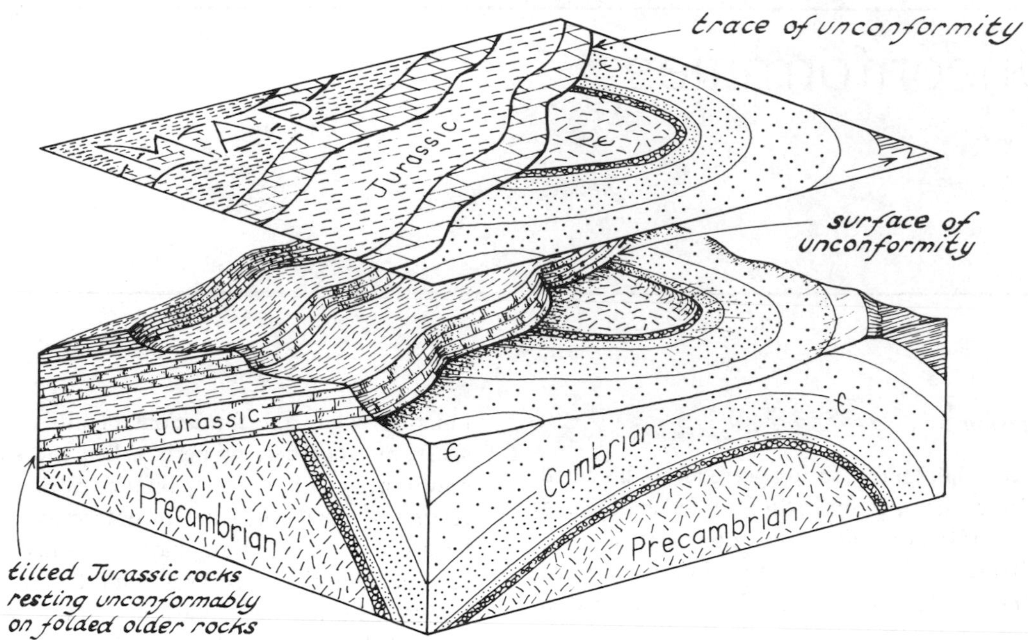

trace of unconformity
MAP
Jurassic
Pє
Є
N
surface of unconformity
Jurassic
Precambrian
Є
Cambrian
Є
Precambrian
tilted Jurassic rocks resting unconformably on folded older rocks

Fig. 7.2 The appearance of an angular unconformity, in block diagram and map view.

unconformable relationship, namely an **angular unconformity**. In contrast to the original use of the term, the time gap is now central to the concept, rather than merely following by implication from the geometrical discordance between the adjacent units.

Geologists also talk about formations resting 'unconformably' upon older rocks, or having an 'unconformable junction'. The surface of unconformity represents the surface of the lower rocks upon which the upper material was deposited. With most unconformities, the younger materials are sedimentary rocks, but they could be volcaniclastic or extrusive igneous rocks, such as the lavas in the example of section 2.3.2. The contacts of igneous intrusions are not regarded as unconformities.

7.3 Recognition on maps

Unconformities are surfaces and therefore appear on maps as linear traces (Fig. 7.2). The map key may give some indication of any unconformities that are present.

Some kinds of unconformity are easier to recognise than others. Angular unconformities are among the most dramatic features that can be seen in rocks, and on maps, too, they can have a conspicuous appearance. The unconformable units meet at the line of unconformity with discordance (Fig. 7.3a) which, if the angularity of the unconformity is large, will be pronounced. The discordance may have to be searched for if the angularity is small, and it may be masked if the outcrop patterns are made irregular by the relief of the land surface (Fig. 7.3b).

Parallel unconformities cannot produce a discordant pattern on maps. They have to be recognised by the detection of missing units, by reference to the map key (Fig. 7.3c). Absence of some unit that may have been deposited only locally is insufficient; the stratigraphic break has to be significant at the scale of the map.

Unconformities can be difficult to distinguish from faults, both in nature if the junction is not exposed and on maps that do not distinguish faulted contacts. In most cases, however, the surveyor will have made a decision in the field, and indicated on the completed map any junctions thought to be faults by some particular line symbol. Unconformable junctions, on the other hand, are normally drawn with the same line as for ordinary stratigraphic boundaries, and their nature left for the reader to deduce. That the geological surveyor can have this difficulty is illustrated by the Ten Mile map of the UK. Part of the *third edition* (1979) of this map is reproduced here as Plate 2. Ten kilometres SE of Whitchurch [SJ6035] rocks of various Lower Jurassic age meet Triassic rocks with discordance. The junction is depicted as a fault. However, on the *second edition* (1957) of this same map, the junction appears as an unconformity. Presumably in the years between the two editions of the map, new evidence came to light which prompted the surveying team to reassess the nature of this particular junction.

The analogous problem confronts the reader of a map which does not distinguish between faulted and unconformable contacts. There may be clues. For example, unconformities tend to be horizontal, unless they have been tilted later, whereas faults tend to be steep. Some un-

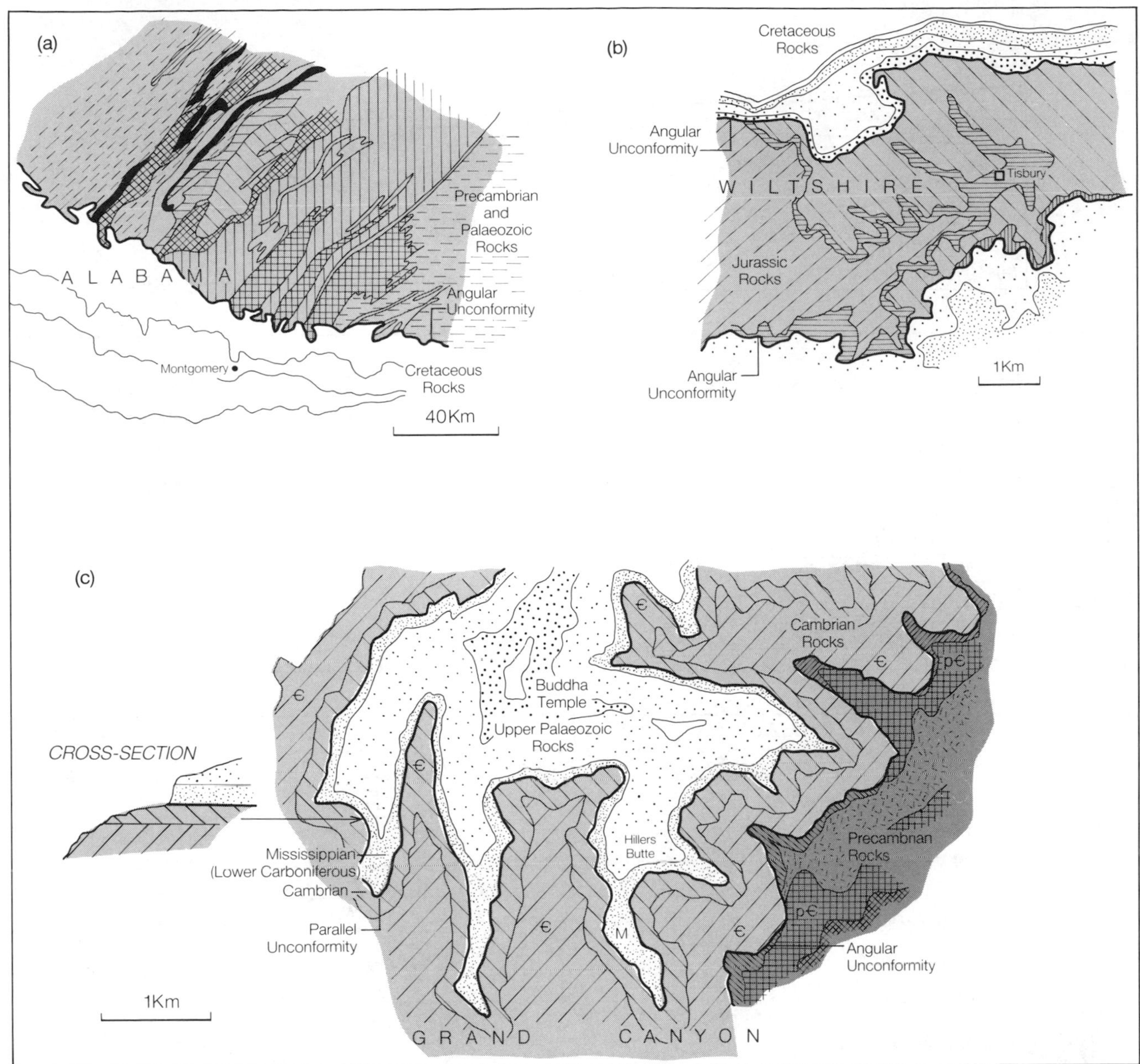
(a)
Precambrian and Palaeozoic Rocks
A L A B A M A
Angular Unconformity
Montgomery
Cretaceous Rocks
40Km
(b)
Cretaceous Rocks
Angular Unconformity
W I L T S H I R E
Tisbury
Jurassic Rocks
Angular Unconformity
1Km
(c)
CROSS-SECTION
Buddha Temple
Upper Palaeozoic Rocks
Cambrian Rocks
pЄ
Є
Mississippian (Lower Carboniferous)
Cambrian
Parallel Unconformity
Hillers Butte
Precambrian Rocks
Angular Unconformity
M
1Km
G R A N D C A N Y O N

Fig. 7.3 Some examples of the appearance on maps of unconformities. (a) SE USA. (b) Shaftesbury district, S England. (c) Grand Canyon, Arizona, USA.

conformities have an irregular form, reflecting an uneven surface of deposition, so their map trace is irregular, unlike the smooth trace of faults. Although the rocks either side of an unconformity may be influencing relief, the surface of unconformity itself rarely has any direct topographic effect. Faults, in contrast, because of the weakening effect they produce on the rocks, commonly induce negative topographic features such as valleys. Nevertheless, in the absence of further knowledge of the rocks in the area, it may remain impossible to distinguish on the map between unconformities and faults.

7.4 Associated features

We can consider the relationship with the surface of unconformity of the rocks below and those above. **Overstep** is concerned with differences in the rocks *below* the unconformity (Fig. 7.4a). It refers to the way in which they are crossed by the overlying unit and depends largely on the way the lower rocks happened to be disposed at the time the material above the unconformity was being laid down. Geologists speak, for example, of the upper unit 'overstepping older rocks northwards', 'overstepping

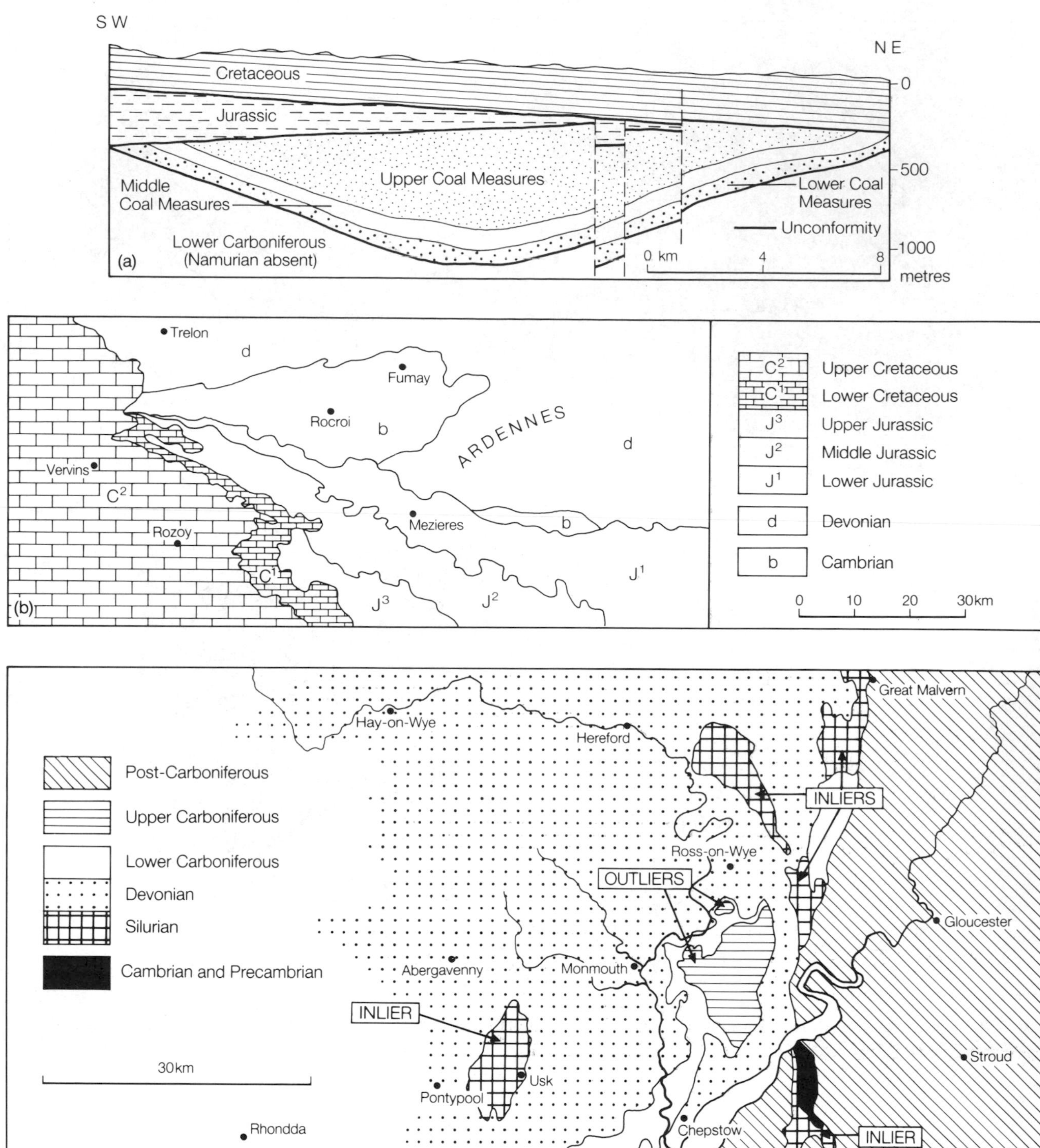
SW
NE
Cretaceous
Jurassic
Upper Coal Measures
Middle Coal Measures
Lower Coal Measures
Unconformity
Lower Carboniferous (Namurian absent)
(a)
0 km 4 8
0
500
1000 metres
Trelon
d
Fumay
Rocroi
b
ARDENNES
d
Vervins
C2
Rozoy
C1
Mezieres
b
J1
J3
J2
(b)
Upper Cretaceous
Lower Cretaceous
Upper Jurassic
Middle Jurassic
Lower Jurassic
Devonian
Cambrian
0 10 20 30km
Great Malvern
Hay-on-Wye
Hereford
Post-Carboniferous
Upper Carboniferous
Lower Carboniferous
Devonian
Silurian
Cambrian and Precambrian
INLIERS
Ross-on-Wye
OUTLIERS
Gloucester
Abergavenny
Monmouth
INLIER
Stroud
30km
Usk
Pontypool
Rhondda
Chepstow
INLIER
(c)

Fig. 7.4 Some features associated with unconformities. (a) The concealed coalfield of Kent, SE England, in cross-section, showing three unconformities. The unconformity at the base of the Cretaceous shows overstep, the Cretaceous rocks overstepping the Jurassic onto Coal Measures. (b) A map, simplified from the 1 : 1 000 000 map of France, showing Devonian unconformably overlying Cambrian rocks (because Ordovician–Silurian strata are absent), and both systems unconformably overlain by Mesozoic rocks. j^2 overlaps j^1, and C^2 overlaps C^1. (c) A map, simplified from the Ten Mile map of the UK, showing examples of inliers and outliers. (The northern part of this area is included in Plate 1, and the south-central part enlarged in Plate 7.)

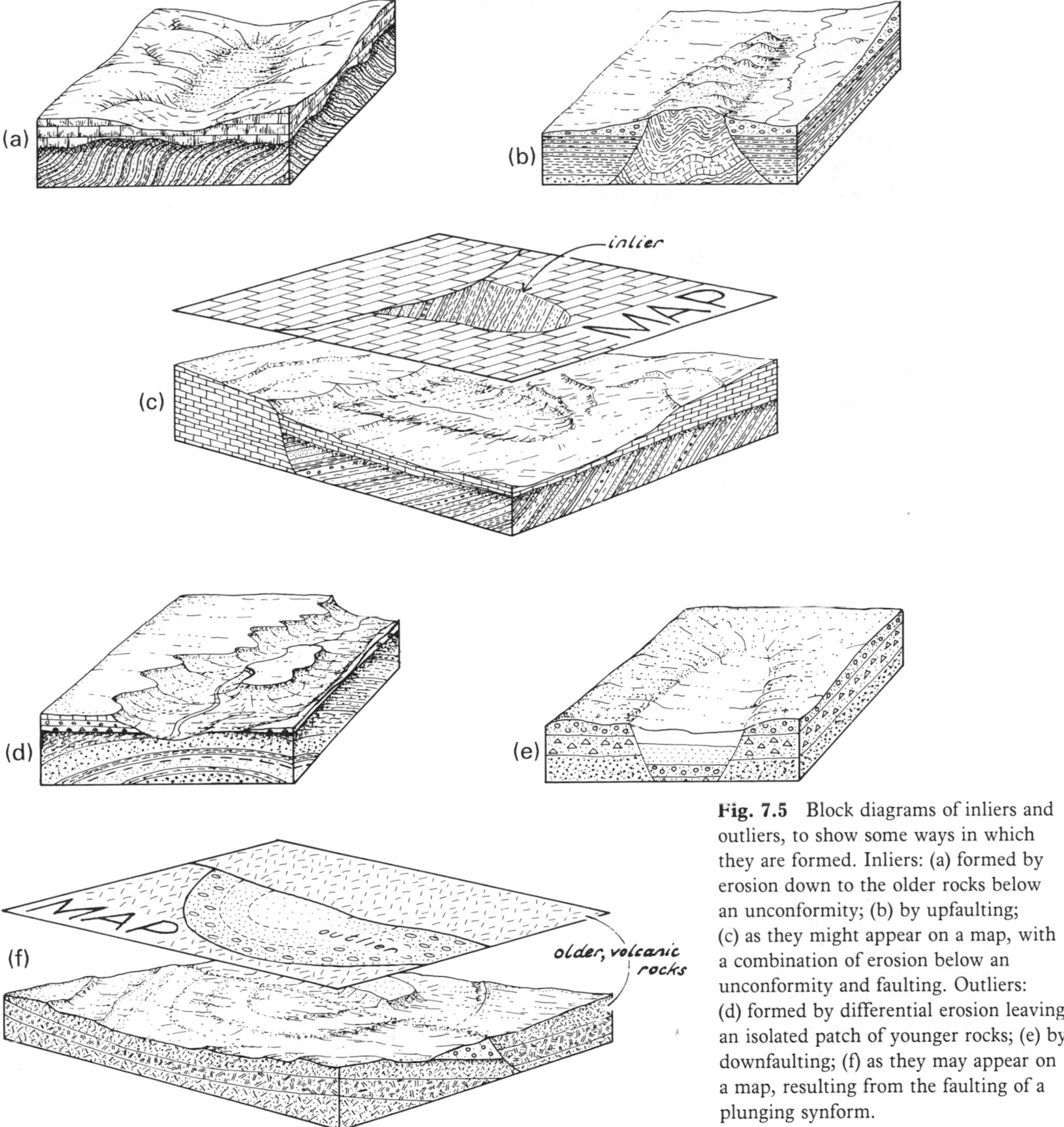
(a)
(b)
inlier
MAP
(c)
(d)
(e)
MAP
outlier
(f)
older, volcanic rocks

Fig. 7.5 Block diagrams of inliers and outliers, to show some ways in which they are formed. Inliers: (a) formed by erosion down to the older rocks below an unconformity; (b) by upfaulting; (c) as they might appear on a map, with a combination of erosion below an unconformity and faulting. Outliers: (d) formed by differential erosion leaving an isolated patch of younger rocks; (e) by downfaulting; (f) as they may appear on a map, resulting from the faulting of a plunging synform.

highly folded rocks in the south', or 'overstepping limestones east of the river'. Overstep can only arise with an angular unconformity.

Other terms are concerned with the arrangement of rocks *above* the unconformity. They are illustrated in Fig. 12.2. If progressively younger formations come into contact with the unconformity, they are said to **overlap** (Fig. 7.4b). If they are sedimentary units, it is common for them to become finer grained rock types as they progressively overlap.

Offlap is the reverse situation. The oldest formation of the upper rocks is everywhere forming the unconformable contact with the lower rocks, and is overlain by successively younger units which have a less and less extensive distribution. In general, fine-grained rocks such as shales and fine limestones are replaced upwards by coarser rocks, such as sandstones and conglomerates.

Two features that commonly arise in association with unconformities, though they are produced in other ways as well, are inliers and outliers (Fig. 7.4c). An area of older

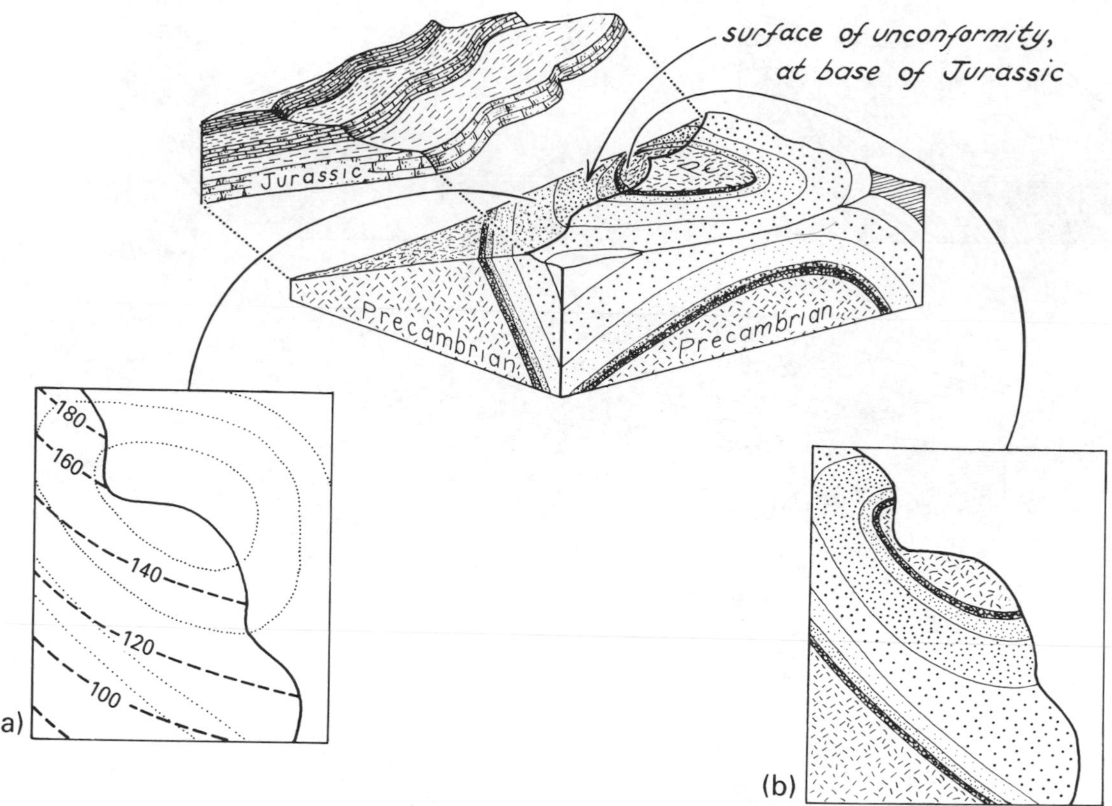
surface of unconformity,
at base of Jurassic
Jurassic
Precambrian
Precambrian
180
160
140
120
100
(a)
(b)

Fig. 7.6 Block diagram of the unconformity shown in Fig. 7.2, 'exploded' at the surface of unconformity to reveal its form and the sub-crop of the older units. (a) Structure contour map of the surface of unconformity. Note that this is the configuration as it is seen *today*, presumably after post-Jurassic tilting had affected the area. Dotted lines indicate the distribution of the Precambrian rocks. (b) Sub-crop map, at the base of the Jurassic.

rocks that appears in map view to be completely surrounded by younger rocks, is called, particularly in the UK, an **inlier**. The converse situation, of younger rocks surrounded by older, is an **outlier**. Both effects can be produced simply by differential erosion, but more significant inliers and outliers are produced where the junction between the younger and older rocks is an unconformity or set of faults, or a combination of both (Fig. 7.5). Inliers provide 'windows' through the covering rocks to what is below. Outliers can give a glimpse of the younger rocks that were once more areally extensive.

7.5 Use on maps

Probably the most usual application of unconformities as they appear on maps is their great value in helping decipher the geological history of an area. The gap in the stratigraphic record will prompt palaeoenvironmental explanations why beds were not deposited during the unrepresented interval, or why they were removed by erosion. Moreover, the three-dimensional shape of the unconformity surface provides a record of the land surface at the time the upper beds were deposited. The pattern of covering of the lower rocks – whether they are 'blanketed' by the upper material or overlapped by successively younger beds – gives information on the depositional environments of the younger sediments. Interpretations of geological histories in these ways are developed in section 12.2.

Unconformities can have practical significance, too. For example, impermeable beds overlying porous reservoir rocks can form important ground water accumulations and petroleum traps. A number of the oil and gas fields in the North Sea involve unconformities. Here, the precise shape of the unconformity can influence the location and method of hydrocarbon production and the economics. In situations like this, it is necessary to treat unconformities in a more quantitative way. Because unconformities are surfaces, structure contours can be drawn to quantify their shape. The contours are drawn in exactly the same way as for other geological boundaries. If the unconformity outcrops at various known altitudes (section 3.5), it may be possible to draw the structure contours from a geological map alone, although usually supplemental borehole information will be required, especially if the surface of unconformity is irregular.

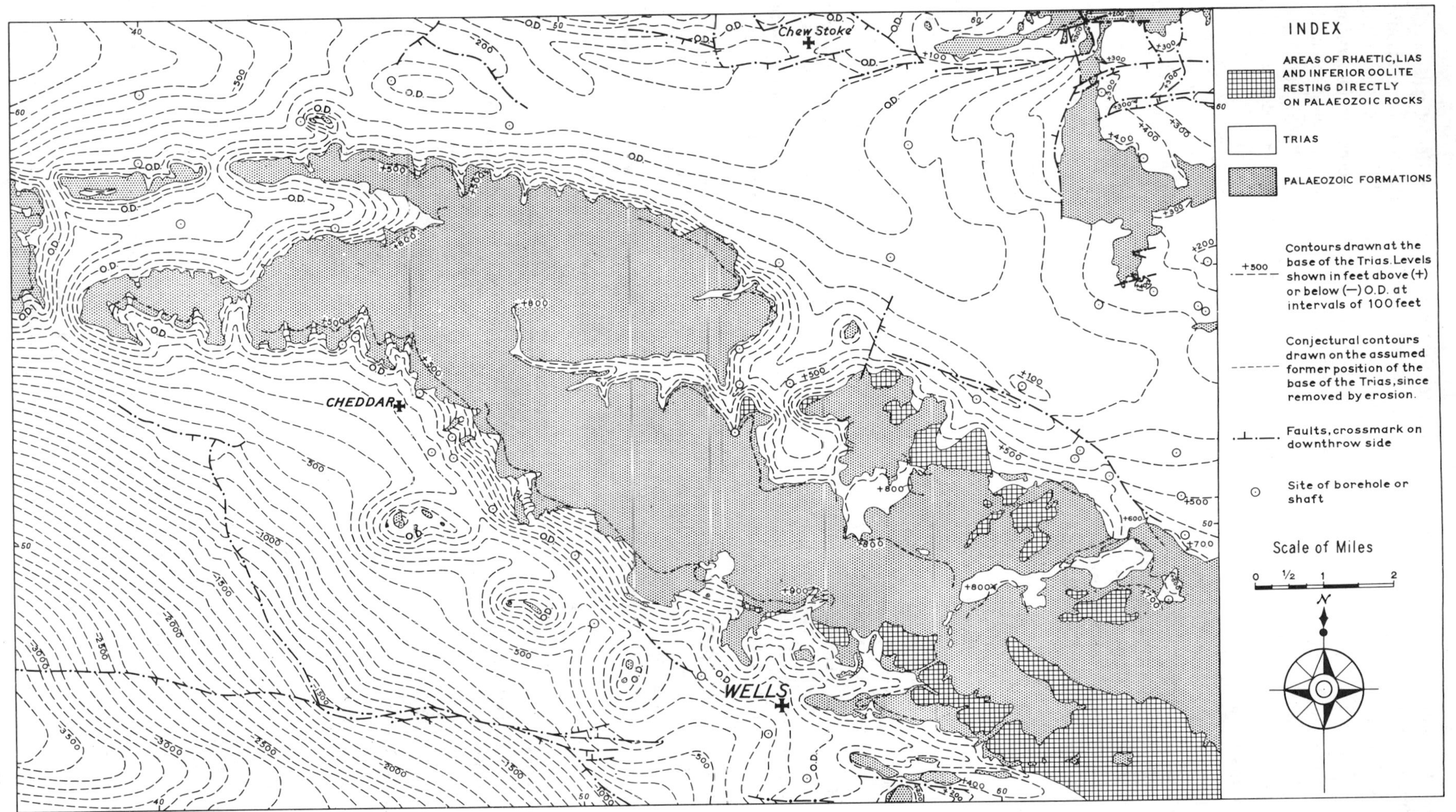
INDEX
AREAS OF RHAETIC, LIAS AND INFERIOR OOLITE RESTING DIRECTLY ON PALAEOZOIC ROCKS
TRIAS
PALAEOZOIC FORMATIONS
Contours drawn at the base of the Trias. Levels shown in feet above (+) or below (−) O.D. at intervals of 100 feet
Conjectural contours drawn on the assumed former position of the base of the Trias, since removed by erosion.
Faults, crossmark on downthrow side
Site of borehole or shaft
Scale of Miles
0
½
1
2
N
Chew Stoke
CHEDDAR
WELLS

Fig. 7.7 An example of a structure contour map for a surface of unconformity, Wells district, England. The structure contours shown here are for the unconformity at the base of the Triassic rocks, which were deposited on an irregular surface of Palaeozoic rocks. Reproduced, at reduced size, from Green and Welch (1965), by permission of the Director, BGS: Crown/NERC copyright reserved.

In the diagrammatic example shown in Fig. 7.6, the surface is fairly smooth and so its structure contours are reasonably straight and evenly spaced. In contrast, the irregular unconformity at the base of the Triassic in the Cheddar area of W England produced the contour pattern shown in Fig. 7.7.

7.6 Palaeogeological maps

The structure contours for the unconformity in Fig. 7.7 can be thought of in a different way. They could equally be regarded as topographic contours for the land surface as it was in Triassic times, when the Triassic sediments were first being deposited. In other words, drawing structure contours for an unconformity can provide information on a past landscape. In the example of Fig. 7.6, the structure contours reflect the land surface when the first Jurassic sediments were being deposited, except that here, judging by the dip which the Jurassic rocks now show, there has been subsequent tilting.

Extending this concept further, it is possible to draw the actual geology of this land surface, as well as its relief, as it was in Triassic times. The younger rocks are mentally stripped away (Fig. 7.6) to reveal the intersections of the older rocks with the Jurassic land surface – what is now the surface of unconformity. Such a map would show the rock outcrops at the land surface in the normal way, but here it is the *Jurassic* land surface. Because those outcrops are now subsurface, buried by the younger deposits, this kind of construction is called a **sub-crop map**.

Maps such as those mentioned above, which attempt to reconstruct some aspect of the geology of a bygone time, are called **palaeogeological maps** (e.g. Levorsen, 1960). Every palaeogeological map has to specify the stratigraphic time for which it is constructed. Unconformities are amenable to this kind of treatment, but in principle any kind of evidence can be used to help assemble palaeogeological maps, hence they take on very varied forms.

In some instances, a whole series of palaeogeological maps has been devised for a particular area, thus mapping its evolution through geological time. Reconstructions of past geological conditions is another major attribute of geological maps, and the ideas will be developed later (chapter 12). Before doing that, however, we have to develop further the three-dimensional considerations of maps; so far we have taken map formations to be more or less planar, in the form in which they were deposited. There are profound repercussions for mapwork if stresses in the earth have deformed the beds from their original shape.

7.7 Summary of chapter

1. An unconformity is a significant time break in the stratigraphic succession of an area.
2. It is usually visualised as the contact between the adjacent units that have differing stratigraphic ages. This surface of unconformity represents the time-span that separates the formations.
3. Angular unconformities are usually readily recognisable on maps from the discordance between units, but the identification of parallel unconformities requires stratigraphic information from the map key.
4. The unconformity may overstep the older rocks in different ways, and the upper rocks may be arranged with overlap or with offlap.
5. Unconformities are valuable in reconstructing the geological histories of regions. Sub-crop and palaeogeological maps can sometimes be constructed from them.

7.8 Selected further reading

Roberts, J. L. (1982). *Introduction to geological maps and structures*, Oxford, Pergamon Press.
(Chapter 7 contains a detailed discussion of the use of unconformity and related terms.)

MAP 11 The Helderberg, South Africa

The map opposite is reproduced from de Villiers (1983), by permission of the Geological Society of South Africa. It is of an area known as the Helderberg, near Stellenbosch, in the Cape Province of South Africa. Outside the northeast corner of the area shown, the Table Mountain Group, predominantly a tough sandstone, connects with the rocks that make the famous Table Mountain at Cape Town. The term foliation, mentioned in the key, refers to planar structures developed in the metamorphic and igneous rocks.

What is the nature of the junction at the base of the Table Mountain Group?

What is its approximate orientation?

What term can be applied to the outcrop of the Table Mountain Group around the Dome?

Why does the Table Mountain Group not appear elsewhere in the area?

Draw a NE–SW cross-section across the map area to illustrate the geological arrangement of The Dome.

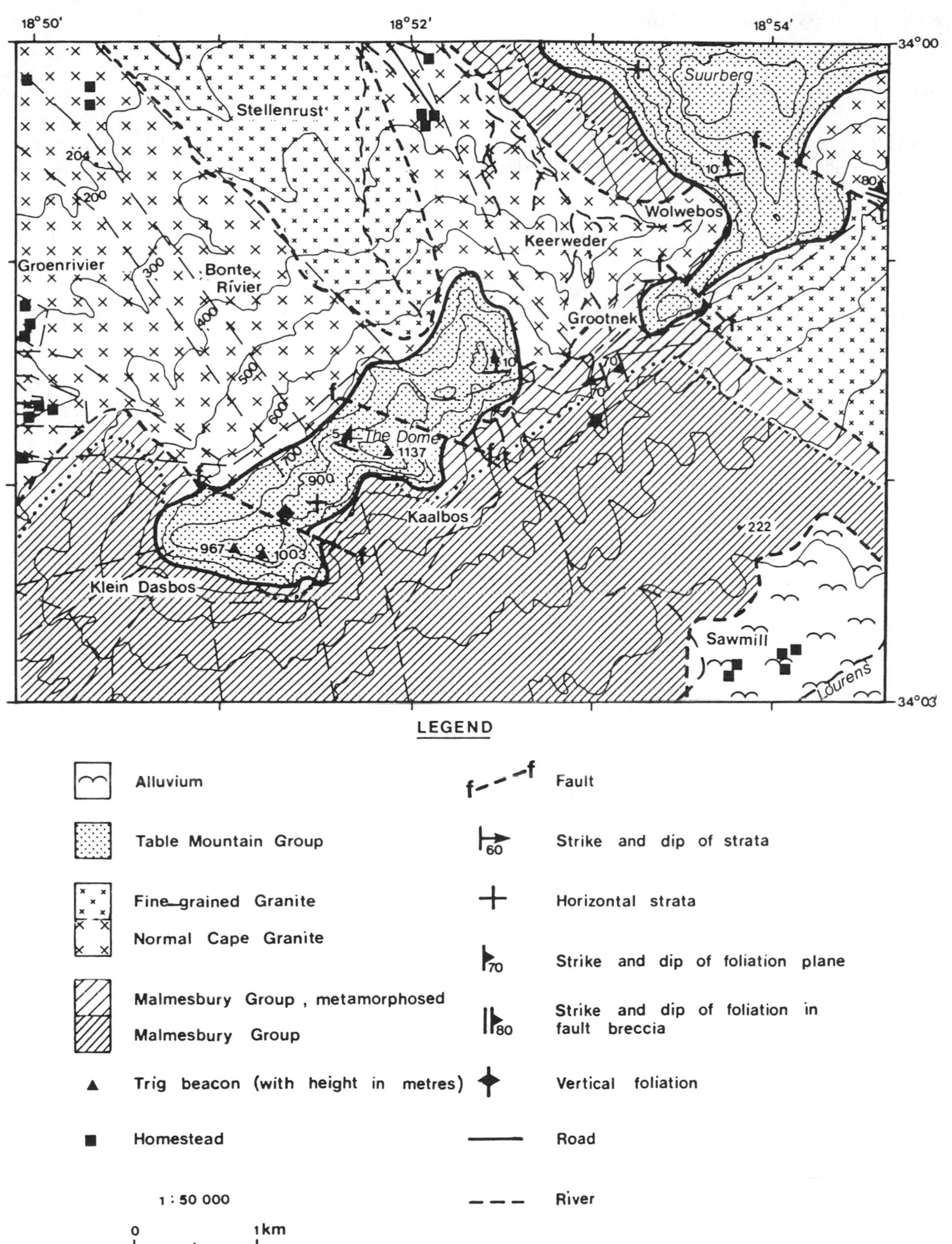
18°50'
18°52'
18°54'
34°00
34°03
Suurberg
Stellenrust
Wolwebos
Keerweder
Groenrivier
Bonte Rivier
Grootnek
The Dome
1137
Kaalbos
967
1003
Klein Dasbos
222
Sawmill
Lourens
204
200
300
400
500
600
700
900
LEGEND
Alluvium
Table Mountain Group
Fine-grained Granite
Normal Cape Granite
Malmesbury Group, metamorphosed
Malmesbury Group
Trig beacon (with height in metres)
Homestead
1 : 50 000
0
1km
Fault
Strike and dip of strata
Horizontal strata
Strike and dip of foliation plane
Strike and dip of foliation in fault breccia
Vertical foliation
Road
River
Farm boundaries

MAP 12 A sub-Permian unconformity and inlier

The map opposite is of the kind of geology found in the north of England. The conspicuous unconformity is at the base of the Permian, which in northern England includes units known locally as the Magnesian Limestone and the Brockram.

What evidence is there on the map for an unconformity at the base of the Carboniferous?

Comment on any structure shown by the Lower Palaeozoic, and by the Carboniferous rocks.

Trace with a coloured pencil the course of the unconformity at the base of the Permian. Notice that the surface of unconformity is highly uneven, so that structure contours drawn for it will be irregular. The locations of a number of boreholes are indicated on the map, together with the *depth* in feet at which they encountered the sub-Permian rocks. Using this borehole data together with the topographic information, carefully construct structure contours for the sub-Permian unconformity.

Describe, from the structure contours, the form of the land surface as it was in early Permian times.

Can you detect any structure in the pre-Permian rocks that may help explain the form of this landscape?

Is there any other junction on the map area, besides the sub-Permian and sub-Carboniferous boundaries, that could be referred to as an unconformity?

Further examples of unconformities on maps

Say what you can about the unconformity at the base of the Coalport Group on Map 5.

Discuss the nature of the unconformities that appear on Map 6, of the Boyd area, Australia.

Locate and identify the various unconformities that appear on Plate 5, of Sanquar, Scotland; on Plate 6, of the Heart Mountain district, Wyoming, USA; and on Plate 8, of Malmesbury, England.

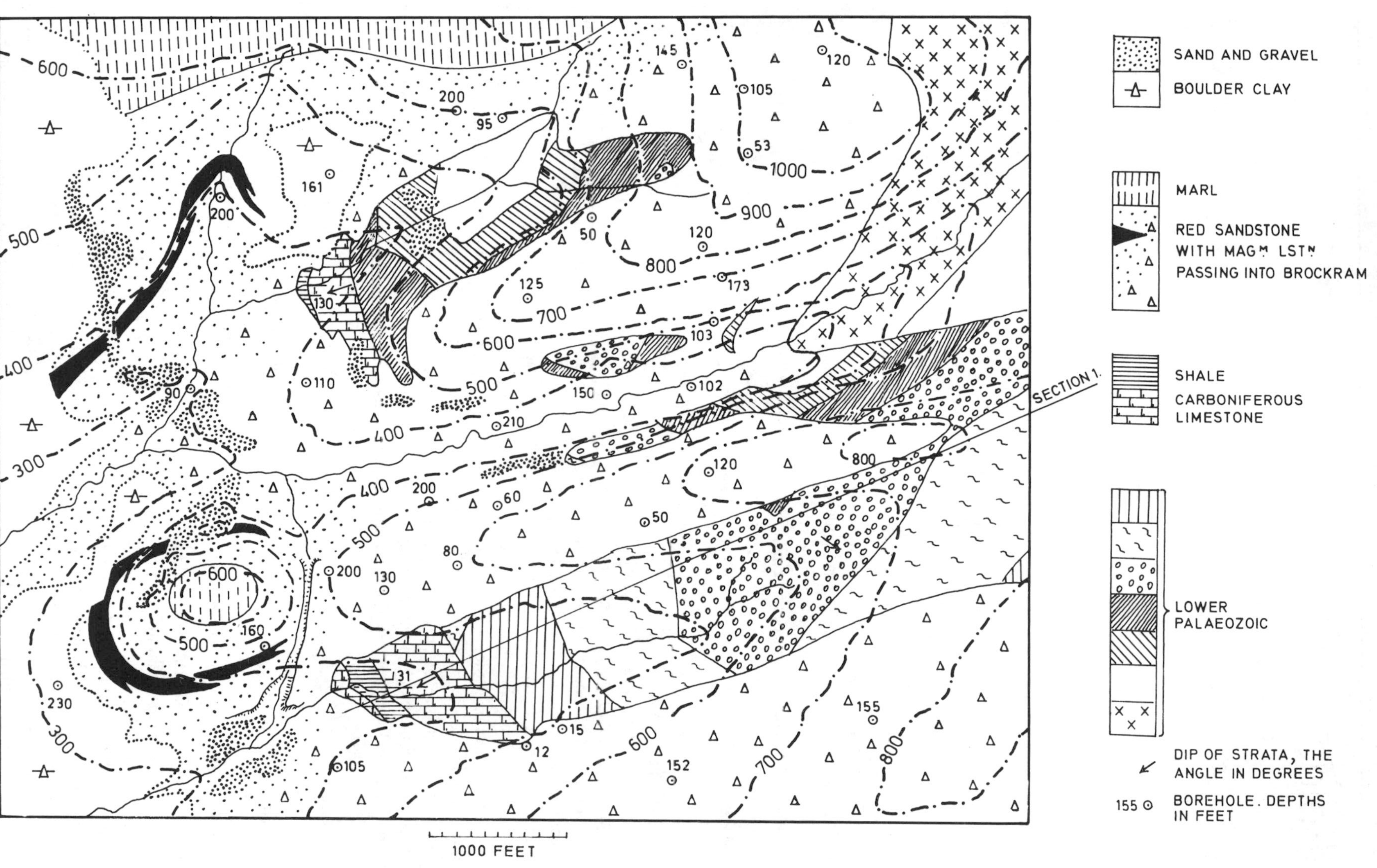

SAND AND GRAVEL
BOULDER CLAY
MARL
RED SANDSTONE WITH MAGm LSTn PASSING INTO BROCKRAM
SHALE
CARBONIFEROUS LIMESTONE
LOWER PALAEOZOIC
DIP OF STRATA, THE ANGLE IN DEGREES
155 BOREHOLE. DEPTHS IN FEET
SECTION 1
1000 FEET

8 Folds

8.1 Introduction

Geologists are still discovering the extent to which the rocks of the earth are mobile. Movements that take place within the earth generate stresses which can be capable of deforming rocks, that is, changing their overall shape. This deformation can occur in a brittle way, where the rocks change shape by fracturing, or in a ductile way. In the latter case, because of factors that come about at depth in the earth, such as increased pressure and temperature and longer times of deformation, the rocks respond to any stress by flow, and there is no fracture. The common way in which bedded sedimentary rocks deform in a ductile way is by warping into the wave-like shapes known as **folds**.

We saw something in chapter 2 of the way folded units are detected on maps. Any folds will certainly have to be taken into account in our interpretations of the underground arrangement of the beds. Folds can be of great economic significance (in section 3.3 we had a glimpse of the importance of certain kinds of fold to the oil industry) and we now take a closer look at how to deal with folded formations as they appear on geological maps and sections. We begin by defining a few basic parts of folds in order to be able to report the nature of any folds we see. The chapter goes on to outline the great variety of appearances which natural folds can have, and how they are recognised and measured on maps.

8.2 Description from maps

8.2.1 The parts of a fold

Most folds do not look like half cylinders. In cross-section, a fold typically has a narrow zone of sharper curvature, called the **hinge zone** (Fig. 8.1). It occurs between two broad, less curved zones called the **limbs**. We can imagine the greatest curvature in three-dimensions making a line running along the folded bed. For introductory purposes, this is the **fold axis**. Advanced work requires a more precise definition (e.g. see Fleuty, 1964; Ramsay and Huber, 1987). Similarly, the definition of the **fold axial surface** has to be rigorous if it is to cover all circumstances but here it is sufficient to regard it as the surface which passes through the axes of the successive beds in a fold. Commonly, although by no means always, the axial surface has the appearance of dividing the fold into two fairly symmetrical halves.

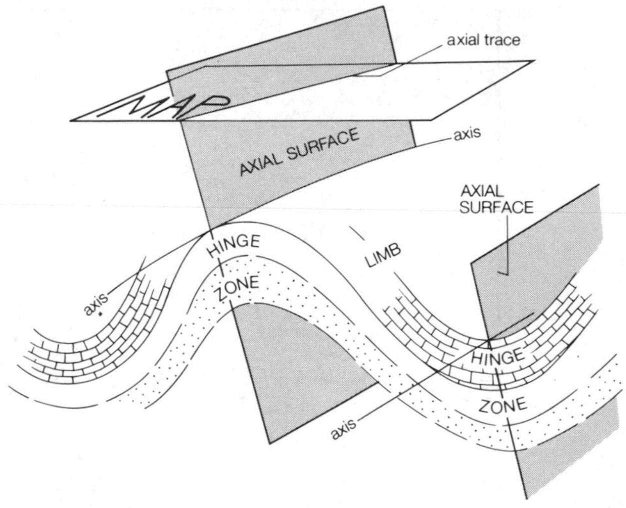
axial trace
MAP
axis
AXIAL SURFACE
AXIAL SURFACE
HINGE
ZONE
LIMB
axis
HINGE
ZONE
axis

Fig. 8.1 The parts of a fold.

The intersection of the axial surface with another surface, such as a map, cross-section, or the ground, is called the **fold axial trace**. It is often useful to draw on maps of areas of folded rocks the courses of the axial traces. It will emerge later that the axial trace on a map will not normally coincide with the axis of the fold.

8.2.2 Fold orientation

The value of the terms fold axis and axial surface lies in their ability to report succinctly the three-dimensional orientation of a fold. However, as we shall see in sections 8.3 and 8.4, it is much more difficult than you might first think to work out from a geological map the orientation of a

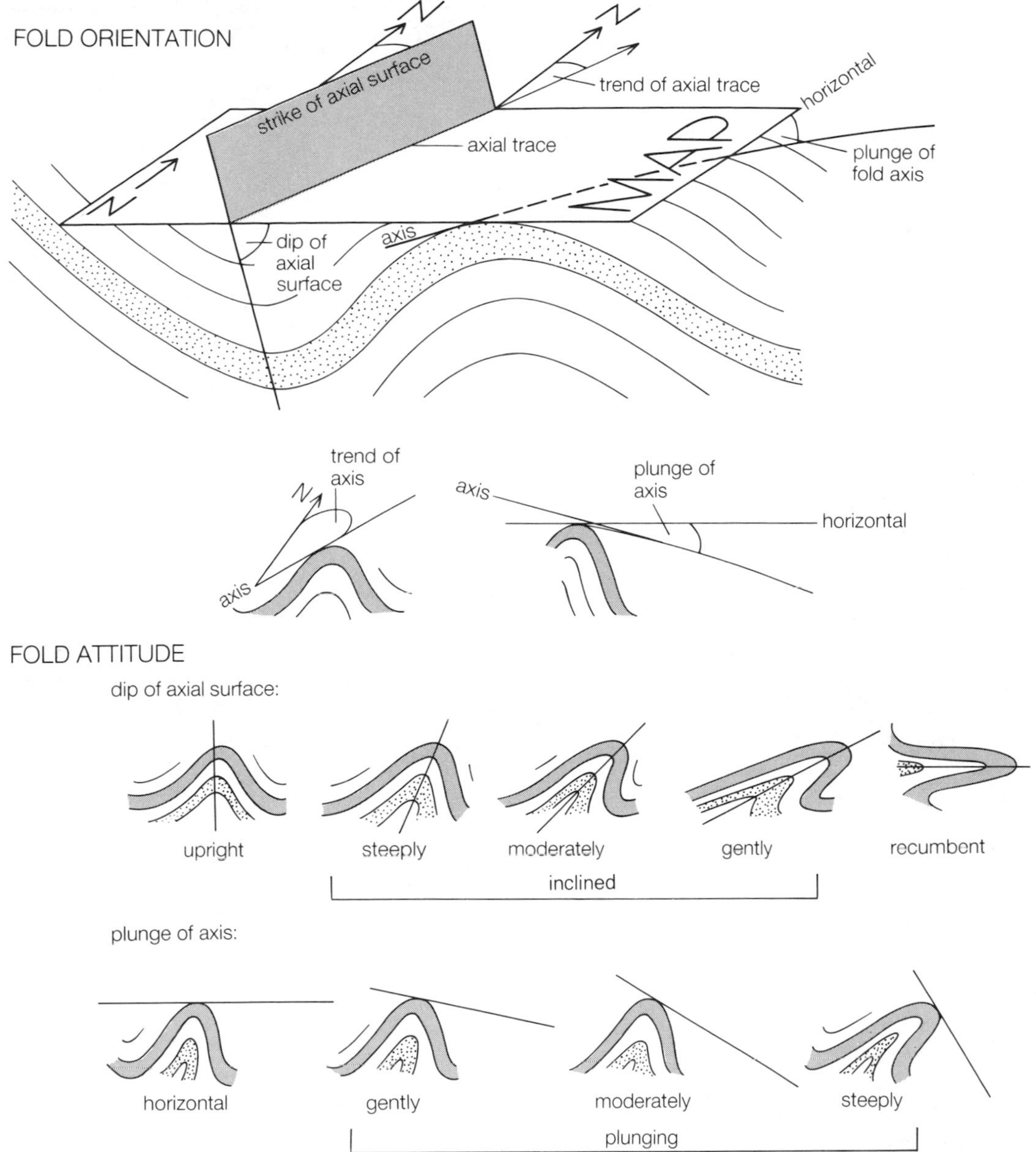
FOLD ORIENTATION
N
strike of axial surface
trend of axial trace
horizontal
axial trace
MAP
plunge of fold axis
dip of axial surface
axis
trend of axis
axis
plunge of axis
horizontal
FOLD ATTITUDE
dip of axial surface:
upright
steeply
moderately
gently
recumbent
inclined
plunge of axis:
horizontal
gently
moderately
steeply
plunging

Fig. 8.2 Fold attitude and orientation.

fold. Hence, the geological surveyor usually makes a point of measuring fold axes and axial surfaces *in the field*, where it is a relatively straightforward operation (McClay, 1987). These measurements are then reported on the map by symbols such as those shown in Fig. 4.2. Even if the surveyor cannot actually see a fold in its entirety, there are routine methods for finding its orientation from indirect field observations (e.g. see Ramsay and Huber, 1987).

Many geological maps, then, have marked on them symbols to indicate the orientation of any folds in the area. A fold axial surface is reported as a strike and dip (Fig. 8.2), exactly analogous to bedding or any other geological plane (section 4.2), and a fold axis or an axial trace, both being lines, are given as a plunge and trend (section 4.2). Remember, from section 4.2, that the trend is expressed as a compass bearing from north. Thus geologists commonly speak loosely of folds 'trending northeastwards' and the like, though it really should be specified whether the axial trace or the axis is meant. The plunge of the axial trace will normally average out as horizontal, being in the horizontal map plane, but it may fluctuate locally as the axial surface crosses various topographic slopes.

8.2.3 *Fold attitude*

In addition to specifying the spatial orientation of a fold, geologists often record in words how much the fold itself is inclined on its side or tipped on end, that is, the fold's

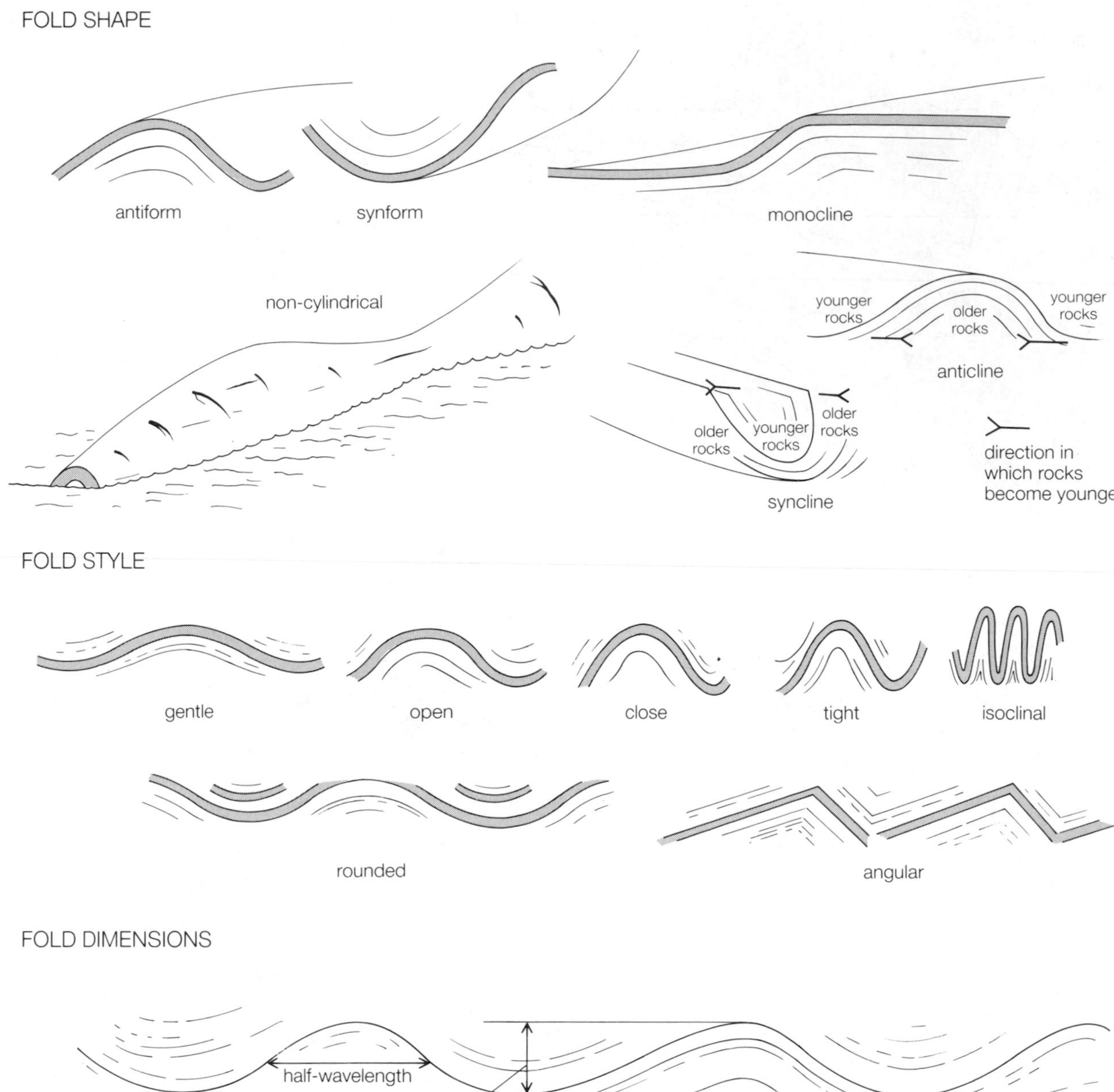
FOLD SHAPE
antiform
synform
monocline
non-cylindrical
younger rocks
older rocks
younger rocks
anticline
older rocks
younger rocks
older rocks
syncline
direction in which rocks become younger
FOLD STYLE
gentle
open
close
tight
isoclinal
rounded
angular
FOLD DIMENSIONS
half-wavelength
amplitude

Fig. 8.3 Fold shape, style, and dimensions.

attitude. The terms commonly used for this are given in Fig. 8.2. For example, it is sometimes useful to speak of a map area being dominated by steeply plunging folds, without specifying in degrees the exact range of plunge values.

8.2.4 Fold shape

We saw in section 2.3.3 how map units can be folded into basins and arches, synclines and anticlines. Although these terms are useful on the regional scale being discussed there, for smaller structures the terms **antiform** and **synform** are used. They are illustrated in Fig. 8.3. As introduced in section 2.3.3, a fold with the oldest rocks in its inner part is called an **anticline** and with the youngest rocks in the middle, a **syncline** (Fig. 8.3). It follows from the discussion of the age sequences seen on tilted beds (section 2.3.1 and Figure 2.1) that ordinarily antiforms will be anticlines, and synforms will be synclines. This is not necessarily so, however, because in highly deformed areas, outside the scope of this book, folds can become entirely inverted, such that synforms have the oldest rocks in the middle, etc.

Figure 8.3 illustrates the single-limbed deflection of beds known as a **monocline**, and also the term **non-**

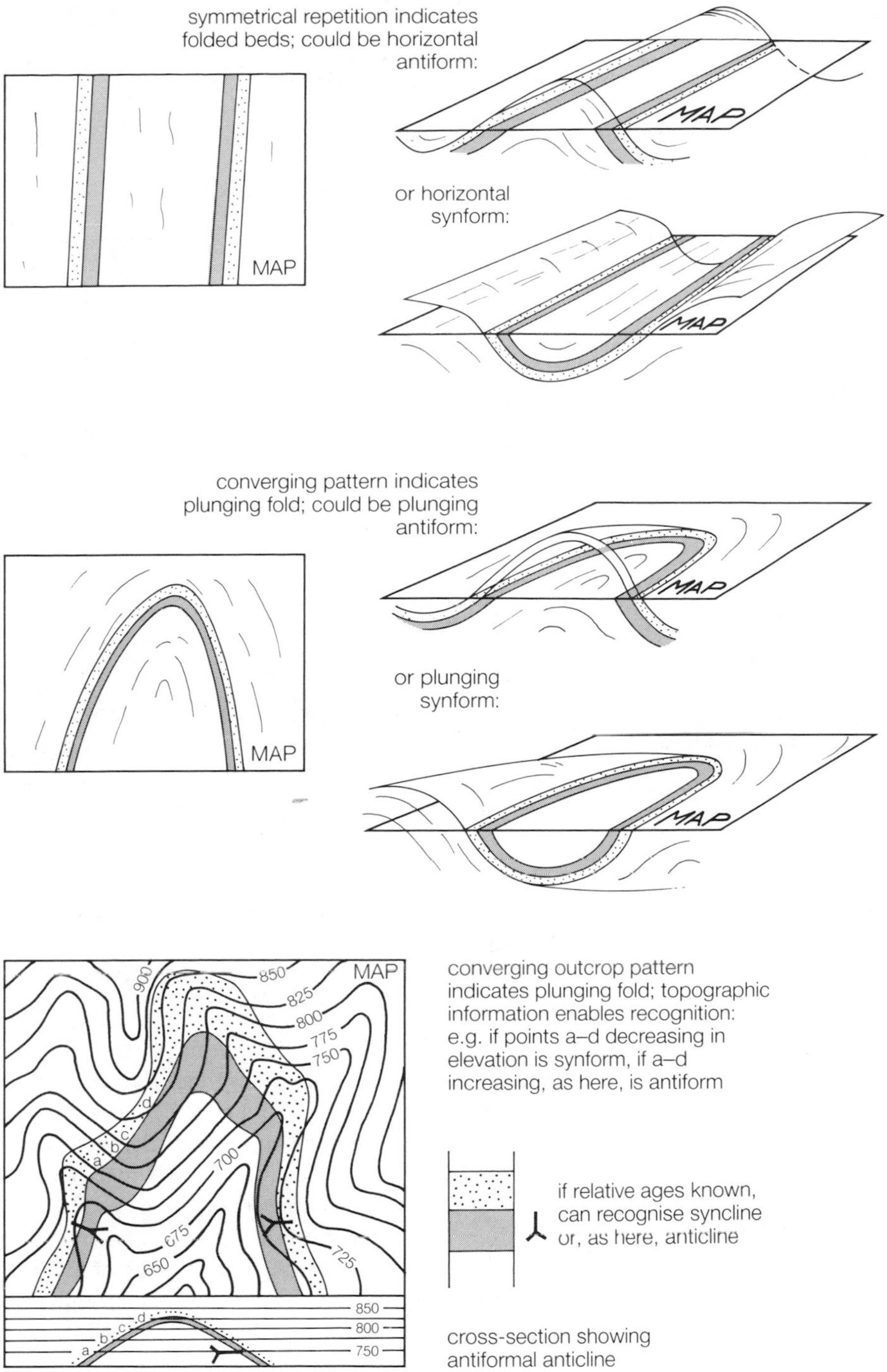

symmetrical repetition indicates folded beds; could be horizontal antiform:

MAP

or horizontal synform:

MAP

converging pattern indicates plunging fold; could be plunging antiform:

MAP

or plunging synform:

MAP

converging outcrop pattern indicates plunging fold; topographic information enables recognition: e.g. if points a–d decreasing in elevation is synform, if a–d increasing, as here, is antiform

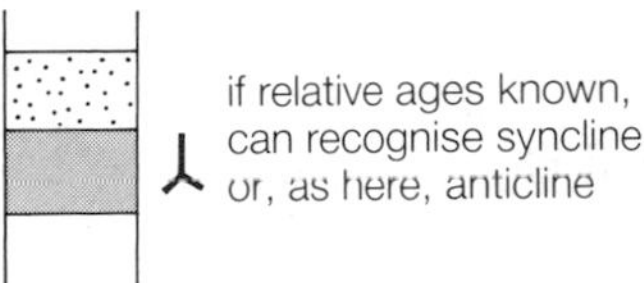

if relative ages known,
can recognise syncline
or, as here, anticline

cross-section showing antiformal anticline

Fig. 8.4 Some guides to the visual assessment of folds on maps.

cylindrical. This means that the axis varies in plunge along its length. You should make sure you can visualise what this signifies for the three-dimensional appearance of a fold. A situation commonly seen on maps is a non-cylindrical fold with steepest plunges at the ends of its axial trace and least plunge in the centre. Such folds are referred to as being **periclinal**. It is in effect a small-scale dome or basin. Thus those folds discussed in section 2.3.3 with a roughly circular outcrop pattern must be non-cylindrical.

8.2.5 Fold style

In addition to describing the basic shape of a fold using the above terms, geologists find it useful to mention what is called the **style** of a fold. The adjectives commonly used for this are given in Fig. 8.3. Describing the fold style is not just a point of detail, as it has major implications for structural geologists interested in the mechanics of how folds form, for more advanced graphical constructions involving beds, and for quantitative estimates of the volumes

DOWN-PLUNGE
VIEWING OF FOLDS

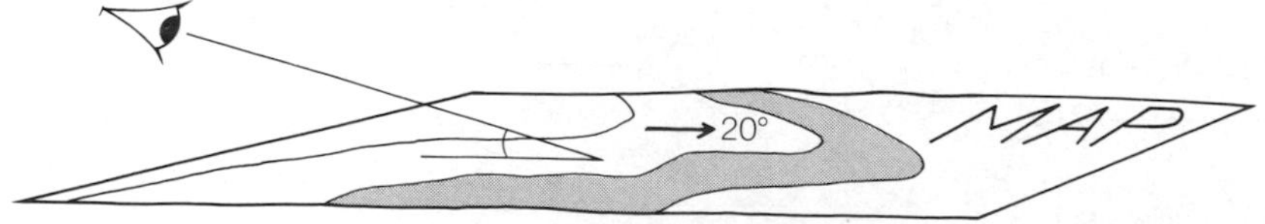
20°
MAP

line of sight at same angle from map as fold plunge

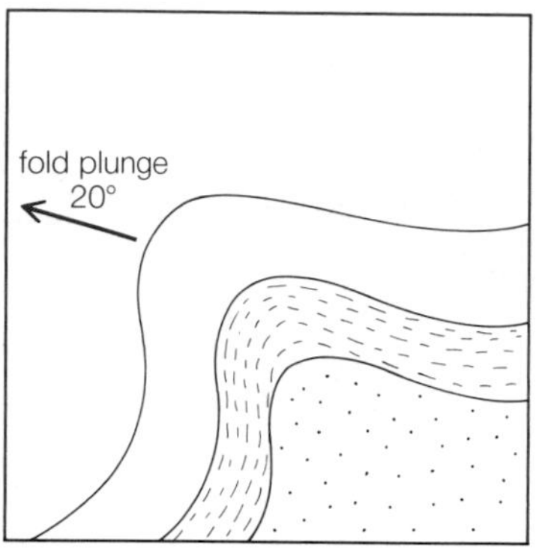
fold plunge
20°

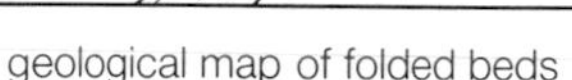

geological map of folded beds

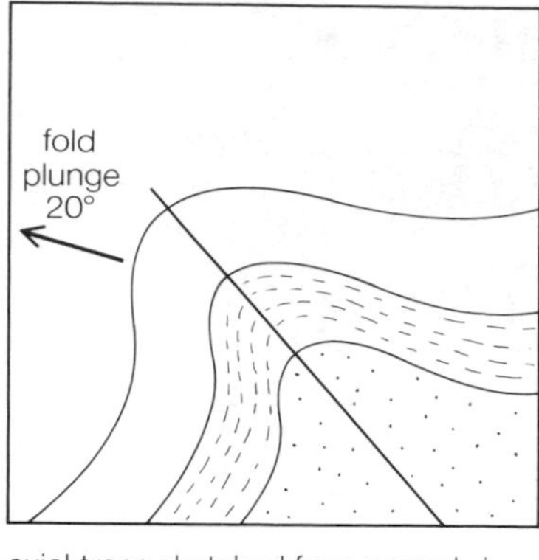
fold
plunge
20°

axial trace sketched from normal view

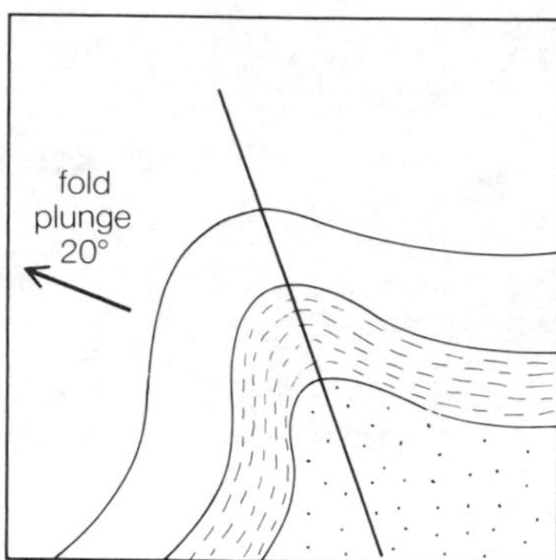
fold
plunge
20°

axial trace from down-plunge view

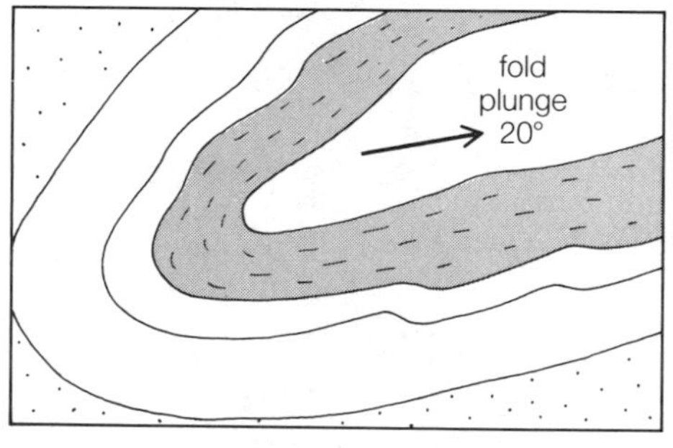
fold
plunge
20°

Geological map of folded beds. Down-plunge view shows synform with highly-overturned limb

Fig. 8.5 Illustrations of the down-plunge method of viewing plunging folds on maps.

of industrial materials involved in folded rocks (e.g. Badgley, 1959).

8.2.6 *Fold dimensions*

Finally, to communicate usefully what a particular fold or collection of folds looks like, the size needs to be indicated. The simplest approach to this is to treat the folds as waves, and to measure the fold amplitude and half wavelength (Fig. 8.3).

8.3 Visual assessment on maps

Many folds are too large to be observable in the field Therefore, it is common for their presence to be detected through the compilation of information on a map. Dip directions may systematically reverse, representing the different limbs of folds, or outcrop patterns may emerge which indicate folded units. Figure 8.4 shows the kinds of outcrop patterns produced on maps by folds which are horizontal or of very shallow plunge. They are essentially symmetrical repetitions of the same beds outwards from the hinge zone of the fold. Note that this pattern of repetition differs from that produced by faults (section 9.5). With increasing plunge of the fold axis there is a growing tendency for the beds on the two limbs of the fold to converge. If the plunge is sufficient, the beds meet and the hinge zone of the fold then appears on the map (Fig. 8.4). Open folds give arcuate patterns like those seen in Fig. 2.2c, whereas tighter folds give more rapidly convergent shapes. Note, however, that on large-scale maps all these appearances can be complicated by an irregular relief.

Unless we have some other information, it is not possible to deduce anything further about the nature of the fold. In fact, at first glance the converging appearance of the beds can be confused with the effects of topography discussed in chapter 6, such as the 'V-shape' made by dipping beds crossing a valley. On a large-scale map without the topography marked, it may not be possible to recognise folded beds with certainty, but normally topographic effects tend to be small and local in comparison with the appearance of folds. If symbols are provided on the map or there is information on the topography, it should be possible to assess the dip of the beds and hence to ascertain whether the fold is a synform or an antiform. It may help to sketch in a few structure contours on each limb to find which way the limbs are inclined (Fig. 8.4).

An important point to understand is that the outcrop pattern of the folded beds does not necessarily indicate the shape or style of the fold. The converging pattern of the beds on the map does not show directly whether the fold is an antiform or synform. The map view is just a horizontal section through the folds. These may well be plunging and, especially if there is marked topographic relief, producing illusory effects. Similarly, a cross-section can be misleading. Only if the fold is horizontal will the cross-section give a true portrayal of the appearance of the fold. There will be distortion in a cross-section through a plunging fold. To see plunging folds properly we should construct a section through the fold *at right angles to the fold axis*, a section which is called the **fold profile**.

A handy device for the visual assessment of fold profile is 'down-plunge' viewing of the map. By inclining your line of sight to the map at an angle roughly equal to the fold plunge, the outcrop pattern you see will approximate the fold profile (Fig. 8.5). Sketching where you think the axial surface runs in this profile view gives a better estimate of its course than normal 'head-on' viewing of the map. Figure 8.5 gives an example of how the axial trace drawn this way can differ from where you might draw it without looking down the fold plunge. It is necessary, though, in order to employ this useful technique for visually assessing folds, to have knowledge of the fold plunge. If this is indicated on the map by a symbol there is no problem; otherwise you will first have to visualise or sketch the structure contours in the hinge zone of the fold (see next section).

Figure 8.6 shows some of the outcrop patterns typically seen on geological maps of folded areas. Almost all of them have some element of the converging aspect so common with folds. Folds can be highly non-cylindrical, so beware of assuming that all the folds which look alike at first glance are of the same kind. Notice also that to tell whether the folds are anticlines or synclines, we must have information on the relative ages of the units. This may well be provided in the key; otherwise, it could be impossible to tell. In weakly deformed areas it is likely that the beds become younger in the dip direction, that antiforms are anticlines, etc. but, if there is suspicion that beds may be inverted, this assumption could be invalid.

8.4 Measurements on maps

If the locations of fold axes are known on a map and they are horizontal, then true cross-sections can be constructed in the normal way at right angles to the axes. Being a fold profile, the attitude, shape, style and scale of the fold can be determined directly. Difficulties arise where the folds are not horizontal. If the plunge is less than 30° or so, then the usual vertical cross-sections may well be sufficient for most purposes, but otherwise the information from a cross-section may be misleading, especially on the large-scale maps likely to be used for measurement purposes. It would be necessary to establish the fold profile, a time-consuming procedure to carry out by hand.

The amount of fold plunge may be given on the map by a symbol; if not, a few structure contours will have to be drawn in the hinge zone of the fold. From their spacing the plunge can be derived either graphically or by trigonometry (Fig. 8.7). To obtain the axial trace on a map it will be necessary to construct at least two sections across the fold, and add vertical axial traces to each section in order to derive points where the axial surface intersects the ground surface. These can then be connected to route the axial trace in map view. If the axial trace is suspected to curve, several sections may be needed. Bear in mind, though, that all this is only approximate if the folds plunge significantly, when fold profiles should really be employed.

We are now in a position to consider the strike and dip of the axial surface. If the fold axial trace is available on the map and crosses topographic contours, it may be possible to sketch in some structure contours in order to derive the orientation of the fold axial surface. Its strike will be the same as the trend of the axial trace, if the latter is horizontal and not crossing topographic slopes. A vertical cross-section, drawn perpendicular to the horizontal axial trace, will reveal the true dip of the axial surface.

There are more sophisticated ways of dealing with folded beds, such as the use of stereographic projections (e.g. Ramsay and Huber, 1987). These methods provide a much more direct treatment of plunging folds but can be difficult for beginners. All this underlines the usefulness of obtaining as much information as possible on folds while in the field. This is why most completed geological maps, especially those concerned with folded units, have much of the orientation data already marked on the map. Although folds on maps commonly produce visually attractive outcrop patterns, they have to be interpreted with care.

8.5 Summary of chapter

1. The axis and axial surface are useful concepts in specifying the orientation of a fold – as plunge and trend, and strike and dip, respectively.
2. This orientation information is awkward to interpret from outcrop patterns; it is commonly provided on the map by symbols.
3. Folds are recognised on maps by the symmetrical repetition of units in a horizontal fold, and by the converging outcrops of a plunging fold.
4. It may be possible to interpret from a map something about the attitude, shape, style, and dimensions of folds, but the appearance of plunging folds on maps and sections can be illusory.

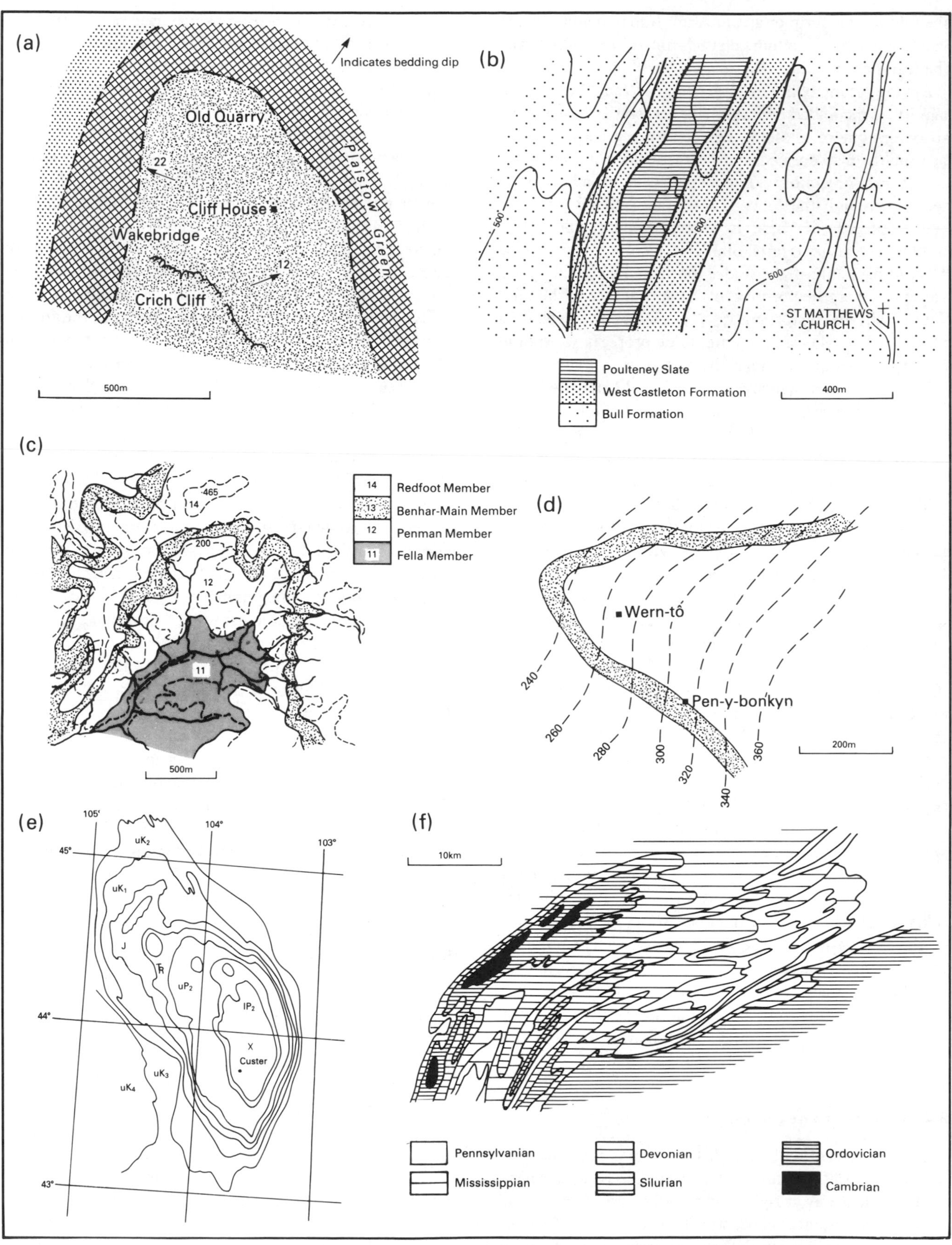

(a)
Indicates bedding dip
Old Quarry
22
Cliff House
Wakebridge
12
Crich Cliff
Plaistow Green
500m
(b)
500
600
500
ST MATTHEWS CHURCH
Poulteney Slate
West Castleton Formation
Bull Formation
400m
(c)
465
14
200
13
12
11
500m
14 Redfoot Member
13 Benhar-Main Member
12 Penman Member
11 Fella Member
(d)
Wern-tô
Pen-y-bonkyn
240
260
280
300
320
340
360
200m
(e)
105°
104°
103°
45°
44°
43°
uK_2
uK_1
J
₸R
uP_2
IP_2
X
Custer
uK_3
uK_4
(f)
10km
Pennsylvanian
Mississippian
Devonian
Silurian
Ordovician
Cambrian

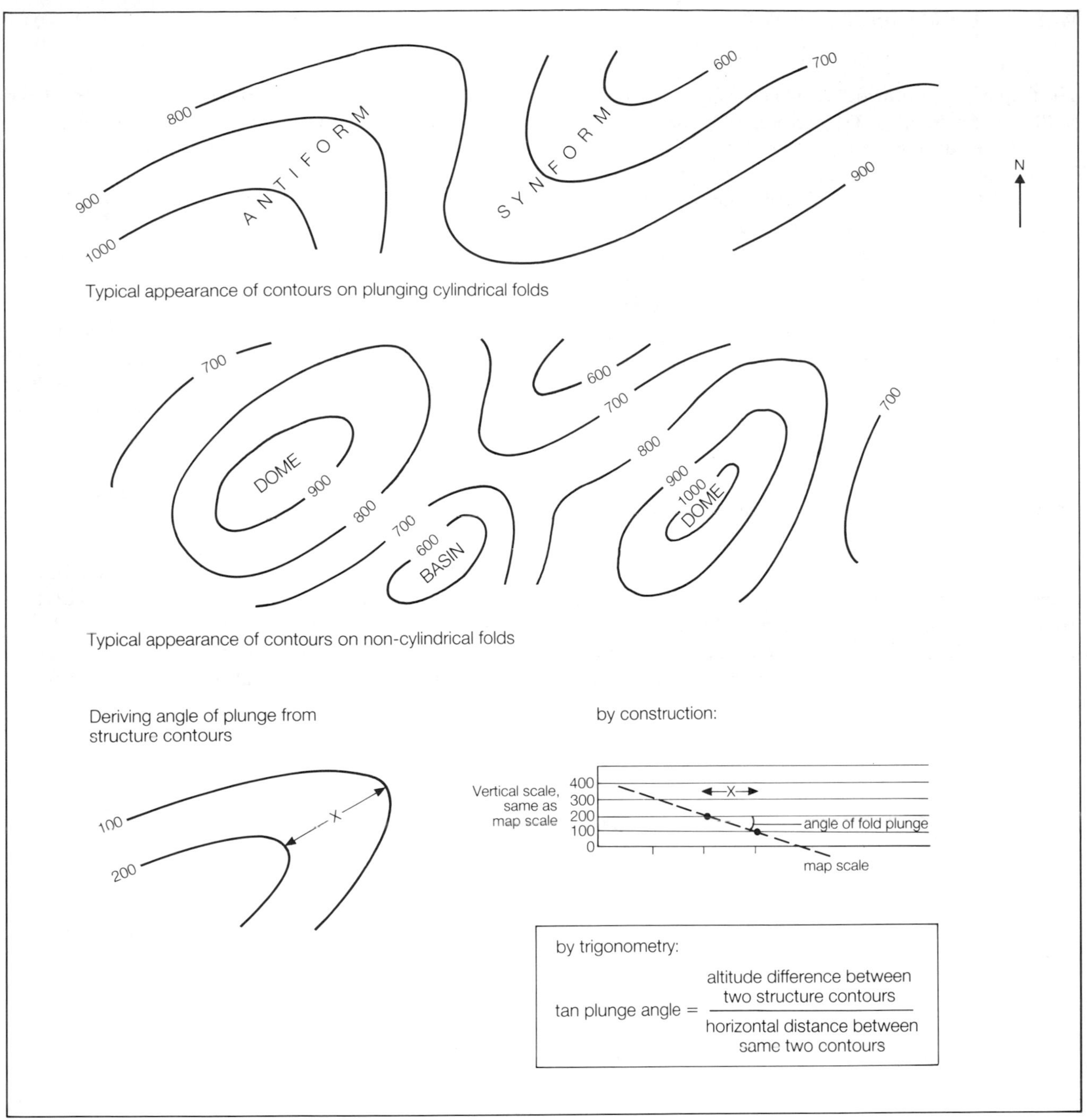

800
900
1000
ANTIFORM
600
700
SYNFORM
900
N
Typical appearance of contours on plunging cylindrical folds
700
600
700
DOME
900
800
800
700
600
BASIN
900
1000
DOME
700
Typical appearance of contours on non-cylindrical folds
Deriving angle of plunge from structure contours
100
200
X
by construction:
Vertical scale, same as map scale
400
300
200
100
0
X
angle of fold plunge
map scale
by trigonometry:
tan plunge angle = altitude difference between two structure contours / horizontal distance between same two contours

Fig. 8.7 Illustrations of how structure contours represent folded surfaces, and simple graphical and trigonometric methods for deriving fold plunge.

Fig. 8.6 (opposite) Examples of outcrop patterns of folds. (a) Arcuate outcrop pattern suggests a plunging fold; lack of relation with cliff suggests a non-topographic effect. Dip symbols confirm presence of antiform. May be an anticline, but relative ages of rocks not known. Near Crich, Derbyshire, England. (b) Symmetrical repetition of formations suggests a fold; relative ages of formations suggest a syncline. Near Lake Bomoseen, Vermont, USA. (c) Arcuate pattern suggests folding present; contours show it is not a purely topographic effect. Relative ages of rocks show a syncline in the NW, an anticline in the S. Near Balclutha, Kaitangata Coalfield, New Zealand. Based on Harrington (1958). (d) Without further information, arcuate outcrop could represent a fold, but is adequately explained by a uniformly dipping unit crossing a hillside. Compare with Fig. 6.2. Near Llanidloes, Wales. (e) Symmetrical repetition of units suggests a fold; unlikely to be a topographic effect at this scale (note degrees of latitude and longitude). Relative ages (K = Cretaceous, J = Jurassic, T = Triassic, etc.) indicate an anticline. Black Hills, S Dakota, USA. (f) Relative ages of rocks show anticlines to NW and synclines to SE; doubly convergent form of outcrops indicate periclinal nature of folds. Appalachians, Pennsylvania, USA.

MAP 13 Llandovery, Dyfed, Wales

The map opposite provides detail of the district appearing on Plate 1 around [SO8338], northeast of Llandovery. The rocks at Llandovery were discussed in section 2.3.1 as examples of dipping beds. However, in a number of places on Plate 1 the outcrops curve, suggesting that, as there is no indication of pronounced topography, the units are folded. Notice, incidentally, that these rocks belong to the lowest series of the Silurian, known in the UK and elsewhere as the 'Llandovery'. They are therefore in their 'type' area. Map 13 is based, by permission of the Geological Society, on a map by Jones (1949).

Based on visual assessment, what is the structure of the area shown?

Draw lightly on the map where you gauge the axial traces to run.

Carefully construct structure contours for the three stratigraphic boundaries shown. (Draw the tentative contours lightly in pencil; when 'firming up' use coloured pencils or different line symbols to distinguish the different sets of contours.)

By what amount does the fold plunge in the Cwm Crychan-Bryn Ffoi area? And by what in the Cwm Clyd-Cefn-y-gareg area?

Is this fold showing any tendency to be periclinal?

How does its plunge compare with that of the adjacent anticline?

At a point between Pen-y-rhiw and Cwm Coed-Oeron, draw a NW–SE cross-section (note the orientation of north on this map) across the Middle Llandovery outcrop. How does the dip on the northwest limb of the fold compare with that on the southeast limb?

On the cross-section draw a line representing the fold axial surface. The intersection of the line with the land surface gives the position of the axial trace on the map. How does its position derived in this way from a cross-section compare with your earlier location from the map alone? (Note that the axial trace has still not been properly located. This would require a fold *profile*, i.e. a section at right angles to the fold axis, which the vertical section you have drawn is not.)

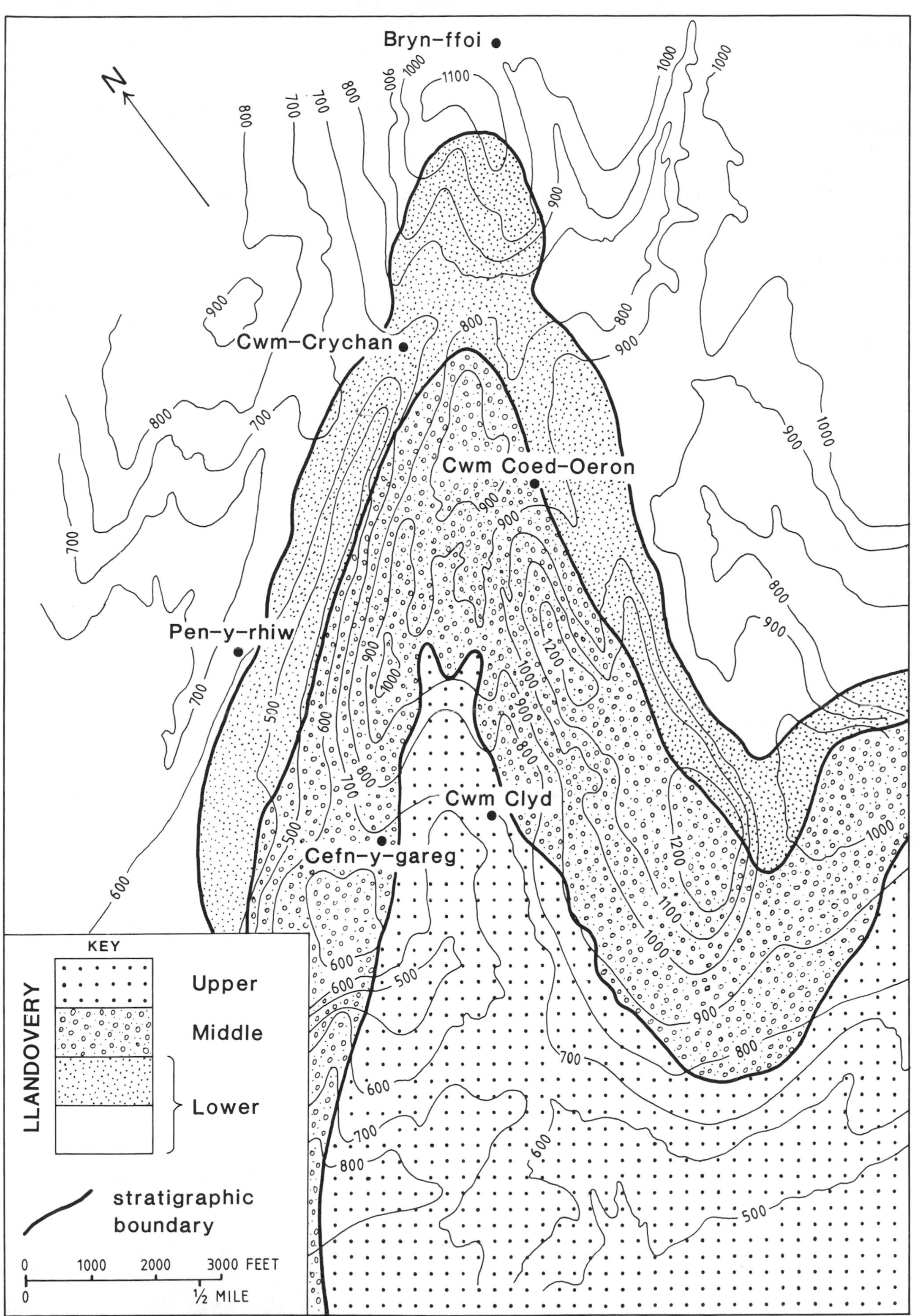

Bryn-ffoi
N
Cwm-Crychan
Cwm Coed-Oeron
Pen-y-rhiw
Cwm Clyd
Cefn-y-gareg
KEY
LLANDOVERY
Upper
Middle
Lower
stratigraphic boundary
0 1000 2000 3000 FEET
0 ½ MILE

MAP 14 Folded Millstone Grit

The facing map, at a scale of 1:25 000, is of the kind of geology found in parts of the Pennines of northern England. The 'Millstone Grit' is a time-honoured name for the coarse sandstones, once much used for millstones, which dominate the Namurian series of the Carboniferous in this region. Many parts are uniformly shallow-dipping, but in some places the beds have been folded by the Variscan earth movements that arose towards the end of the Palaeozoic era.

Describe, from visual assessment, the kind of fold illustrated in Map 14.

One of the Millstone Grit bands has a much wider outcrop in the northwest of the area than in the east. Why might this be?

Using the dip information provided, draw an E–W cross-section in the vicinity of Black Gill.

In order to illustrate the plunge of the fold, draw a N–S cross-section across the hinge zone outcropping in the south of the area. Because the values of dip indicated are so variable, a more accurate section will result from drawing structure contours for some of the surfaces.

Is there any relationship in the area between the geology and the relief of the land surface?

Further examples of folds on maps

On Map 4, of Maccoyella Ridge, New Zealand, having constructed structure contours for the base of the Te Were sandstone, calculate the plunge of the major synform and describe its form.

Consider the rocks lying below the sub-Permian unconformity in Map 12. Interpret visually the structure in each of the Lower Palaeozoic inliers. Construct structure contours in the southern inlier for the top of the unit with an open circle ornament, and in the northern inlier for the junction of the two units with diagonal line ornaments. Describe the form of the structures revealed by the contours.

Note that the questions accompanying Plate 4, Root River, Canada, involve the interpretation of folded units, and that folds appear on Plate 7, of Marraba, Australia, and Plate 8, of Malmesbury, England.

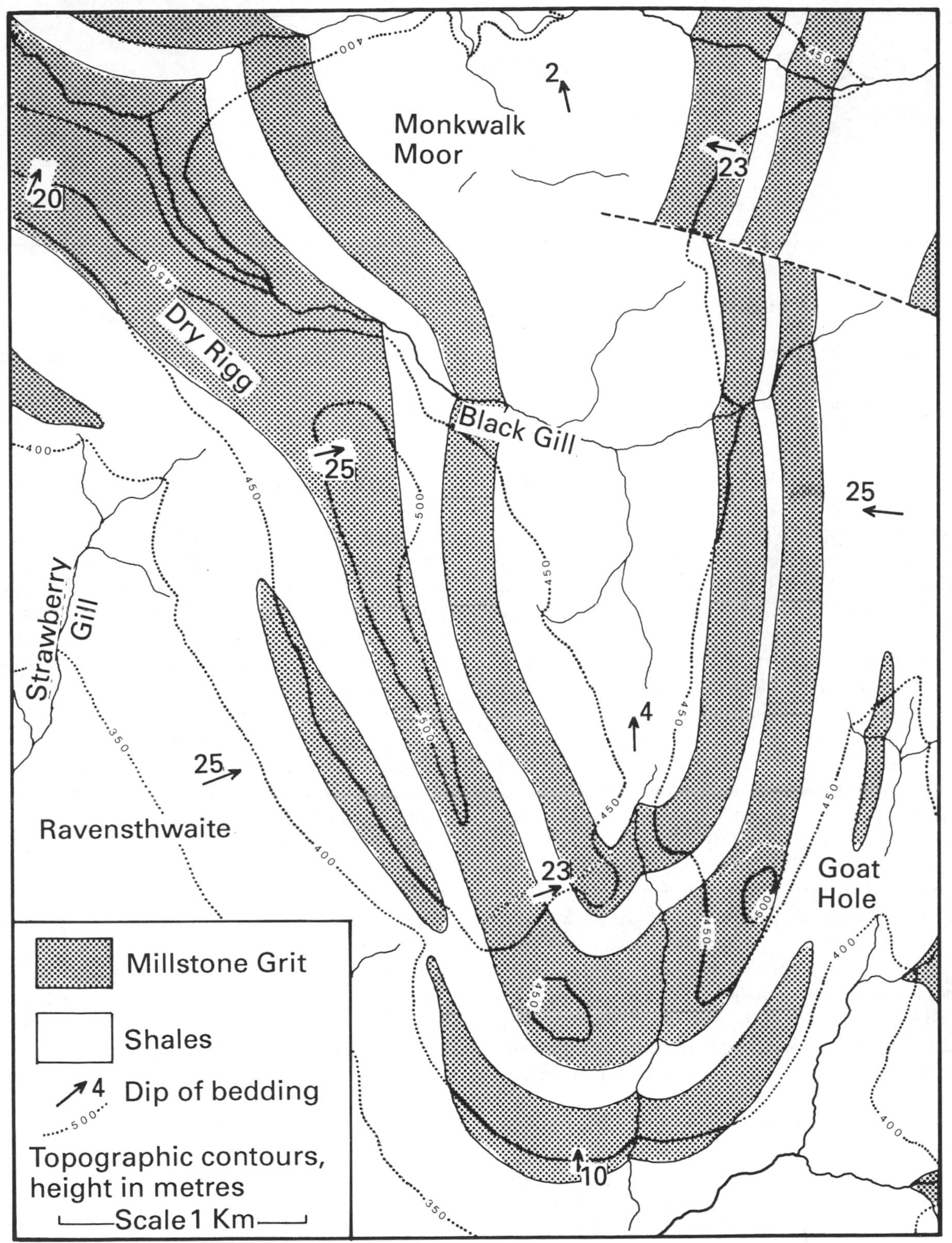

Monkwalk Moor
Dry Rigg
Black Gill
Strawberry Gill
Ravensthwaite
Goat Hole
2
20
23
25
25
4
25
23
10
400
450
500
350
Millstone Grit
Shales
4 Dip of bedding
500
Topographic contours, height in metres
Scale 1 Km

9 Faults: the fundamentals

9.1 Introduction

Faults are perhaps the most frustrating structures to deal with on maps. On the one hand, they are tremendously important features, in both academic and industrial work. They can, for example, interfere with the predictions of the mining geologist and cause special problems for the civil engineer. Even non-geologists may well know something about faults, if only the devastating effects of earthquakes that can arise from earth movements along them. And faults are usually conspicuous features on maps.

Yet, on the other hand, it can be very difficult to deduce much from a map about a fault. The amount by which the rocks either side of the fault have moved is commonly extremely elusive; even the direction of movement is often unclear. Moreover, faults are very awkward to classify and describe in a rigorous way. Much of the terminology that surrounds them is very inexact, but deeply entrenched. We will have to be careful in this chapter to distinguish between those terms that are used in a time-honoured but loose way, and those that have to be employed exactly.

We saw in section 8.1 that stresses in the earth's crust sometimes cause rocks to deform in a ductile way, producing folds. In other circumstances, in general where the stresses are operating near the earth's surface, rocks can respond in a brittle way. This behaviour is characterised by fracture of the rocks. Faults result from brittle behaviour. These geological terms brittle and fracture mean exactly what they do in everyday speech.

By far the most common fractures in rocks are **joints**, along which there has been no movement of the rocks. Virtually every rock exposure you see has joints in it, and they can be very important in contexts such as engineering geology. Rarely, however, are joints represented on general geological maps. It is those fractures along which there has been displacement of the rocks – **faults** – which are important for map work, especially if the amount of movement has been large enough to affect the outcrop patterns on the map.

Let us look at faults in the same order as we considered folds: first, outlining some basic descriptive features so that we can report on faults more efficiently, and then looking at some ways in which faults are dealt with on maps.

9.2 Fault parts, orientation and dimensions

Faults commonly have an undulating form, but are often loosely referred to as planes. For most map work, it is realistic to think of a fault as a single plane, although on the ground there may be a broad zone of broken rocks, or a network of smaller fractures. Treated as a single surface the fault appears on a map or cross-section as a **fault trace** (Fig. 9.1). It is dealt with exactly like any other line that arises from a plane intersecting with the map surface. Hence, if the fault trace crosses topographic contours, it should be possible to work out something of the three-dimensional orientation of the fault plane. Like other geological surfaces, its orientation can be specified as a strike and dip. The fault trace on the map is given as a trend and plunge. The dip of the fault as seen in cross-section will be an apparent value, unless the section is drawn at right angles to the strike, in the true dip direction of the fault (cf. section 5.2).

Either side of the fault trace, in most cases the map units will appear to have moved. Either or both sides may have actually carried out the movement; it is normally impossible to tell which. We can refer to the result of this movement, irrespective of the direction in which we are looking, as the **displacement**. This is a very useful but loose term, and by no means necessarily represents the *actual* movement along the fault. The tricky matter of attempting to deduce the real three-dimensional movement is deferred until section 9.6.

Displacement in a steep direction – the 'up and down' part of the movement – is often called the **throw** of the fault, but this is an example of a term that is sometimes used loosely, in the sense just mentioned, and other times with the precise meaning given in section 9.6. The relative movement directions each side of the fault, called the **sense** of displacement, are often represented by paired half-arrows (Fig. 9.1). If the displacement direction is

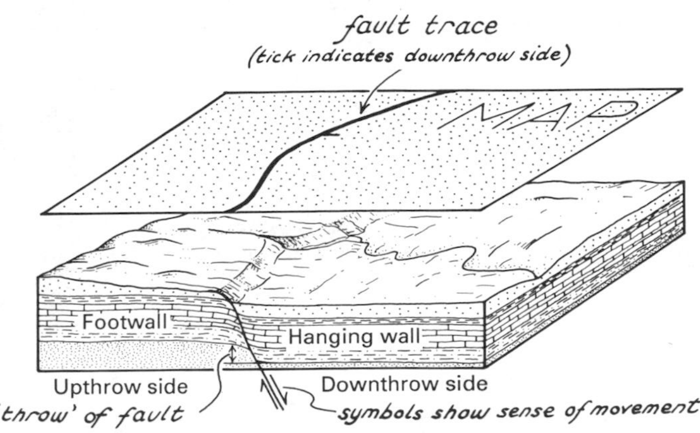
fault trace
(tick indicates downthrow side)
MAP
Footwall
Hanging wall
Upthrow side
Downthrow side
'throw' of fault
symbols show sense of movement

Fig. 9.1 Block diagram to show the main elements of faults relevant to mapwork.

steep, it is usually possible to distinguish the **upthrow** from the **downthrow** side of the fault. With a dipping fault, the side above the fault is called the **hangingwall** and the side below is the **footwall**. These two terms supposedly derive from where miners used to hang their lamps and put their feet. Most of the rich vocabulary that miners used for fault features has now disappeared, but these two terms have recently surged back into technical usage.

The size of a fault is most simply stated by its length and maximum displacement. The horizontal length at surface is readily measured from its map trace; it is the amount of displacement which causes trouble and needs to be considered very carefully.

9.3 Fault displacement

Displacement is absolutely central to the concept of faulting, but working out by how much the rocks have actually moved can be very awkward. The difficulty arises because the displacement seen in one view, say on a map or cross-section, is just the component of movement in that plane. It may or may not reflect the amount of movement in other directions. The problem does not arise in certain special situations involving horizontal or vertical units, but in the general case all kinds of deceptive appearances can be produced.

It is usual to consider displacement from two different aspects: slip and separation. **Slip** is the displacement of formerly adjacent *points* along a fault, in a particular specified direction and *measured in the fault plane* (Fig. 9.2b). Used in this way, slip is a precise term. **Net-slip** is an unambiguous measure of total fault movement. The more loose terms **strike-slip** and **dip-slip** are useful for indicating the dominant movement directions. Note that the 'strike' and 'dip' parts of these terms refer to the *fault*, not the strike and dip of the displaced units. The disadvantage of working with slip is that it is not common to be able to establish *points* which have been relatively displaced. In practice, the points usually arise from the intersection of lines with the fault surface, but even this circumstance is not very common.

It is much more usual to see the result of *planes* having been displaced, that is, the outcrop traces on a map or section. Here, separation is the relevant term. **Separation** is the distance between two formerly adjacent *lines*, and measured in any specified direction, not necessarily in the fault plane (Fig. 9.2). Separation is therefore a much more accessible measure than slip; the snag is that it may not be particularly meaningful. Take the vertical displacement of faulted, very steeply dipping beds: the separation will be small in map view, even though the vertical throw could be huge. With a fault that dips obliquely to dipping beds, the amount of separation, even when consistently measured in a particular direction, will vary according to *where* the measurement is made. It will vary, for example, from cross-section to cross-section.

Separation is therefore an important practical measurement in mapwork, but it is merely a guide to the actual amount of fault movement. It is imperative when dealing with faults on maps to keep clear in your mind the concepts of displacement, slip and separation.

9.4 Classification of faults

Much has been written about the best way to classify faults. Several schemes involve the stresses and mechanics of fault generation but for our purposes a descriptive system, based on what can be observed on maps, is appropriate. Most practical is a scheme which divides faults according to what is judged to be the dominant slip direction, with a few descriptive terms added to enable some sub-division (Fig. 9.3). Thus, if the main displacement seems to be along the strike of the fault we have a **strike-slip fault**, whereas a **dip-slip fault** shows displacement chiefly in the dip direction of the fault. Where the displacement is neither strike-parallel nor dip-parallel but somewhere in between, it is an **oblique-slip fault**. Do notice that the term slip is not being employed in the rigorous sense defined in the previous section, for rarely is the fault classification applied with reference to displaced points.

For dip-slip faults a further division is useful based on the sense of displacement with respect to the fault dip. Where the fault dips towards the downthrow side it is a **normal fault** and where the fault dips towards the upthrow side it is a **reverse fault**. Alternatively, we could think of a normal fault as having its hangingwall downthrown and a reverse fault as having its hangingwall upthrown. The end result is the same in both definitions. The terms normal and reverse are said to come from British coal mining practice: if a coal seam was faulted out, the miners judged the kind of fault and adopted either the normal or the reverse procedures of tunnelling to relocate

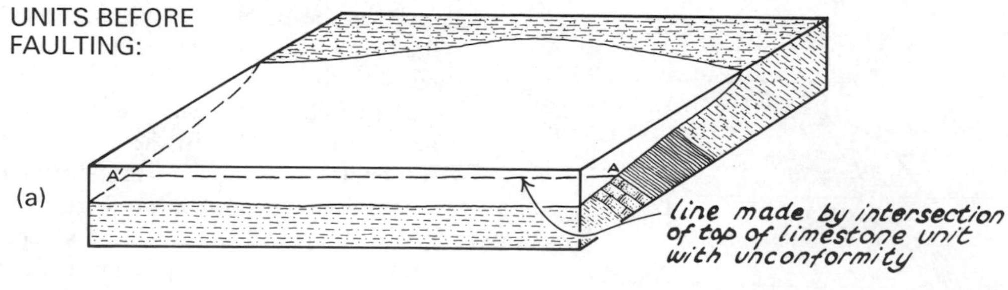
UNITS BEFORE
FAULTING:
(a)
A'
A
line made by intersection
of top of limestone unit
with unconformity

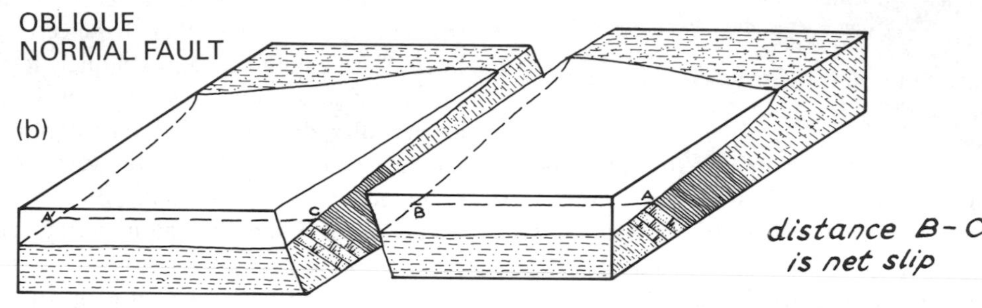
OBLIQUE
NORMAL FAULT
(b)
A'
C
B
A
distance B-C
is net slip

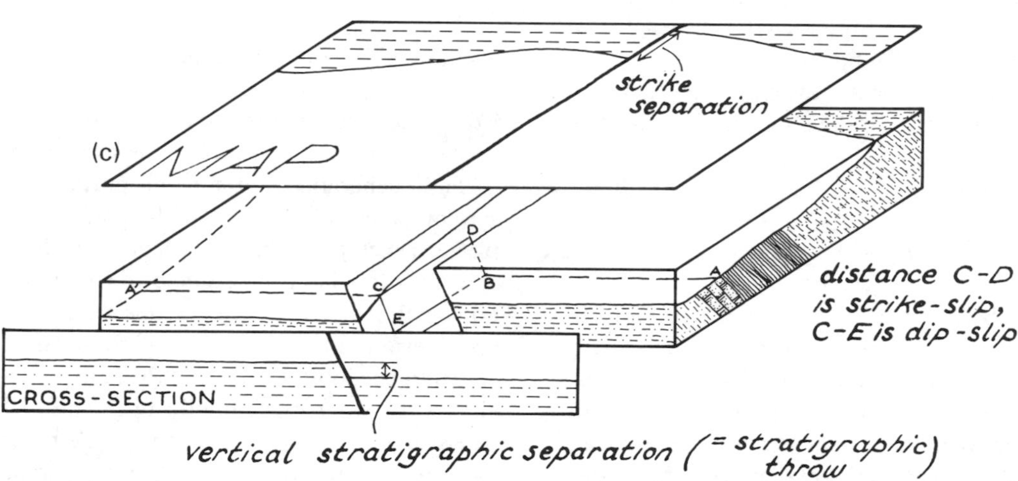
strike
separation
(c)
MAP
D
A'
C
B
E
A
distance C-D
is strike-slip,
C-E is dip-slip
CROSS-SECTION
vertical stratigraphic separation (= stratigraphic
throw)

Fig. 9.2 Block diagrams to show some aspects of fault displacement. (a) shows the rocks before faulting. The unornamented unit unconformably overlies dipping units. The intersection of the top of the limestone unit (brickwork ornament) with the surface of unconformity makes a *line* (dashed). This line makes a *point* on intersecting other planes, such as the edges of the block, at A and A′. (b) shows the same rocks after faulting. The A–A′ line has been displaced; the two points it makes on intersecting the fault plane, B and C, give the net-slip. (c) The same rocks as (b), showing the horizontal component of slip along the fault, C–D, the strike-slip; and the component of slip in the dip direction of the fault, C–E, the dip-slip. These three-dimensional diagrams show the displacement of *points*, and so reveal the oblique-slip nature of the fault, the amount of net-slip in the oblique direction, and the strike-slip and dip-slip components. In map and section view, however, only the *separation* of planes is seen, such as the strike separation and the vertical stratigraphic separation.

the seam. The terms have become extremely widely used, and will be employed here, especially for somewhat isolated faults. Note, however, that it is a somewhat arbitrary classification. Because the name given to the fault depends on the attitude of the fault, which can vary along its length, unclear situations can arise. Hence, normal and reverse

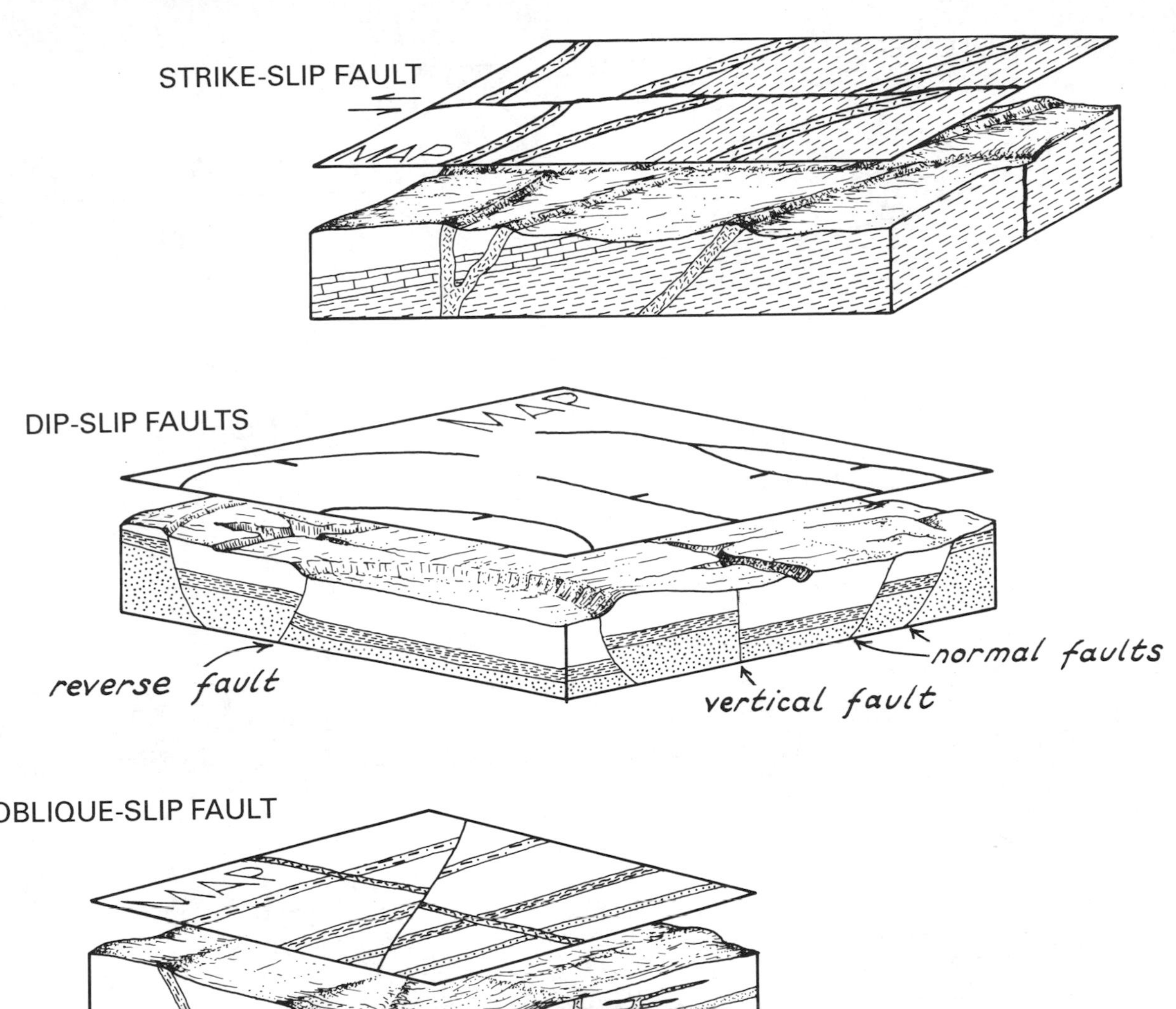
STRIKE-SLIP FAULT
MAP
DIP-SLIP FAULTS
MAP
reverse fault
vertical fault
normal faults
OBLIQUE-SLIP FAULT
MAP

Fig. 9.3 Block diagrams to illustrate the main kinds of faults.

faults are being increasingly referred to as extension and contraction faults, respectively, as discussed in chapter 10.

This basic distinction of strike-slip, normal and reverse dip-slip, and oblique-slip faults is made more informative by the addition of descriptive modifiers. It can be indicated, for example, whether the fault dips at a high or low angle. The distinction between high- and low-angle faults is often placed at 45°, although this is an arbitrary, intermediate figure – there is no intrinsic difference between a reverse fault dipping at 40° and one dipping at 50°. Some low-angle faults, however, are sufficiently distinctive and important to justify their own terms and these will be considered in chapter 10. Some further descriptive terms are given in Fig. 9.4. Thus, a reasonably informative but concise picture of a set of faults is conveyed by something such as 'en echelon high-angle normal faults'.

9.5 Visual assessment on maps

It can be tricky deciding in the field whether or not a particular junction between two different rock units is a fault. Usually on a finalised geological map the surveyor will have indicated a decision. If the contact is thought to be faulted, it will be shown by a line of different weight or colour. There may be some symbolism to distinguish the downthrow side (Fig. 4.2).

On a less complete map, it may fall to the reader to infer the presence of faults from the outcrop patterns; indeed, because faults in nature are rarely exposed, it is often from maps that they are detected. Interruption of the stratigraphic succession may indicate faulting parallel to the strike of the outcrops. Units which should be present but do not appear at surface may be affected by a strike-parallel

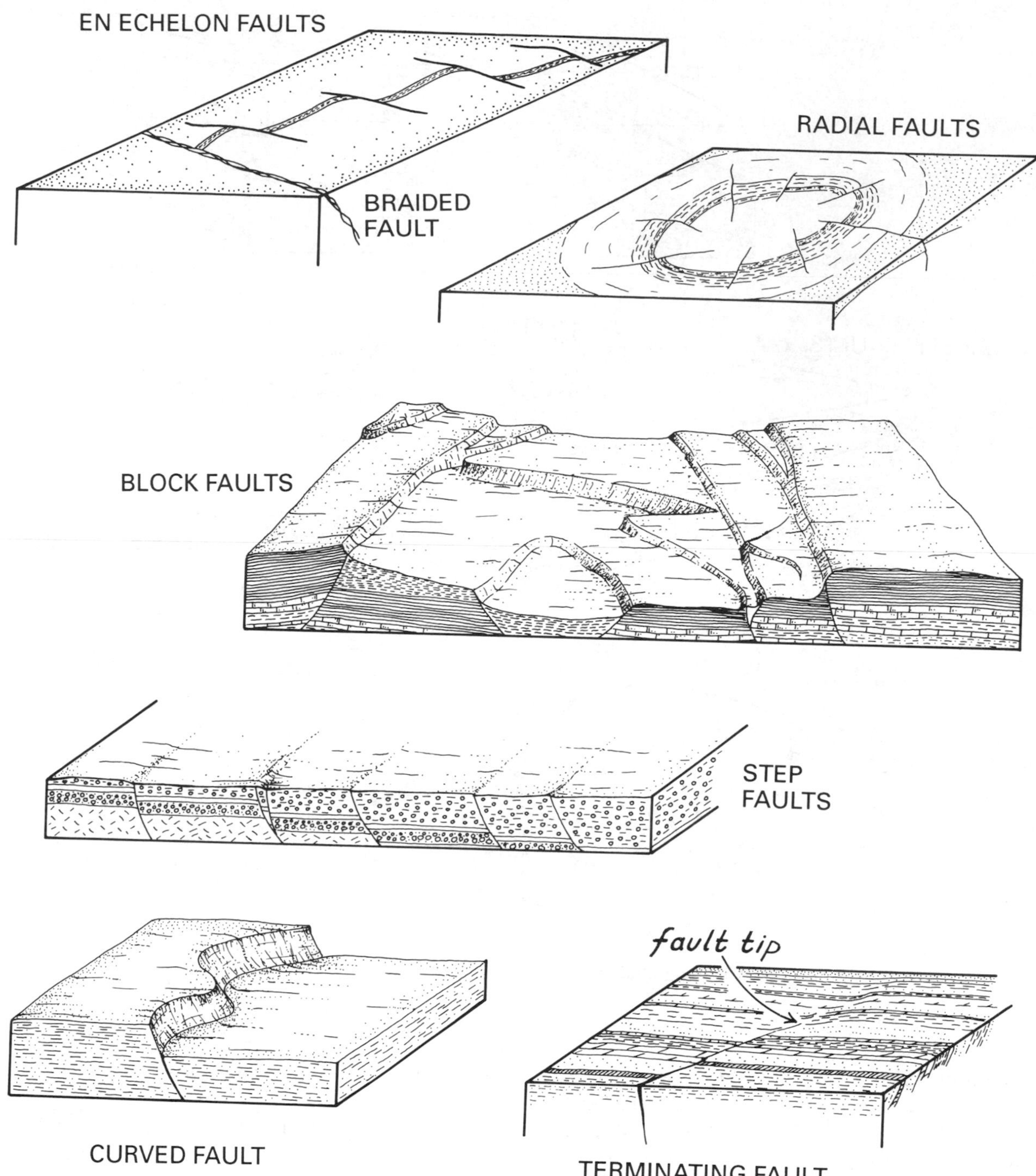
EN ECHELON FAULTS
BRAIDED FAULT
RADIAL FAULTS
BLOCK FAULTS
STEP FAULTS
fault tip
CURVED FAULT
TERMINATING FAULT

Fig. 9.4 Some descriptive terms for faults.

fault dipping in the same direction as the beds (Fig. 9.5), although the absence could also indicate an unconformity (the distinction between faults and unconformities was discussed in section 7.3). Repetition of beds, on the other hand, can only indicate a strike-parallel fault, dipping in the opposite direction to the beds (Fig. 9.5). Note how this pattern of repetition due to faulting contrasts with the kind of repetition produced by folding (section 8.3). If horizontal beds are involved, small-scale strike-slip

Fig. 9.5 (opposite) Block diagrams to show the effects in map and section views of the fault displacement of horizontal beds. Note that the strike-slip fault has no apparent effect. With the oblique-slip fault, the strike-slip component appears to have no effect, whereas the dip-slip component has the same effect as a normal fault.

Normal fault

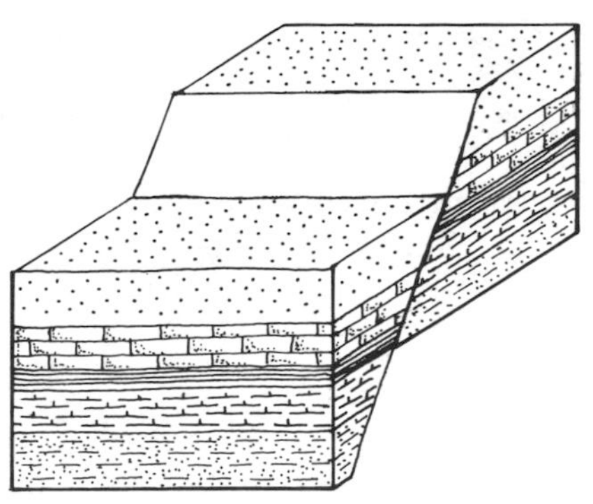

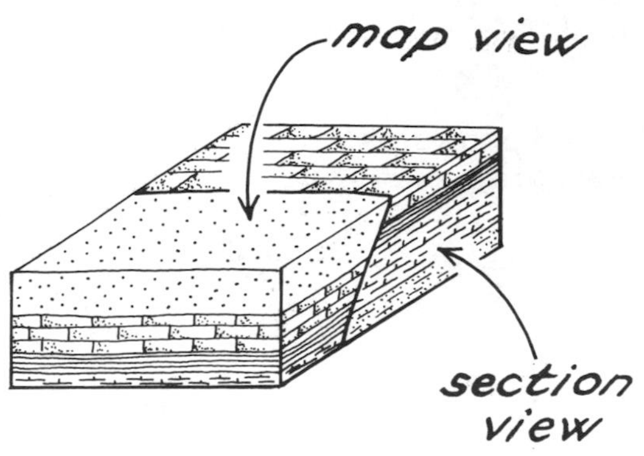
map view
section view

Reverse fault

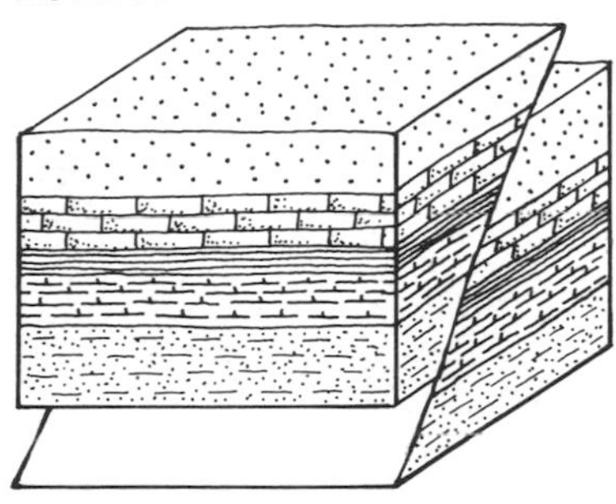

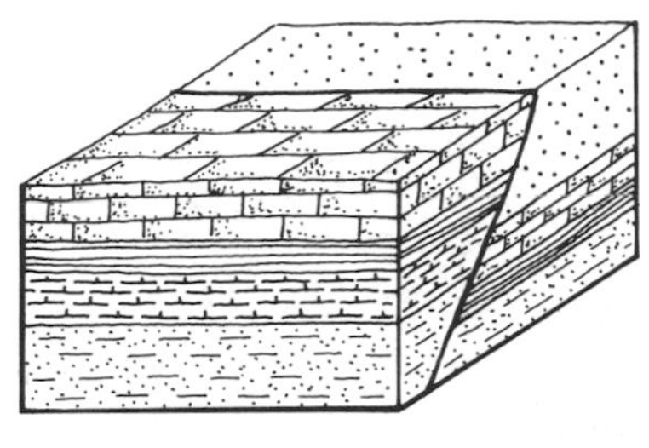

Strike-slip fault

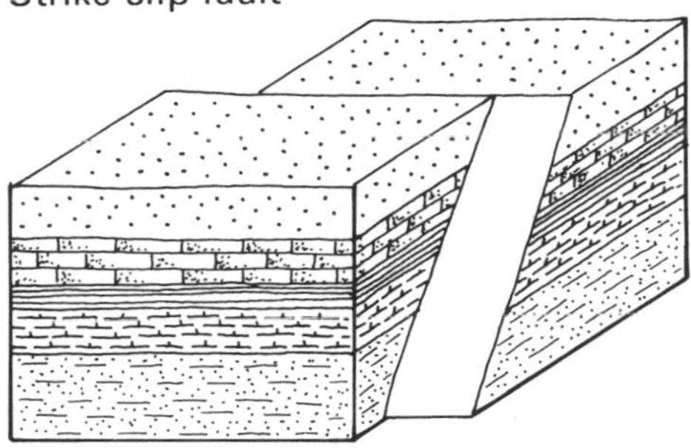

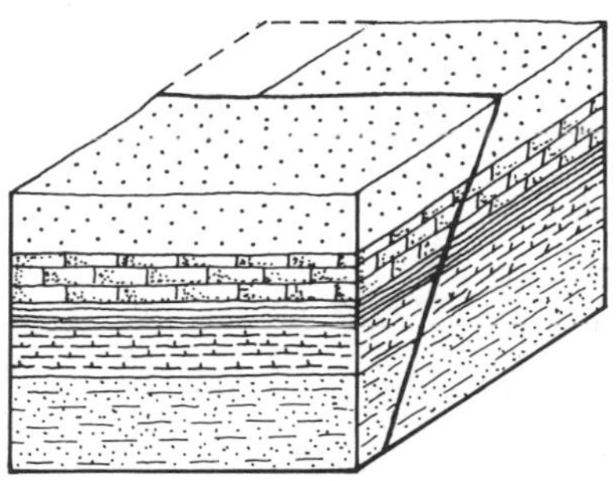

Oblique-slip fault

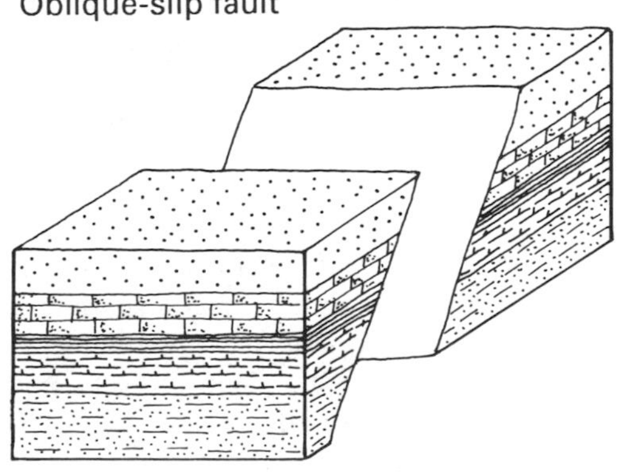

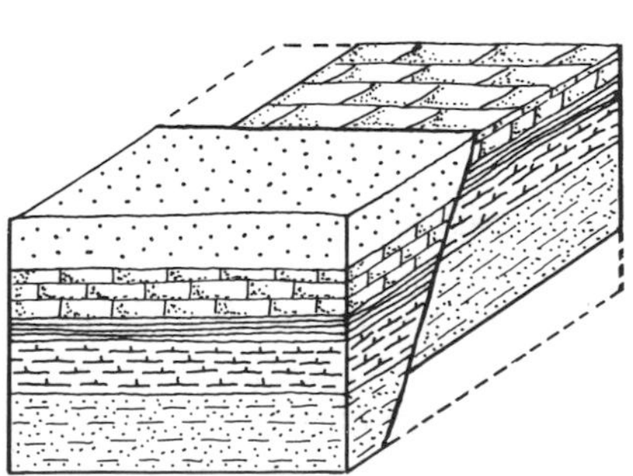

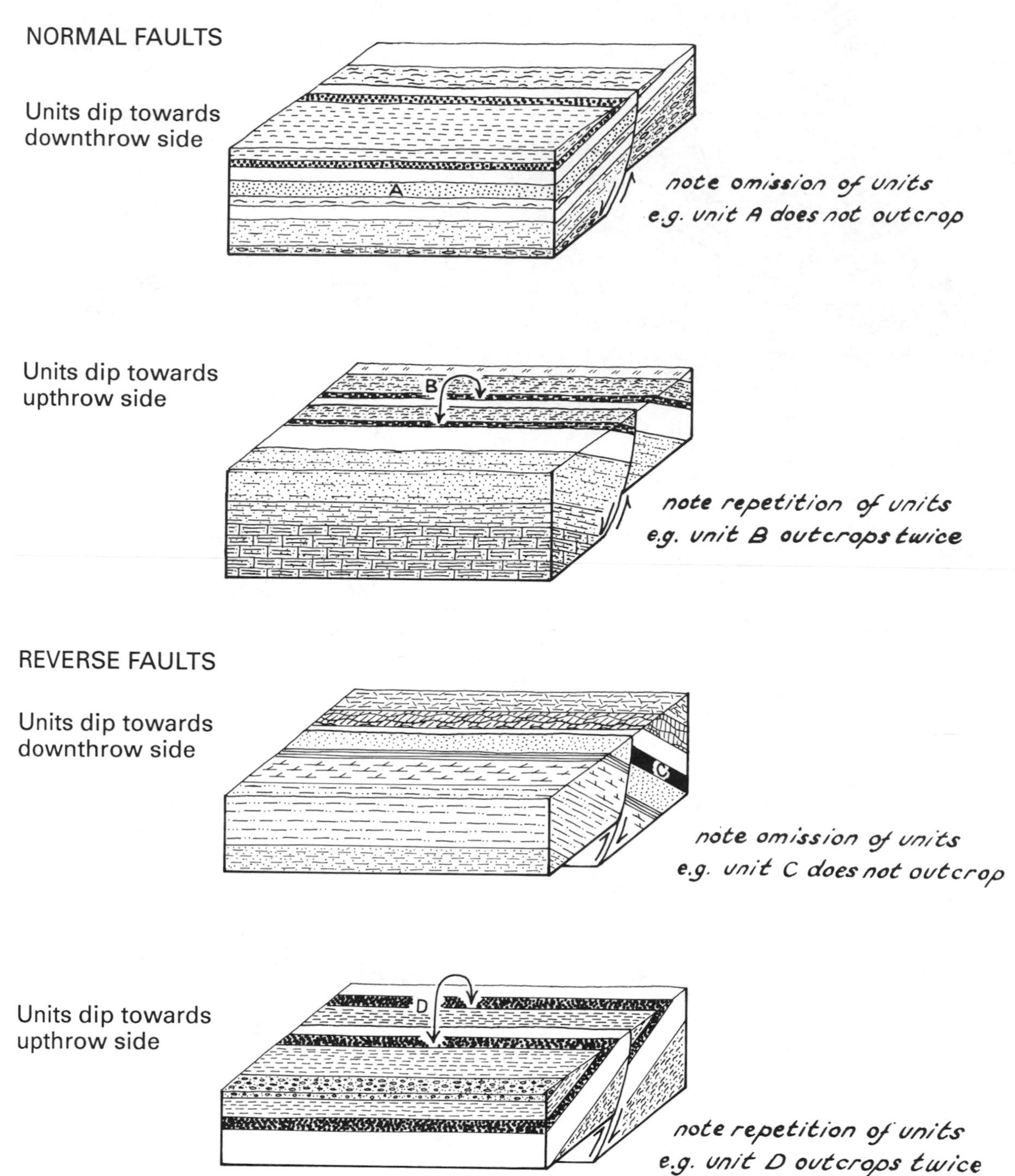
NORMAL FAULTS
Units dip towards downthrow side
A
note omission of units
e.g. unit A does not outcrop
Units dip towards upthrow side
B
note repetition of units
e.g. unit B outcrops twice
REVERSE FAULTS
Units dip towards downthrow side
C
note omission of units
e.g. unit C does not outcrop
Units dip towards upthrow side
D
note repetition of units
e.g. unit D outcrops twice

Fig. 9.6 Block diagrams to show the effects on dipping units of dip-slip faults parallel to the strike of the units.

faulting may not be apparent in either map or section view (Fig. 9.6).

Abrupt displacements of outcrop traces on the map indicate faults which are not strike-parallel (Fig. 9.7). Similar effects are produced by both strike-slip and dip-slip faults if the beds are dipping. For a particular amount of net-slip, the amount of horizontal displacement decreases as the fault becomes more oblique to the strike of the beds (Fig. 9.7). The sense of displacement in the horizontal for a given fault depends on the dip direction of the beds, except where the fault is perpendicular to the strike of the beds (Fig. 9.8). A characteristic double displacement effect results from a dip-slip fault displacing both limbs of a fold (Fig. 9.9).

In general, then, the presence of a fault on a geological map is not too difficult to spot. Recognition of the kind of

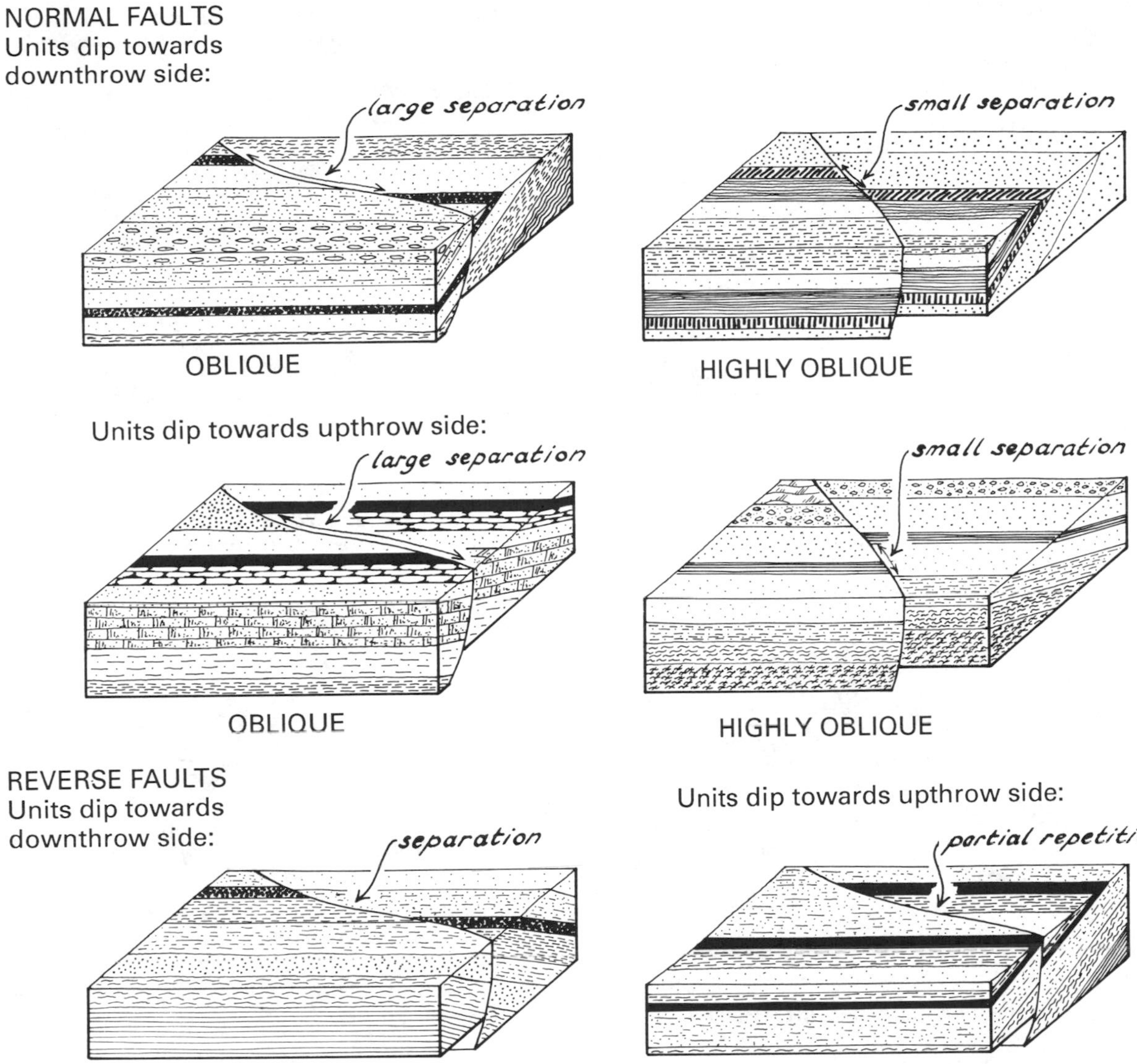

NORMAL FAULTS
Units dip towards
downthrow side:

large separation

small separation

OBLIQUE

HIGHLY OBLIQUE

Units dip towards upthrow side:

large separation

small separation

OBLIQUE

HIGHLY OBLIQUE

REVERSE FAULTS
Units dip towards
downthrow side:

separation

Units dip towards upthrow side:

partial repetition

Fig. 9.7 Block diagrams to show the effects on dipping units of dip-slip faults oblique to the strike of the units.

fault is a different matter. Horizontal displacement of beds may be conspicuous, but, as mentioned above, if the beds are dipping it could be due to either strike-slip or dip-slip faulting. It may not be possible to tell which. Similarly, on a cross-section vertical displacement of beds can result from either strike-slip or dip-slip movement, *if the beds are dipping*. In short, discrimination between minor strike-slip and dip-slip faults is commonly difficult. Section 10.4.2 discusses the recognition of major strike-slip faulting.

There may be clues. If the fault surface is markedly curved, it is likely that the displacement was principally along the axis of curvature (Fig. 9.4). If the dip of the units varies, or there are other features present of a different dip (e.g. sheets of igneous rock), then the same horizontal displacement will be maintained for all dips by a strike-slip fault, whereas it will vary with a dip-slip fault. On a cross-section, the same vertical displacement will be preserved

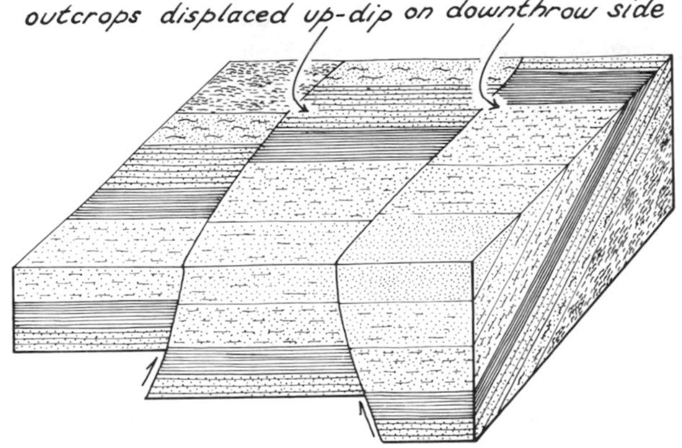
outcrops displaced up-dip on downthrow side

Fig. 9.8 Block diagram to show the effects on dipping units of dip-slip faults at right angles to the strike of the units.

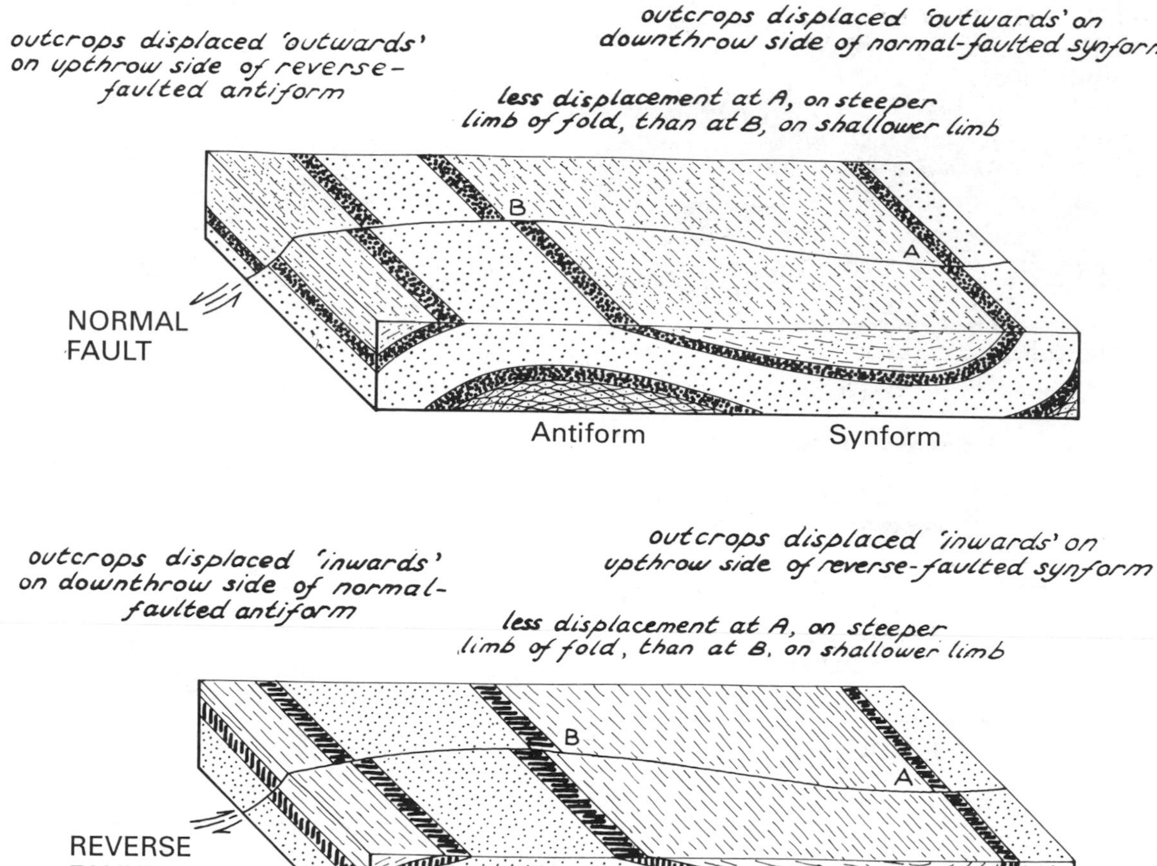
outcrops displaced 'outwards'
on upthrow side of reverse-
faulted antiform
outcrops displaced 'outwards' on
downthrow side of normal-faulted synform
less displacement at A, on steeper
limb of fold, than at B, on shallower limb
B
A
NORMAL
FAULT
Antiform
Synform
outcrops displaced 'inwards'
on downthrow side of normal-
faulted antiform
outcrops displaced 'inwards' on
upthrow side of reverse-faulted synform
less displacement at A, on steeper
limb of fold, than at B, on shallower limb
B
A
REVERSE
FAULT
Antiform
Synform

Fig. 9.9 Block diagrams to show the effects of dip-slip faults on folded units. Note the opposite displacement effects on opposing limbs of the folds. The effect decreases as faults decrease in obliquity to the strike of the units.

by a dip-slip fault that affects differently dipping features, whereas a strike-slip fault will produce various amounts of vertical displacement.

It can be helpful to adapt the 'down-plunge' viewing method for folds (section 8.3) to faults. If it is possible to look down the dip of the displaced units, a truer impression will be given of their separation. If the fault strikes obliquely to the units, it is more realistic to view the separation down a line of intersection made by one of the dipping surfaces with the fault plane.

If the fault is deduced to be dip-slip, then it is usually possible to identify its upthrow and downthrow sides from the relative ages of the strata on either side. In general, older rocks will be brought up on the upthrow side; younger rocks will appear on the downthrow side. Keep an eye on the bed dips though, and this generalisation can easily be undermined by any unconformities and folds which are present. Having deduced that a fault is dip-slip and recognised the upthrow and downthrow sides, the next step is to seek information on the dip of the fault in order to find whether it is normal or reverse. The map may provide a symbol which records the fault dip. The interaction between the fault trace and the topography may provide sufficient information. For example, the principles developed for map units crossing hillslopes and valleys (chapter 6) apply equally to fault planes. If no information on fault dip is available, the fault should be regarded as vertical, and no further classification will be possible. Examples of the assessment of faults from maps are given in Fig. 9.10.

Fig. 9.10 (opposite) Some examples of interpreting faults on maps. (a) Near Dorking, Surrey, England; based on Hayward (1932). (b) Near Newtown, E Wales; based on Earp (1938). (c) Near Swinden, Lancashire, England; based on Hudson and Dunnington (1944). (d) Part of the Rangeley oilfield, Colorado, USA; based on Lalicker (1949).

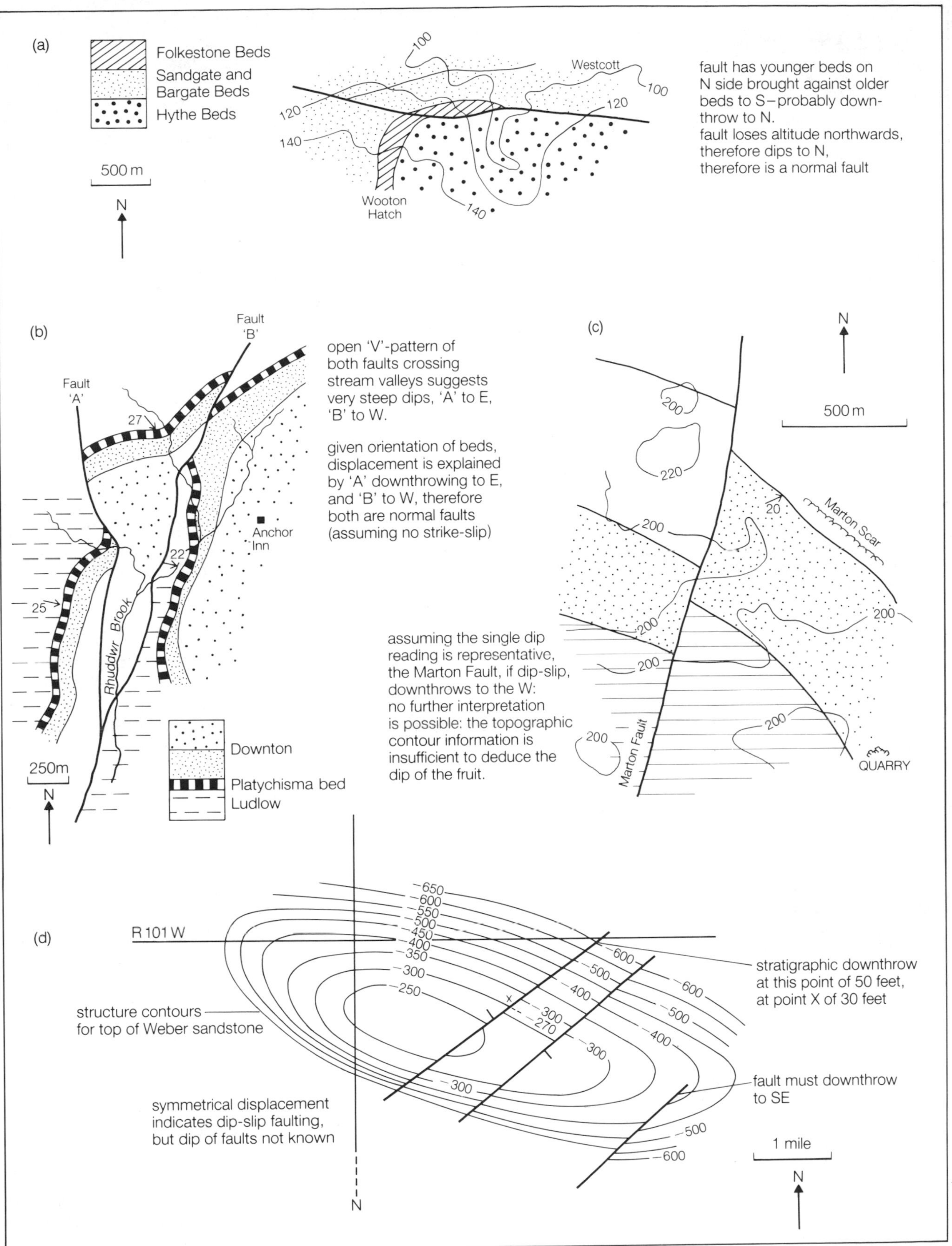
(a)
Folkestone Beds
Sandgate and Bargate Beds
Hythe Beds
500 m
N
100
Westcott
100
120
120
140
Wooton Hatch
140
fault has younger beds on N side brought against older beds to S–probably downthrow to N.
fault loses altitude northwards, therefore dips to N, therefore is a normal fault
(b)
Fault 'B'
Fault 'A'
27
open 'V'-pattern of both faults crossing stream valleys suggests very steep dips, 'A' to E, 'B' to W.
given orientation of beds, displacement is explained by 'A' downthrowing to E, and 'B' to W, therefore both are normal faults (assuming no strike-slip)
Anchor Inn
22
25
Rhuddwr Brook
Downton
Platychisma bed
Ludlow
250m
N
(c)
N
200
500 m
220
20
Marton Scar
200
200
200
200
assuming the single dip reading is representative, the Marton Fault, if dip-slip, downthrows to the W: no further interpretation is possible: the topographic contour information is insufficient to deduce the dip of the fruit.
200
200
Marton Fault
QUARRY
(d)
R 101 W
650
600
550
500
450
400
350
300
250
600
500
400
600
500
400
300
270
300
300
stratigraphic downthrow at this point of 50 feet, at point X of 30 feet
structure contours for top of Weber sandstone
fault must downthrow to SE
symmetrical displacement indicates dip-slip faulting, but dip of faults not known
500
600
1 mile
N
N

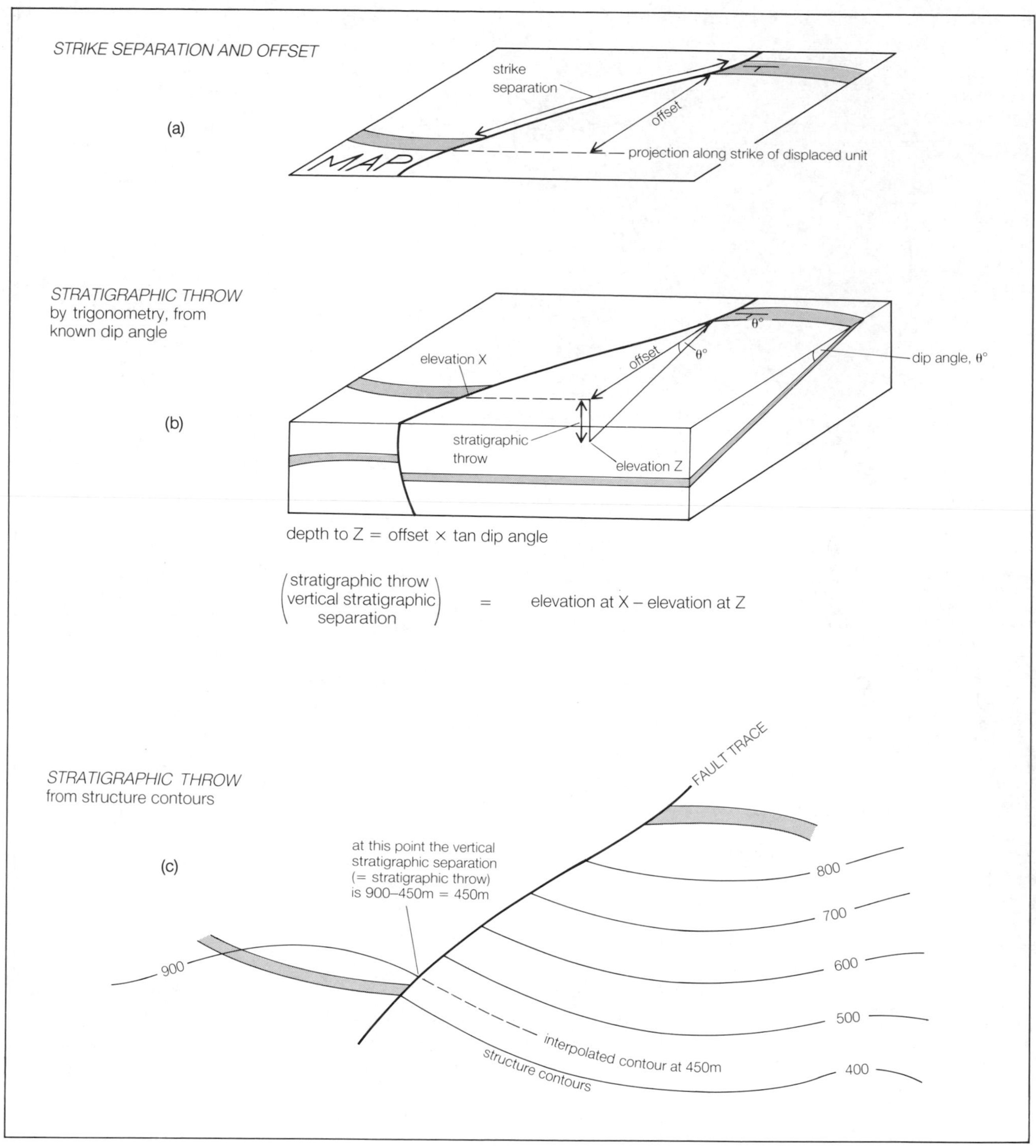
STRIKE SEPARATION AND OFFSET
(a)
strike
separation
offset
MAP
projection along strike of displaced unit
STRATIGRAPHIC THROW
by trigonometry, from
known dip angle
(b)
elevation X
offset
θ°
θ°
dip angle, θ°
stratigraphic
throw
elevation Z
depth to Z = offset × tan dip angle
(stratigraphic throw
vertical stratigraphic
separation) = elevation at X – elevation at Z
STRATIGRAPHIC THROW
from structure contours
(c)
FAULT TRACE
at this point the vertical
stratigraphic separation
(= stratigraphic throw)
is 900–450m = 450m
800
700
600
500
400
900
interpolated contour at 450m
structure contours

Fig. 9.11 Some fault measurements that can be made from maps. (a) Measurement of strike separation and offset directly from the map. (b) Derivation of stratigraphic throw by trigonometry, and (c) from structure contours. Note that the trigonometric method assumes constant dip at depth; the extent of this assumption in method (c) depends on the control on the structure contours.

9.6 Measurements on maps

The length of the fault trace is readily measurable on a map. A minimum value can be given if the trace continues off the map. If the trace is curved it may be necessary to follow it with a piece of thread, which is then held tautly against a ruler.

Displacements in the horizontal are easily measured.

The **strike separation**, measured parallel to the fault strike, and **offset**, measured normal to the strike of the units (Fig. 9.11a), are two readily cited values. The snag is, to emphasise the point again, that they may not mean very much. If the beds either side of the fault are known to dip steeply, then the horizontal separations are likely to be greatly underrepresentative. Conversely, faulting of shallow-dipping beds produces considerable horizontal displacement without much steep movement. Relief of the land surface can also contribute to misleading appearances. If values of the horizontal separations are all that can be obtained from the map, a comment should be made on how meaningful they are likely to be.

Clearly some measure of the steep movement is desirable, and on many maps it is possible to derive at least the vertical separation of the beds, referred to as the **stratigraphic throw**. There are two ways of approaching this. One involves the trigonometric estimation of bed depth (section 4.5, Fig. 4.9). Bed dips have to be known, and assumed to be constant. From the offset of a displaced bed and the tangent of the dip angle, the bed depth can be calculated and subtracted from its elevation at the surface on the other side of the fault (Fig. 9.11b). The difference that results is the stratigraphic throw. With faults oblique to bedding it will be necessary to project horizontally the value of bed depth to the fault trace, to bring it next to its displaced counterpart. The projection is done *along the strike* of the bed.

The second method requires the construction of some structure contours (Fig. 9.11c). On one side of the fault at least two contours will have to be known so that their spacing can be established. From this, assuming constant dip, further contours can be added if necessary. Only one contour will have to be known on the other side of the fault, provided the dip of the beds is taken to be the same, from which additional contours can be sketched. Where any two contours on either side of the fault abut, the elevation difference between them is the stratigraphic throw. The most closely constrained contours are likely to give the most reliable value. If no contours meet directly, then interpolation will be necessary on one side of the fault. The more structure contours that can be drawn from the information given on the map, the greater the control and the less significant will be the assumption of constant dip.

Where two units which are not adjacent stratigraphically are brought together at the fault plane, it may be possible to establish, either by a series of measurements from the map (section 4.4) or by reference to the map key, the thickness of stratigraphy that has been excised. This value is called the **stratigraphic separation**. This thickness, being measured at right angles to the boundaries of the unit, is independent of the orientation of the fault.

Any further useful information on fault displacement requires knowledge of the dip of the fault. This may be cited on the map, or it may be possible to draw some structure contours for the fault surface itself (at least two, if constant dip can be assumed). Several further components of displacement then become measurable (e.g. Roberts, 1982). It also becomes possible to construct an accurate cross-section through the fault to show the fault dip and the displacement magnitude in this vertical plane. The most useful measure is the **fault throw**. This value, in its precise sense (contrast with the usage in section 9.2), is the vertical separation measured in the dip direction of the fault. Note, that in most cases it will not have the same value as the stratigraphic throw, which involves projection along the strike of the units and does not refer to the dip of the fault (Fig. 9.11c).

Ordinarily in mapwork this is all the useful fault measurement that can be carried out. Unless the fault displacement is somehow known to be purely dip-slip or strike-slip, the value of net-slip still eludes us. We will not be in a position to predict accurately the displacement that will appear in other directions, say across some oblique mine adit or tunnel. Methods for deriving net-slip, all of which require further information about the displaced beds, are discussed by Billings (1954) and Ramsay and Huber (1987). Even these procedures involve assumptions, such as the amount of slip being constant along a fault plane. And this cannot be. After all, faults start and stop somewhere, so the displacement must vary along their length.

9.7 Summary of chapter

1. Faults are fractures along which the rocks have moved.
2. The displacement of rocks that is apparent from one viewpoint is not necessarily representative of the actual movement. Terms have to be used carefully.
3. Slip is the displacement of formerly adjacent points, measured in a specified direction in the fault plane. Separation is the displacement of formerly adjacent points measured in some specified direction.
4. Faults are traditionally classified as strike-, oblique-, or dip-slip faults, the last being further distinguished as either normal or reverse.
5. Faults are usually easily detected on maps, but their interpretation can be elusive.

9.8 Selected further reading

Roberts, J. L. (1982). *Geological maps and structures*, Oxford, Pergamon Press.
(Pp. 131–63 discuss normal and reverse faults, and the problems of terminology.)

MAP 15 Aspen, Colorado, USA

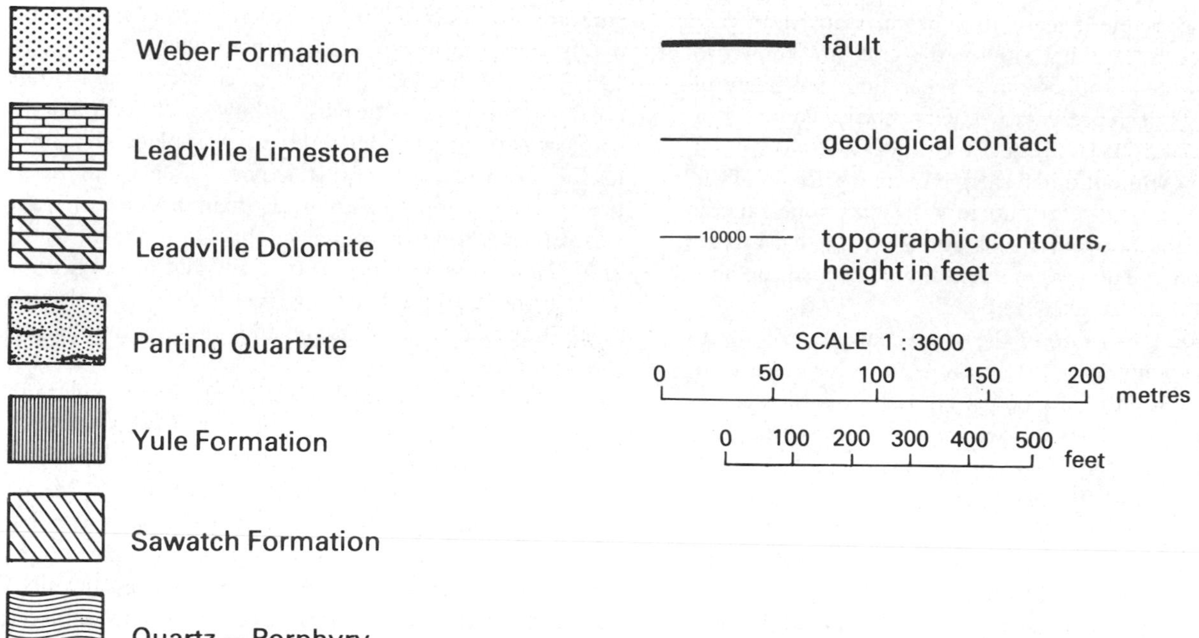
Weber Formation
Leadville Limestone
Leadville Dolomite
Parting Quartzite
Yule Formation
Sawatch Formation
Quartz – Porphyry
fault
geological contact
10000
topographic contours, height in feet
SCALE 1 : 3600
0 50 100 150 200 metres
0 100 200 300 400 500 feet

The map opposite is based on one of a folio of superb, very large-scale maps published by the USGS in 1898 of the Aspen district of Colorado. The detailed study was prompted by the intensive mining for various precious metals in the district, an activity which has now ceased. The numerous faults which were once the miners' bane now criss-cross the slopes used in Aspen's new 'industry' – downhill skiing. The area presented opposite is a part of the 1:3600 Tourtelotte Park Mining District sheet, reproduced here, with some modification, by permission of the USGS.

Is there any overall pattern to the trends of the fault traces?

Judging by the displacements seen on the map, is the Good Thunder Fault likely to be a strike-slip or a dip-slip fault?

Given that the Burro Fault is a dip-slip fault, does it downthrow to the north or south?

In which direction does the Silver Bell Fault dip? (It should be possible to draw a few structure contours for this fault.)

What is the strike separation along the Dixon Fault? What is the stratigraphic throw of the Dixon Fault shown by the top of the Leadville Dolomite? (This can be answered either by using trigonometry, or by constructing structure contours south of the fault and comparing them with their estimated counterparts to the north.)

Construct structure contours for the Dixon Fault. Draw an accurate cross-section in the dip direction of the fault through the point where it is met by the Leadville Dolomite to the N. Project in its dip direction, the top of the Leadville dolomite south of the fault to the cross-section. Measure the throw of the fault.

What kind of fault is the Justice Fault?

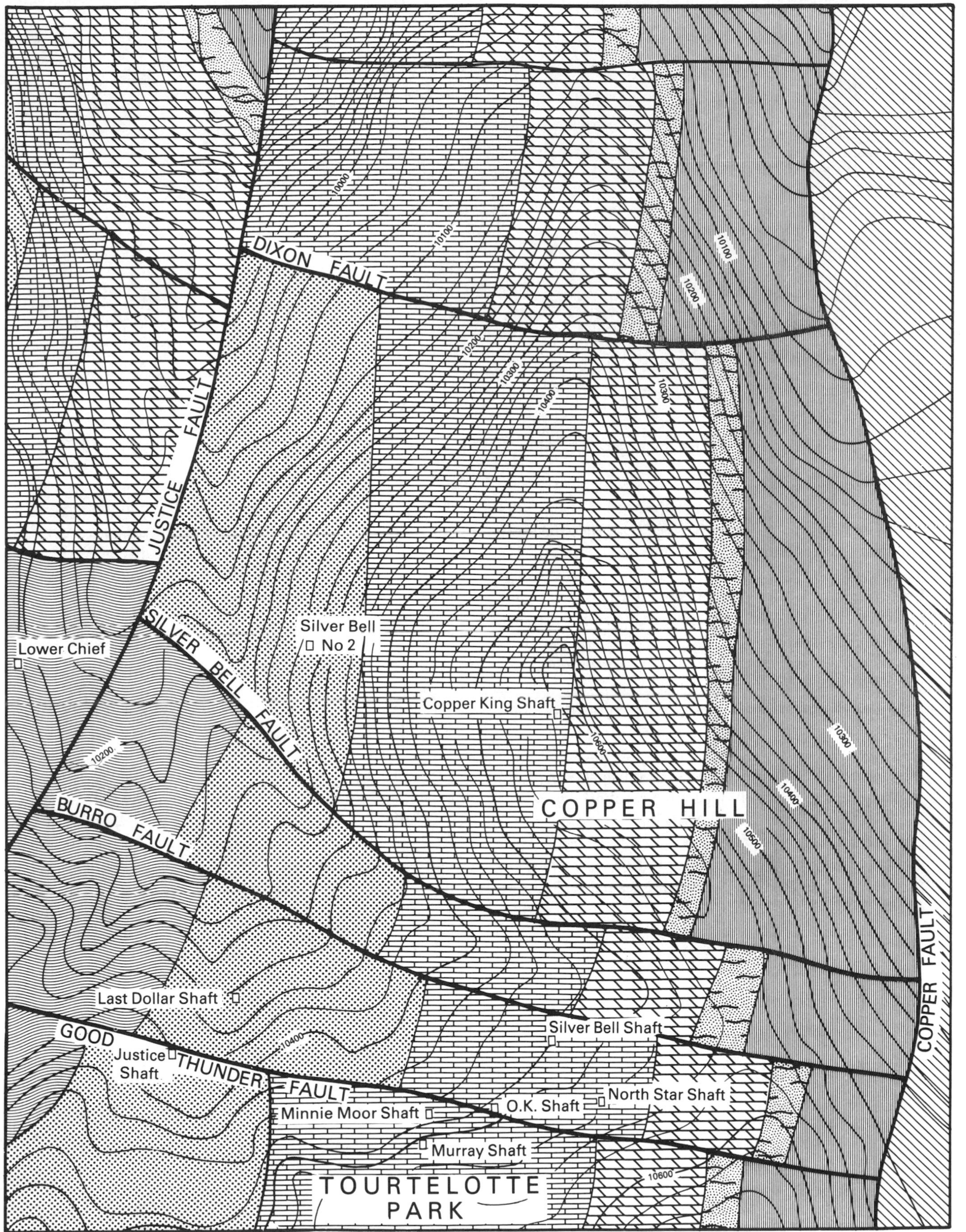

DIXON FAULT
JUSTICE FAULT
10000
10100
10100
10200
10200
10300
10400
10300
SILVER BELL FAULT
Silver Bell
No 2
Lower Chief
Copper King Shaft
10600
10200
10300
10400
10500
COPPER HILL
BURRO FAULT
COPPER FAULT
Last Dollar Shaft
GOOD THUNDER FAULT
Justice
Shaft
10400
Silver Bell Shaft
North Star Shaft
O.K. Shaft
Minnie Moor Shaft
Murray Shaft
10600
TOURTELOTTE
PARK

MAP 16 Alton Pancras, Dorset, England

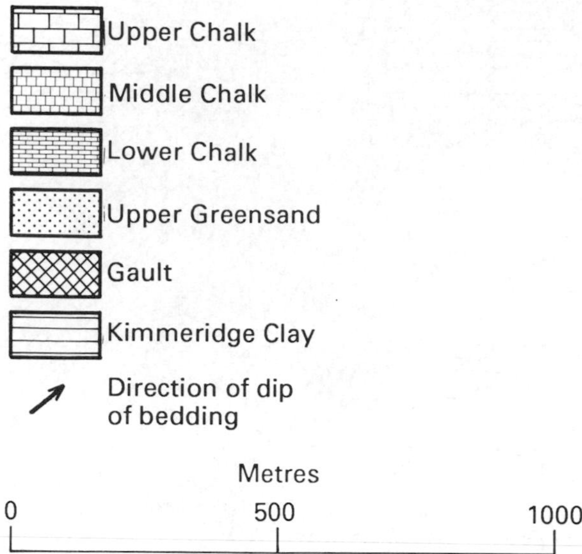
Upper Chalk
Middle Chalk
Lower Chalk
Upper Greensand
Gault
Kimmeridge Clay
Direction of dip of bedding
Metres
0
500
1000

The map opposite is redrawn at a scale of 1 : 14 000 from a sketch-map by Smart (1954). It is used by permission of the Director, BGS: Crown/NERC copyright reserved. The map details the arrangement of the Upper Jurassic and Lower Cretaceous rocks about 10 km north of Dorchester, in SW England. On a hillside just west of the map area, the white chalk was cleared of turf by prehistoric people to form the celebrated figure of the Cerne Abbas giant.

What is the general orientation of the units in the map area?

Why does the N–S fault northeast of Plush appear to displace the Lower Chalk in opposite directions?

Consider the long N–S fault that outcrops between Alton Pancras and Plush. What strike separation is shown by the base of the Upper Chalk? What strike separation is shown by the top of the Lower Chalk? Why might these two amounts be so different? Comment on the value of strike separation as a measure of the actual displacement of a fault. Assuming this fault is a true plane, what do the curves in its trace signify?

From the ages of the rocks on either side of the fault, which is likely to be the downthrow side?

Draw the 210 and 180 m structure contours for the fault. What kind of fault is it?

Draw the 150, 180 and 210 m structure contours for the top of the Lower Chalk for about a kilometre either side of the fault. Because of the nature of the orientation of the map units, the structure contours are likely to be irregular and poorly constrained.

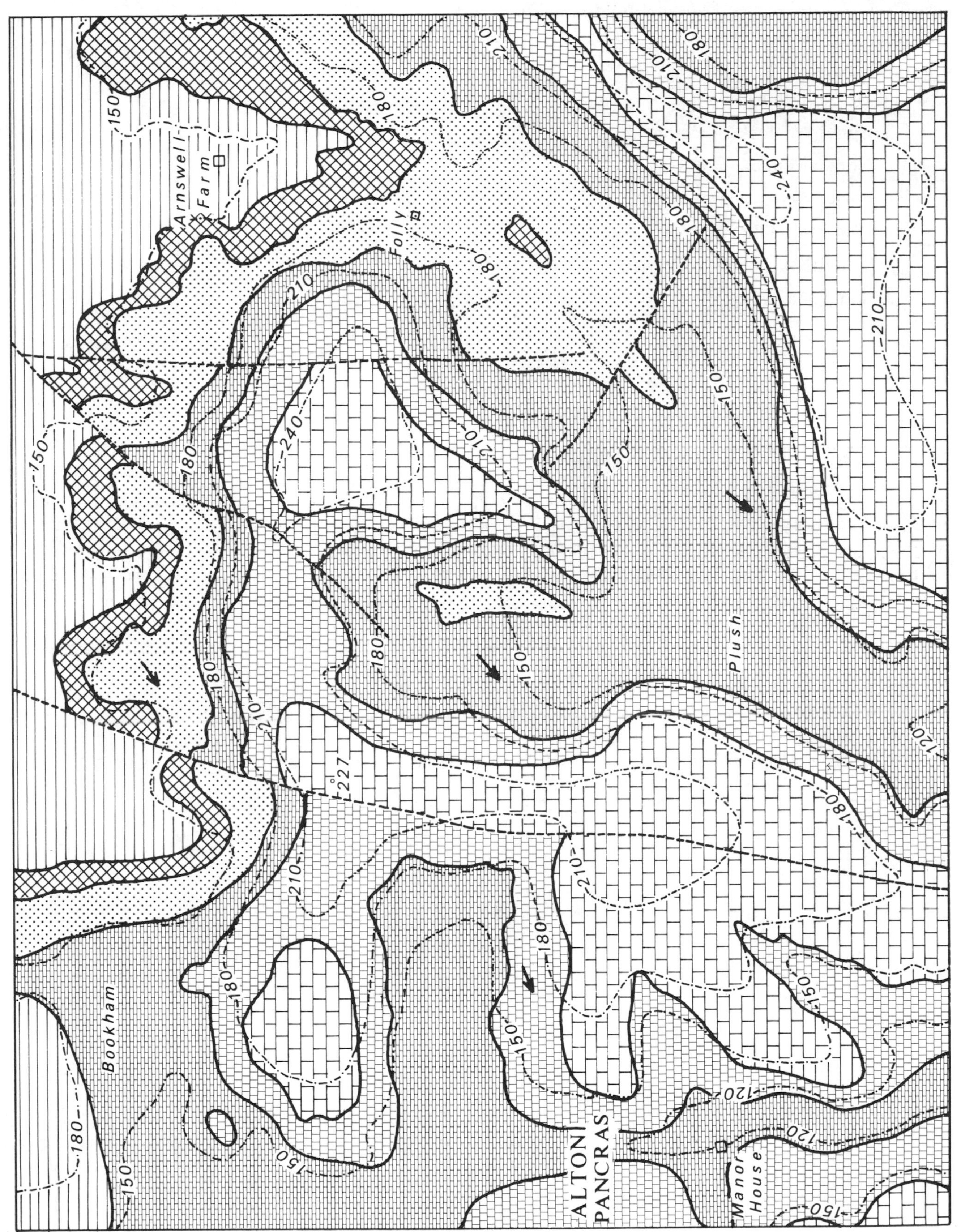
Arnswell Farm
Folly
Plush
Bookham
ALTON PANCRAS
Manor House
227

MAP 17 Wren's Nest, West Midlands, England

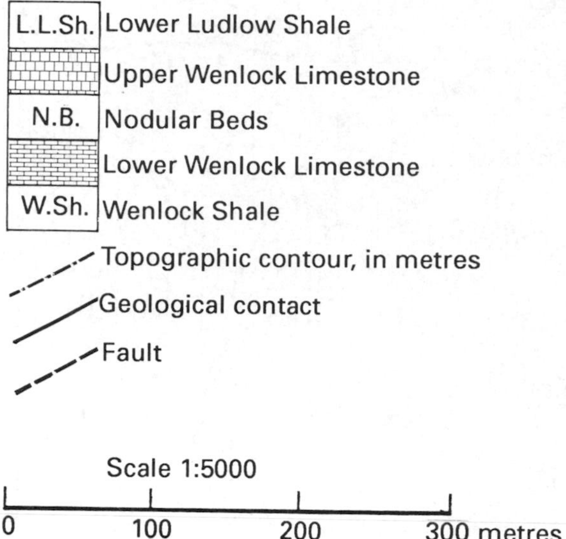
L.L.Sh. Lower Ludlow Shale
Upper Wenlock Limestone
N.B. Nodular Beds
Lower Wenlock Limestone
W.Sh. Wenlock Shale
Topographic contour, in metres
Geological contact
Fault
Scale 1:5000
0
100
200
300 metres

The middle Silurian Wenlock Limestone of Dudley, W Midlands, has long been famous for its abundant, beautifully preserved fossils. The outcrop in the area known as Wren's Nest is now a National Nature Reserve. Map 17 is redrawn, by permission of the Geological Society, from Butler (1939).

Describe the overall structure of the area.

What strike separation and what offset is produced by the fault in the east of the area? What stratigraphic throw does it show?

What is the strike separation of the Lower Wenlock Limestone south of Wren's Nest Farm?

Using the nearest dip value provided, calculate the stratigraphic throw shown by this unit. How does the value compare with that derived by constructing structure contours in the vicinity of Wren's Nest Farm?

Deduce the plunge of the fold in the south of the area.

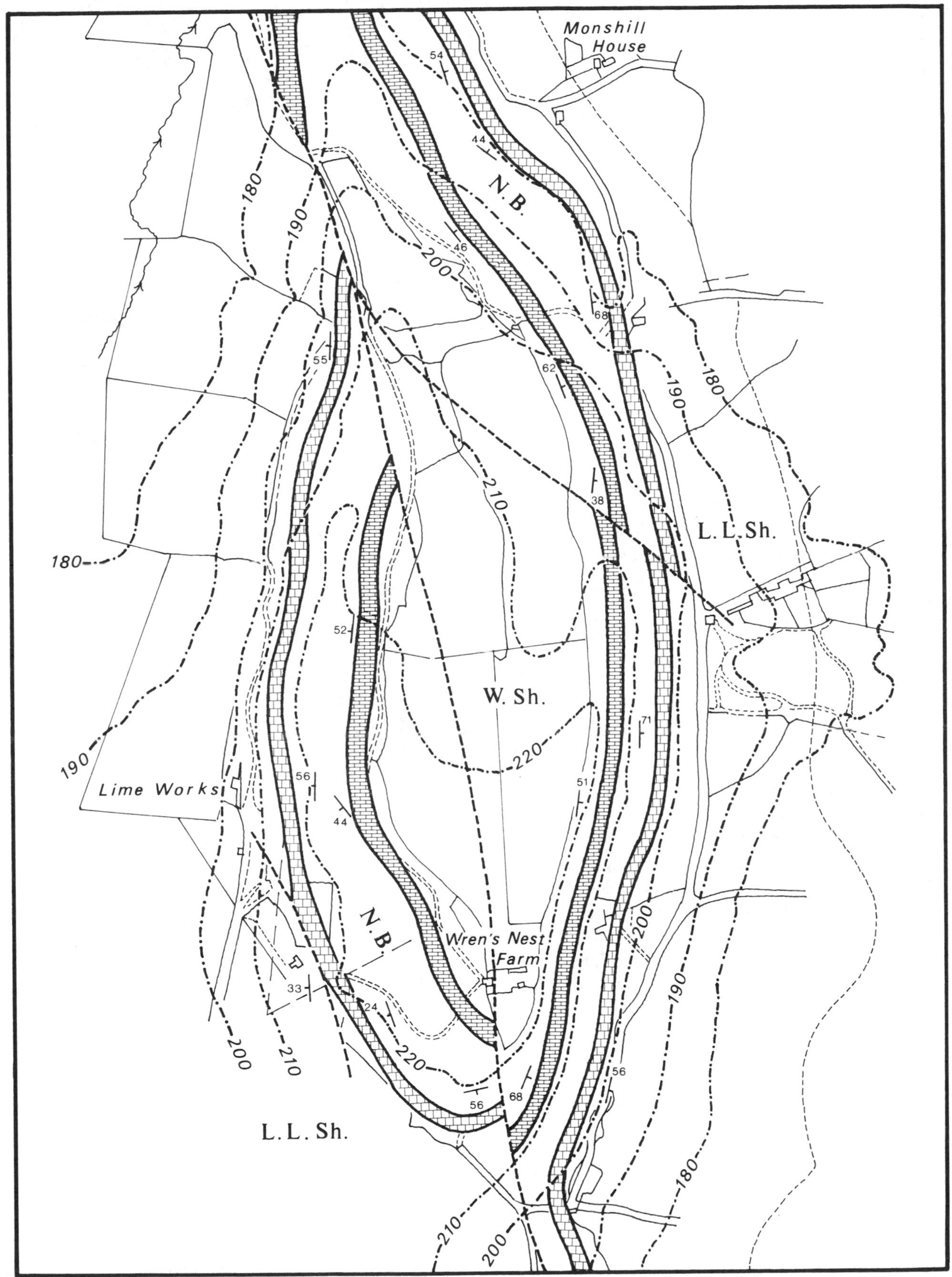
Monshill House
N.B.
L.L.Sh.
W. Sh.
Lime Works
N.B.
Wren's Nest Farm
L.L.Sh.
180
190
200
210
220
54
44
46
68
62
55
38
52
71
51
56
44
33
24
56
68
56

10 More on faults: contraction (thrust), extension, and strike-slip faults

10.1 Introduction

Having outlined in chapter 9 some of the methods for dealing with faults on maps, we can now look at some of the natural situations in which faults are found. It is a rare map which does not show a fault of one kind or another, but this chapter is mainly concerned with those areas of the earth where faults are numerous and dominated by a particular type.

There are long, linear zones made up of faults which have essentially a reverse fault geometry but are of shallow inclination. They are called thrust faults, and the zones in which they predominate are called thrust belts. An example was mentioned in section 2.3.4. Their overall effect, along with any associated reverse faults, is to telescope together the stratigraphic sequence, producing a thick stack of beds and decreasing their horizontal extent. Hence, all these faults can be referred to as **contraction faults**. They have attracted much attention, partly because of the intriguing problem of understanding how the rocks can actually accomplish large amounts of contraction, and partly because in recent years some thrust belts have been the scene of intensive oil exploration.

In contrast, there are areas of the earth which have been 'pulled apart' such that they are now dominated by **extension faults**. The dominant structures are essentially normal faults, but tend to have a low dip-angle overall. The inner parts of these areas tend to be dropped down along the faults more than the outer parts, leading to subsidence and the production of **extensional basins**. These areas, too, are of great importance in oil geology; the North Sea is an example of an extensional basin.

Curiously, although on regional maps thrust belts contrast clearly with extensional basins, on large-scale maps contraction and extension faults can be difficult to distinguish. The two kinds of fault have many similarities in appearance. In a restricted area it might not be possible to match the rocks in the hangingwall with those in the footwall, or the low-angle fault may be exactly parallel to bedding, so that the critical difference of the hangingwall moving up or down will not be recognisable.

Yet other parts of the earth are dominated by zones of strike-slip faulting. These can also give problems in map studies. Typically, these faults have very large displacements and their traces are conspicuous on maps, but correlation across the faults is notoriously difficult, even on small-scale maps, because of the large amount of movement. Even though some of the most widely known geological structures are strike-slip faults, for example, the San Andreas Fault in California, their strike-slip character can be difficult to prove.

10.2 Contraction (thrust) faults

10.2.1 Characteristics

Thrust faults are low-angle dip-slip faults, along which the hangingwall has been upthrown (Fig. 10.1). They are therefore essentially reverse faults (section 9.4), and low-angle reverse faults are sometimes called thrusts. However, it would be misleading to think of this as the only difference; it is the overall character of thrust faults which compels a distinction.

Thrusts rarely occur as isolated faults. Typically they are in groups, which together with splaying and interlocking smaller thrusts and folds, form the long, linear zones known as fold-and-thrust belts or simply **thrust belts**. Families of closely spaced splaying reverse faults called **imbricate zones** may also be involved (Fig. 10.2).

The displacements on the major thrusts of the belt may be substantial and are typically measured in kilometres of movement.

The low dip of thrust faults towards the upthrow side results in bringing more deeply buried rocks up and over shallower rocks. It is a general property of thrusts that they bring older rocks over younger. The hangingwall of a thrust is commonly called a **thrust sheet** and named after the fault at its base.

The shape of an individual thrust is not normally planar over any great distance. There are two general tendencies. One is for the thrust plane to curve smoothly from a steeper dip at its upper end to a shallow dip at depth (Fig. 10.1). This concave-upwards form is called **listric**, from

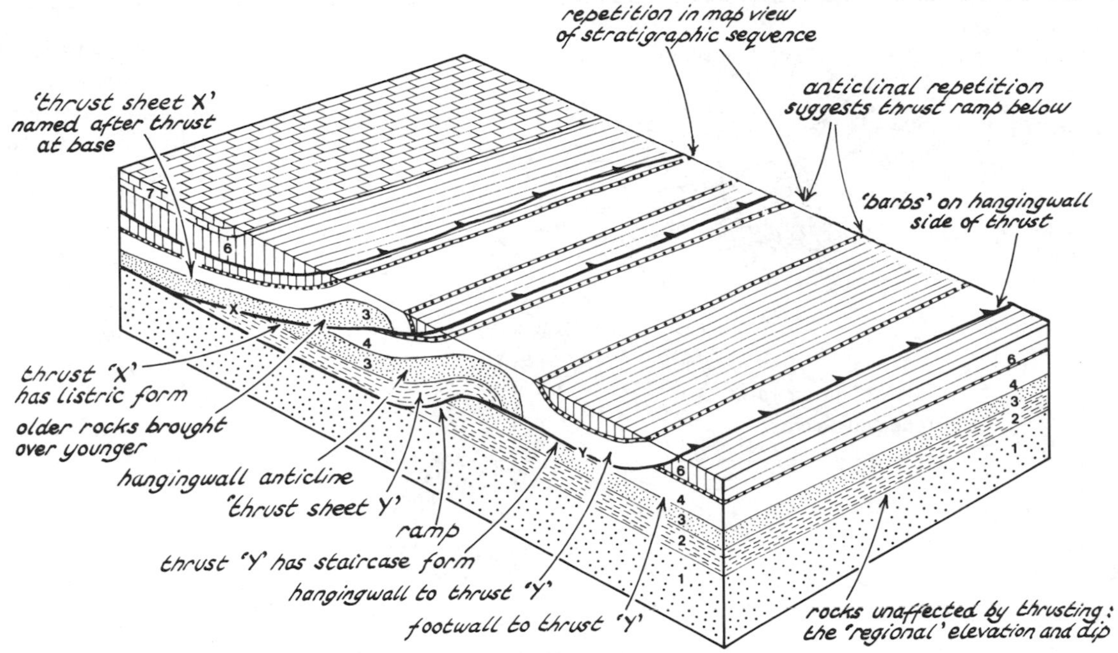
repetition in map view
of stratigraphic sequence
'thrust sheet X'
named after thrust
at base
anticlinal repetition
suggests thrust ramp below
'barbs' on hangingwall
side of thrust
thrust 'X'
has listric form
older rocks brought
over younger
hangingwall anticline
'thrust sheet Y'
ramp
thrust 'Y' has staircase form
hangingwall to thrust 'Y'
footwall to thrust 'Y'
rocks unaffected by thrusting:
the 'regional' elevation and dip

Fig. 10.1 Block diagram to show the main features of thrust faults.

the Greek word for a spoon. The other tendency is towards developing a kind of 'staircase' shape (Fig. 10.1). The **ramps** commonly dip at about 30–35° and occupy a shorter distance than the bedding-parallel **flats**. Some thrusts have bedding-parallel parts several kilometres long.

A consequence of a ramp having developed is that beds moving up and over the ramp take on an antiformal shape (Fig. 10.1). The structure is termed a **hangingwall anticline**.

10.2.2 Recognition on maps

An isolated thrust fault will be recognisable on a map as a low-angle plane on which older rocks overlie younger ones. No other structure can look like this, except for very special cases such as an inverted unconformity. If the various characteristics listed above are also apparent, the diagnosis of thrusting should be straightforward. In any case, it is conventional for thrusts to be indicated on maps by a special symbolism (Figs 4.2 and 10.2). If you are drawing this symbol on a map, do make sure you have the barbs on the hangingwall/thrust sheet side; it is a common beginner's mistake to reverse the position.

A group of thrusts on a map may well have the effect of repeating the stratigraphy several times, and if imbricate zones are present too, the outcrop pattern can be extremely intricate. Stratigraphic repetition is also produced by extension faulting (section 10.3, Fig. 10.5) but there the overall effect of bringing younger rocks over older will be lacking.

10.2.3 Three-dimensional arrangement

Having located and recognised thrust faults on a map, several things can be attempted by way of three-dimensional interpretation. Because of their overall low dip, thrusts are amenable to the methods developed earlier for horizontal and dipping beds (sections 6.2 and 6.3). The map trace of a thrust will tend to follow topographic contours, and will parallel them if the thrust is horizontal. The principle that formations become younger in the dip direction will have to be used with extreme caution, though, as by their very nature thrusts will be upsetting the stratigraphic succession.

If there are topographic contours on the map, or borehole/well information is available, it may be possible to construct structure contours for the thrust surface (cf. sections 3.5 and 3.6). Figure 10.3 gives examples. If the structure contours are closely constrained, they may bring out the listric or staircase shape of the plane. It may be possible to construct sub-crop patterns for the thrust surface (Fig. 10.3) in an analogous way to unconformities (section 7.6).

Note that the dip of the fault at the surface does not necessarily reflect the overall thrust inclination. Projection to depth on a cross-section is precarious without supporting information. It is perhaps safest to draw the thrust trace as a straight line. Some listric form could be included where the beds in the thrust sheet are not greatly different in stratigraphic age from those in the footwall. However, if basement rocks are involved in the hangingwall, the thrust

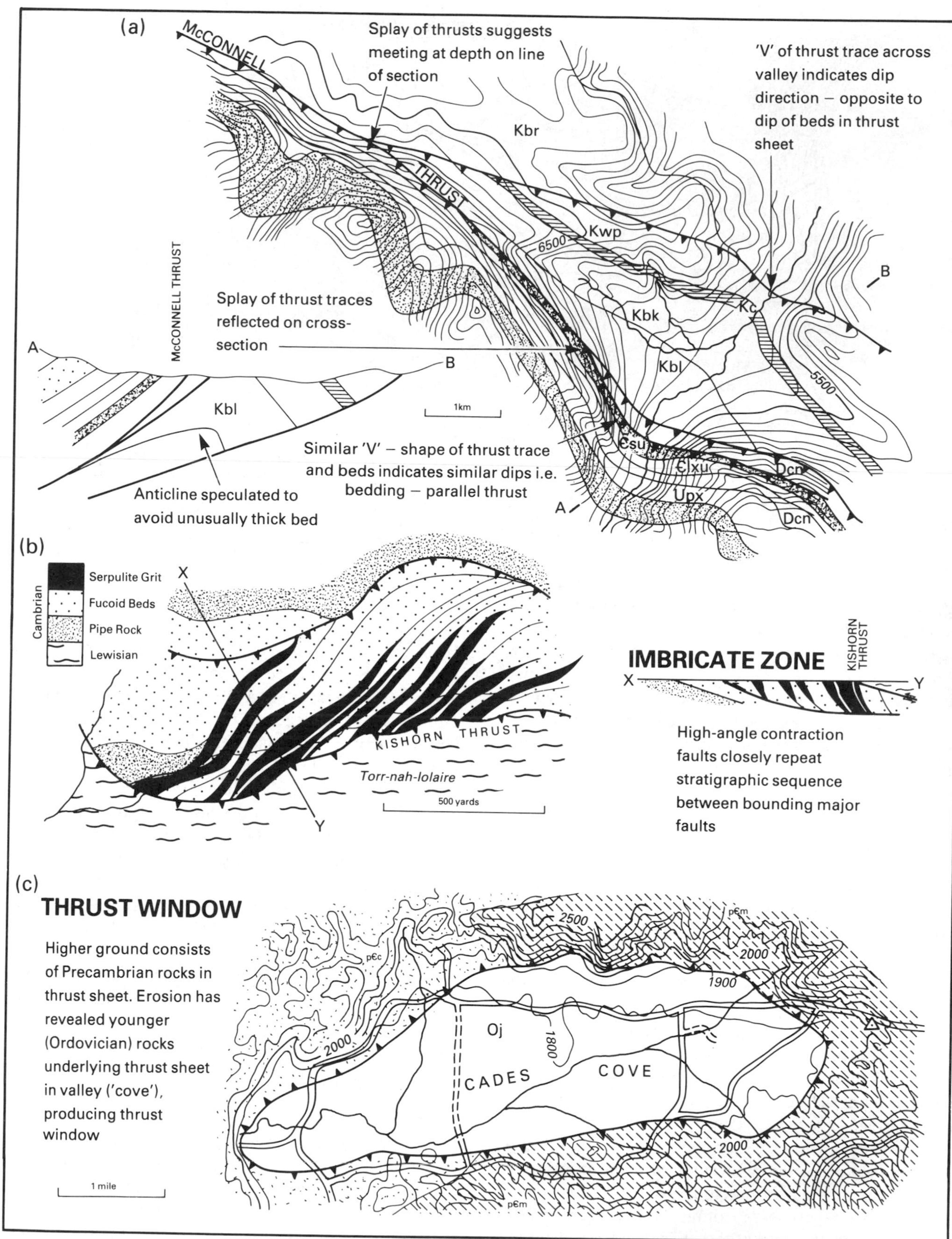
(a)
McCONNELL
THRUST
Splay of thrusts suggests meeting at depth on line of section
'V' of thrust trace across valley indicates dip direction – opposite to dip of beds in thrust sheet
Kbr
Kwp
6500
B
Kc
Kbk
Kbl
5500
McCONNELL THRUST
Splay of thrust traces reflected on cross-section
A
B
Kbl
1km
Similar 'V' – shape of thrust trace and beds indicates similar dips i.e. bedding – parallel thrust
Anticline speculated to avoid unusually thick bed
Ꞓsu
Ꞓxu
Upx
Dcn
Dcn
A
(b)
Cambrian
Serpulite Grit
Fucoid Beds
Pipe Rock
Lewisian
X
KISHORN THRUST
Torr-nah-Iolaire
500 yards
Y
IMBRICATE ZONE
KISHORN THRUST
X
Y
High-angle contraction faults closely repeat stratigraphic sequence between bounding major faults
(c)
THRUST WINDOW
Higher ground consists of Precambrian rocks in thrust sheet. Erosion has revealed younger (Ordovician) rocks underlying thrust sheet in valley ('cove'), producing thrust window
1 mile
2500
p€m
p€c
2000
1900
Oj
1800
2000
CADES
COVE
2000
p€m

Fig. 10.2 Some features of thrust on maps. (a) Redrawn from part of the Geological Survey of Canada 1:50 000 'Whiterabbit Creek' (E) sheet 1388A, by permission of the Geological Survey of Canada. Cross-section inferred from map features. (b) Imbricate zone in map and section. Near Lochcarron, Scotland. (c) Thrust window. Cades Cove, Tennessee, USA. Redrawn from part of the 1:62 500 map in USGS Professional Paper 394-D, 'Geology of the Great Smoky Mountains, Tennessee', by permission of the USGS.

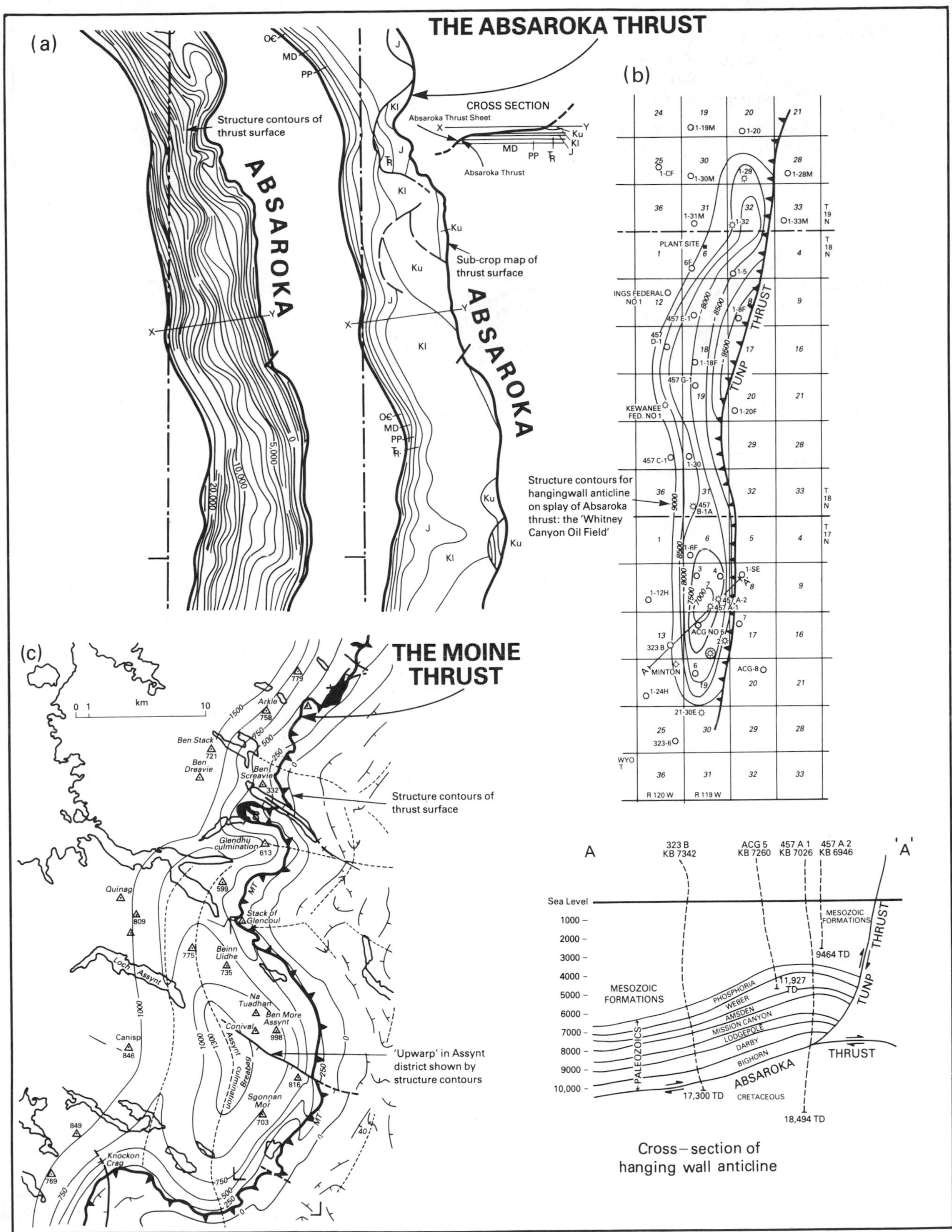

THE ABSAROKA THRUST
(a)
Structure contours of thrust surface
ABSAROKA
CROSS SECTION
Absaroka Thrust Sheet
Absaroka Thrust
Sub-crop map of thrust surface
(b)
Structure contours for hangingwall anticline on splay of Absaroka thrust: the 'Whitney Canyon Oil Field'
TUNP THRUST
(c)
THE MOINE THRUST
Structure contours of thrust surface
'Upwarp' in Assynt district shown by structure contours
Cross–section of hanging wall anticline

Fig. 10.3 Three-dimensional aspects of thrusts on maps. (a) Structure contour and subcrop maps of the Absaroka Thrust, Idaho–Wyoming, USA. Reproduced from Dixon (1982), by permission of the American Association of Petroleum Geologists. (b) Structure contour map of a splay of the Absaroka Thrust, and a cross-section. Reproduced from Ver Ploeg and de Bruin (1982), by permission of the Geological Survey of Wyoming, and based on data of the Amoco Production Company. (c) Structure contour map of the Moine Thrust, NW Scotland. Reproduced from Eliot and Johnson (1980), by permission of the Royal Society of Edinburgh.

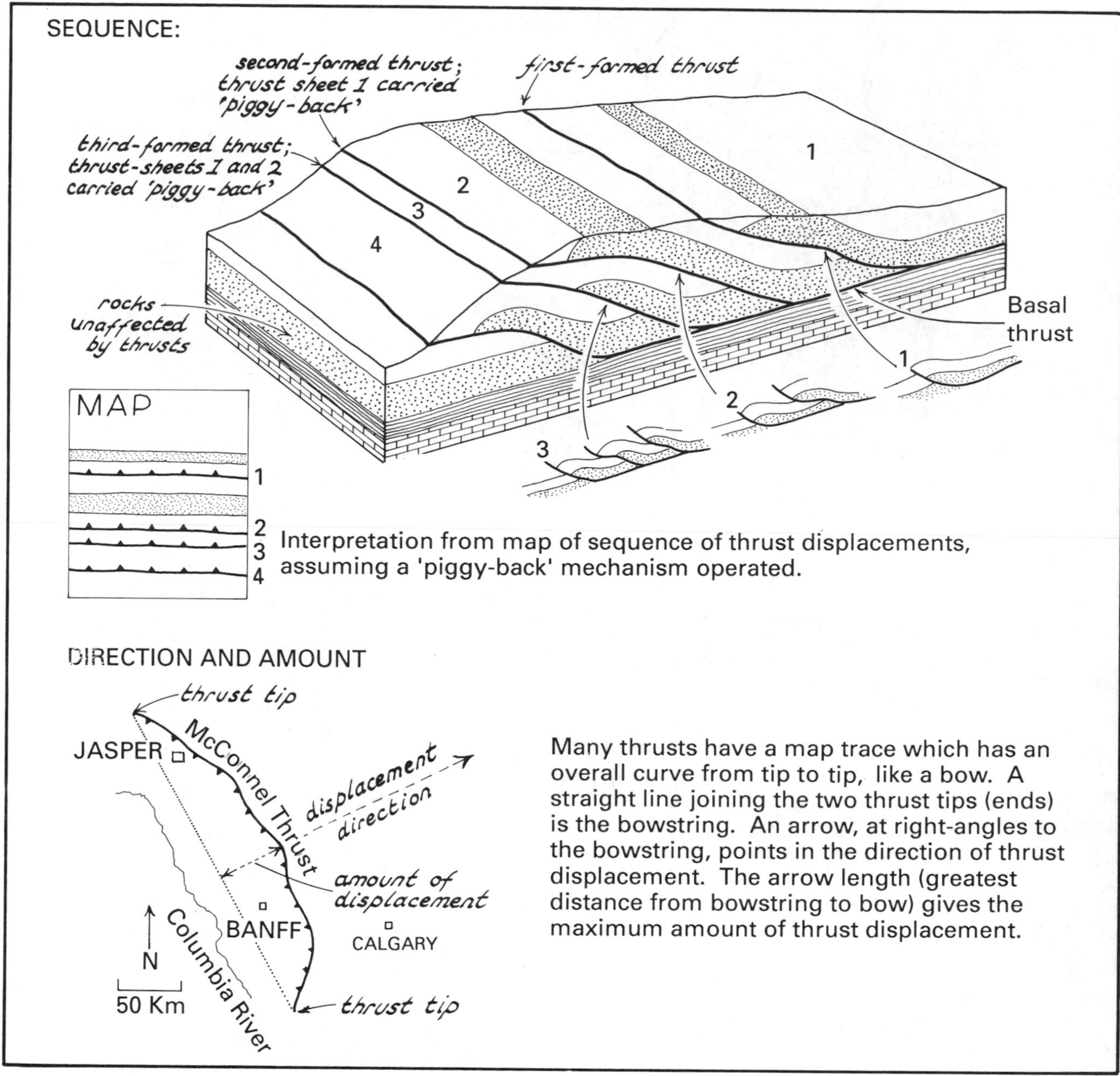
SEQUENCE:
second-formed thrust; thrust sheet 1 carried 'piggy-back'
first-formed thrust
third-formed thrust; thrust-sheets 1 and 2 carried 'piggy-back'
1
2
3
4
rocks unaffected by thrusts
Basal thrust
MAP
1
2
3
4
Interpretation from map of sequence of thrust displacements, assuming a 'piggy-back' mechanism operated.
DIRECTION AND AMOUNT
thrust tip
JASPER
McConnel Thrust
displacement direction
amount of displacement
BANFF
CALGARY
N
50 Km
Columbia River
thrust tip
Many thrusts have a map trace which has an overall curve from tip to tip, like a bow. A straight line joining the two thrust tips (ends) is the bowstring. An arrow, at right-angles to the bowstring, points in the direction of thrust displacement. The arrow length (greatest distance from bowstring to bow) gives the maximum amount of thrust displacement.

Fig. 10.4 Interpretation from maps of the sequence, direction, and amount of displacement on thrusts.

must continue sufficiently deep to have enabled the incorporation of this material. If the map shows the thrust trace to follow certain stratigraphic horizons and crosscut others, it may be reasonable to incorporate these patterns as flats and ramps, respectively, in the cross-section. The presence of a localised anticline next to the map trace of a thrust may be interpreted as a hangingwall anticline, and the fold and ramp included on the section.

Commonly, the drawing of thrust traces in any detail on a section requires additional information, for example, from wells or seismic traces. There are techniques of graphically restoring beds to their pre-thrust position (e.g. Woodward *et al.*, 1985) to provide a first check on the feasibility of the cross-section interpreted from the map. If it turns out to be impossible to restore the section, there must be something wrong with it.

10.2.4 Displacement amount, direction and sequence

Thrust sheets have commonly been displaced substantial distances along the fault at their base. It is usual to seek the amount and direction of this movement, referred to in the context of low-angle faults as the **transport**. *How* the friction between the rocks is reduced to allow this transport

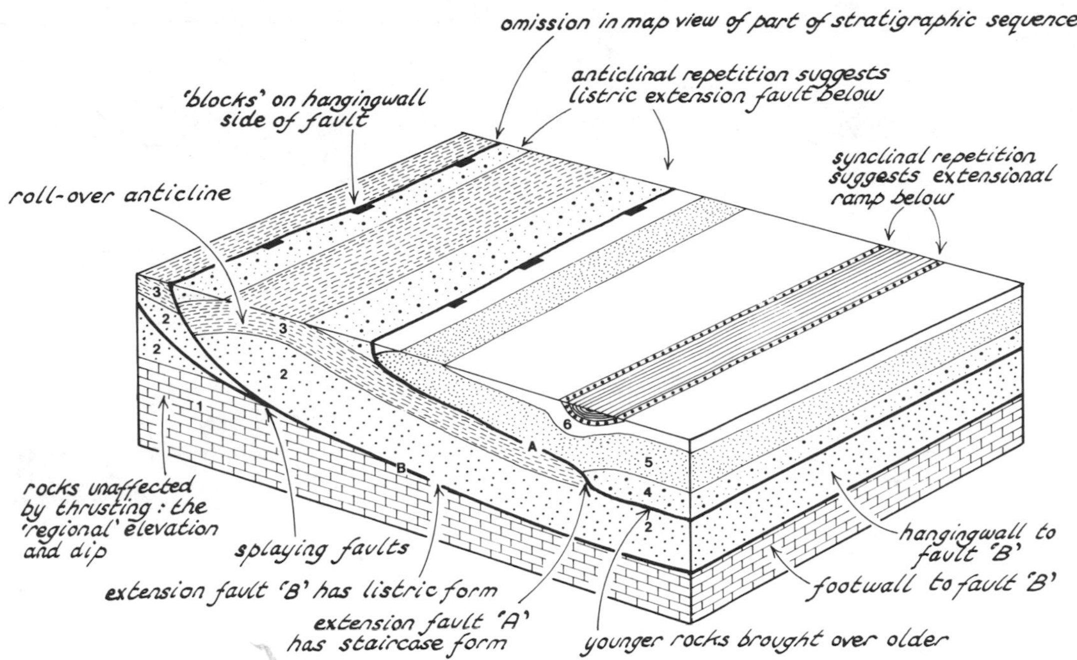
omission in map view of part of stratigraphic sequence
anticlinal repetition suggests listric extension fault below
'blocks' on hangingwall side of fault
synclinal repetition suggests extensional ramp below
roll-over anticline
rocks unaffected by thrusting: the 'regional' elevation and dip
splaying faults
extension fault 'B' has listric form
extension fault 'A' has staircase form
younger rocks brought over older
hangingwall to fault 'B'
footwall to fault 'B'

Fig. 10.5 Block diagram to show the main features of extension faults.

is one of the intriguing questions of structural geology, but is outside the scope of this book.

If the rocks on the hangingwall can be matched on a map with those in the footwall, then the strike separation and offset can be measured, just as for reverse faults (section 9.6). These values measured in the horizontal map plane will be much more meaningful for low-angle faults than for steep structures (cf. section 9.6), as the bulk of the movement has to be at a low angle.

The transport direction is often *assumed* to be at right angles to the trend of the thrust trace on the map. In this case, it may be possible to project marker units back to their pre-faulting position, and derive the amount of horizontal transport. It is a simplistic assumption, but thrust belts are complicated enough without worrying here about oblique slip. A rough but handy guide for interpreting thrust transport from regional maps – the 'bow-and-arrow rule' – is illustrated in Fig. 10.4. Cross-sections designed to show information about a thrust are usually drawn in the supposed transport direction. The sense of displacement (section 9.3) can be depicted on the section. From the definition of a thrust, the hangingwall will have moved up the fault. Put in another way, thrusts generally *cut upwards* through the stratigraphic sequence in the direction of transport.

If one thrust truncates another, it must have formed later (section 12.3). Many coalescing thrusts are thought to form in a 'downward' sequence (Fig. 10.4). In this theory, the topmost thrust forms first, then it and its thrust sheet are carried 'piggy-back' by younger thrusts below. In these ways it may be possible to deduce from maps and sections the sequence in which thrusts were generated.

10.3 Extension faults

10.3.1 General

Extension faults are the exact converse of contraction faults, and yet, paradoxically, the two have a great deal in common. The contrasts are that extension faults are dip-slip faults which dip at a low angle towards their *downthrow* side. They are therefore normal faults of shallow inclination. This form requires that higher rocks are brought down next to lower (younger over older) which is the exact opposite of thrusts. In cross-section the transport direction will be *down* dip. Their overall effect is to attenuate or pull out the stratigraphic sequence laterally, so that it becomes thinner but more areally extensive. Extension faults therefore tend to form basins rather than linear belts.

10.3.2 Characteristics

All the above points form contrasts with thrusts. In most other respects, extension faults have properties markedly similar to contraction faults. Compare the following points with those of section 10.2.1.

Typically, extension faults occur in groups, to form extensional basins. The faults may interlink and have minor splay faults (Fig. 10.5). The resulting basin is by no

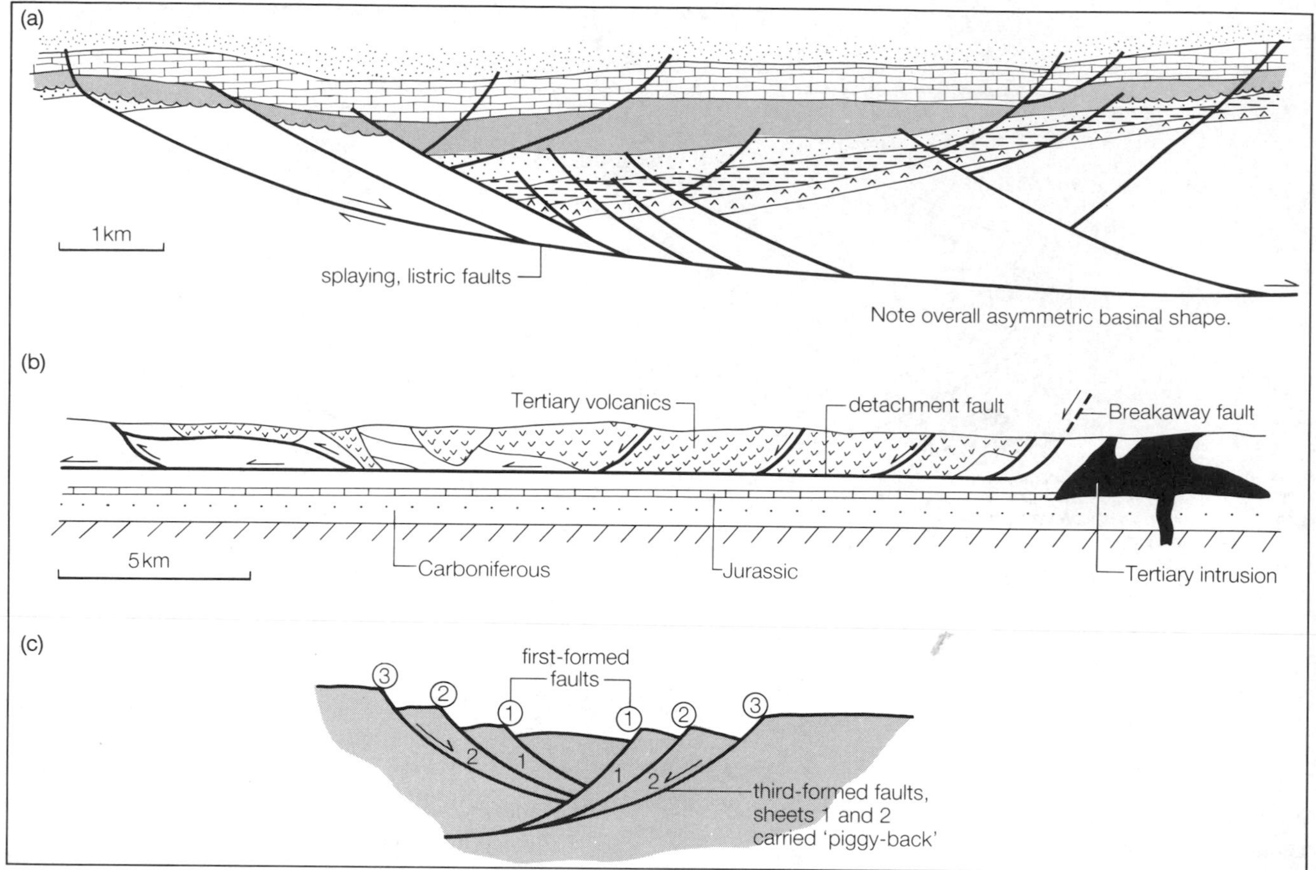
(a)
1km
splaying, listric faults
Note overall asymmetric basinal shape.
(b)
Tertiary volcanics
detachment fault
Breakaway fault
5km
Carboniferous
Jurassic
Tertiary intrusion
(c)
first-formed
faults
third-formed faults,
sheets 1 and 2
carried 'piggy-back'

Fig. 10.6 Some aspects of extension faults. (a) The appearance of an extensional basin in cross-section, Witch Ground, North Sea. Redrawn with modification from Beach (1984), by permission of the Geological Society, from 'Structural evolution of the Witch Ground Graben', A. Beach, (1984) *J. Geol. Soc. London*, **141**. (b) A detachment fault in cross-section. Based on USGS Map I-919, Bearpaw Mountain area, north-central Montana, by permission of the USGS. (c) Interpretation of the sequence of generation of extension faults, assuming a 'piggy-back' mechanism operated.

means necessarily symmetrical. The variable distribution of displacements can produce complex basin shapes. Arrays of high-angle extension faults can form imbricate zones. The faults root into a basal, low-angle **detachment fault** (Fig. 10.6). This is normally at depth, but may reach the surface at its tips. There are areas of the earth where such large, low-angle faults occur more or less singly. A famous and intriguing example forms the subject of Plate 6.

The shapes of extension faults are highly analogous to thrusts. They can have listric or staircase form, or some combination of both.

Like thrusts, production of these fault shapes causes the beds to fold. A characteristic feature is a **roll-over anticline** (Fig. 10.5).

10.3.3 Extension faults on maps

If faults have not been marked as such on a map, the recognition of a single detachment fault could be difficult. With most extension faults, however, some of the features mentioned above will be apparent. The biggest difficulty can be the distinction of extension from contraction faults, if this is not indicated on the map by symbolism. On larger scale maps the distinction might not be possible.

The basic property of extension faults of bringing younger rocks over older may be discernible. On smaller scale maps it may be possible to locate the **breakaway fault** (Fig. 10.6). Whereas contraction faults can *repeat* the stratigraphic sequence – thrusts can cause the same unit to appear on a map in several different places – extension faults tend to cause *omission* of parts of the stratigraphy. A feature which is virtually confined to extension faults is an increased thickness and a progressive displacement of the sedimentary succession on the downthrow side. The implication of this is that the fault was growing at the same time as the sediments were accumulating, a process called **growth faulting**.

Interpretation of the extension fault from its trace on the map is analogous to the procedure for thrusts (section 10.2.2). Because both kinds of faults are low-angle surfaces, they are recognised in the same way. It may be possible to draw structure contour and sub-crop maps. Cross-section preparation is similar. Transport amount and direction can be approached in a similar way, except that the direction will be down the fault dip.

The sequence of fault production is illustrated in Fig. 10.6. The innermost faults are thought to be generated first and younger faults produced successively outwards.

10.4 Strike-slip faults

Strike-slip faults are typically major structures, making conspicuous features on regional maps. They can, however, be small and occupy only a part of a large-scale map. In the latter case, they may represent local adjustments to different, larger structures. Such a local fault has a lot in common with the high-angle faults dealt with in chapter 9. The main difference is simply that the displacement was in the strike direction of the fault rather than the dip direction. Remember, though, that *apparent* horizontal displacement is produced by steep fault movements acting on dipping beds (section 9.5). What follows mainly refers to major strike-slip faults developed on the regional scale.

10.4.1 Characteristics

The fault traces of strike-slip faults are typically long, measured in tens or hundreds of kilometres. The amounts of displacement are commonly of similar magnitudes. The fault surfaces tend to be very steep to vertical. Strike-slip faults tend to have straight courses for long distances. They can curve: the famous 'big bend' of the San Andreas Fault north of Los Angeles is an instance. There may be sub-parallel splay faults. Some faults **splay** and anastomose on a large scale, making broad zones of complex faulting. In fact the geometrical details of these zones have much in common with contractional and extensional faults.

Strike-slip faults are typically long-lived structures. Once such a major fracture is initiated, it responds relatively easily in subsequent times of stress. Consequently, many ancient strike-slip faults are still active today. However, this **reactivation** of the fault does not necessarily occur with the same kind of displacement. Strike-slip faults typically have periods of dip-slip movement in their history.

Finally, it is useful to label a strike-slip fault with its dominant displacement sense (section 9.3), if this is known. Imagine standing on one side of the fault and looking across it: if the opposite side has moved to your left, it is a **left-lateral** or **sinistral fault**; if the opposite side has moved to the right, it is a **right-lateral** or **dextral fault**.

10.4.2 Recognition on maps

It is usually easy enough to recognise major strike-slip faults; it is the displacement history which can be very elusive. The faults tend to make straight traces on maps. This is not only because the faults tend to be straight anyway, but because their steepness, allows them to cut across topographic relief. Moreover, erosion often works preferentially on the weak rocks of the fault zone, producing conspicuous straight valleys. The Great Glen of Scotland, containing the deep, elongate Loch Ness, is formed along a major strike-slip fault, the Great Glen Fault. Such features are distinctive on air photographs and satellite images, and hence tend to be shown boldly on regional reconnaissance maps.

Curiously enough, the huge displacements which can accumulate along these faults are not necessarily a distinctive feature on a map. It may be obvious that the rocks either side of the fault bear little relation to each other, but in the absence of features which match up, the displacement will not be clear. Another complicating factor is that, with the common reactivation of these faults, features of different geological ages will show different amounts of displacement.

Strike-slip movement on smaller faults can be detected by the displacement of vertical features (Figs 9.3 and 10.7a), and by variably oriented features being offset by the same amounts (Fig. 10.7c). Ideally, it is the *oldest* rocks in the map area that we aim to correlate across the fault in order to detect the maximum displacement. However, the old rocks may now be covered by younger deposits. In fact, it is commonly the *younger* features that give the initial clues to the fault displacements, even if they are just the more recent movements. A good example of this is the San Andreas Fault which, although now thought to have accomplished something like 1 000 km displacement, was first detected by the offset of orange groves and present-day streams. The Hope strand of the Alpine Fault of New Zealand is thought to have displaced the bedrock by about 20 km, post-Quaternary river terraces by 160 km (Fig. 10.7b) and, in living memory, farm fences by 3 m (Freund, 1971).

In the absence of suitable features either side of the fault, assessment of the displacement will be difficult. The displacement may be so large that even if such features do exist, they do not fall on a single map. Some clue, at least to the sense of displacement, may be provided by consistent offsets across any minor splays of the major fault. Otherwise, it becomes a matter of attempting to correlate regional features: granite plutons, metamorphic zones, special sedimentary environments, etc. Strike-slip faults

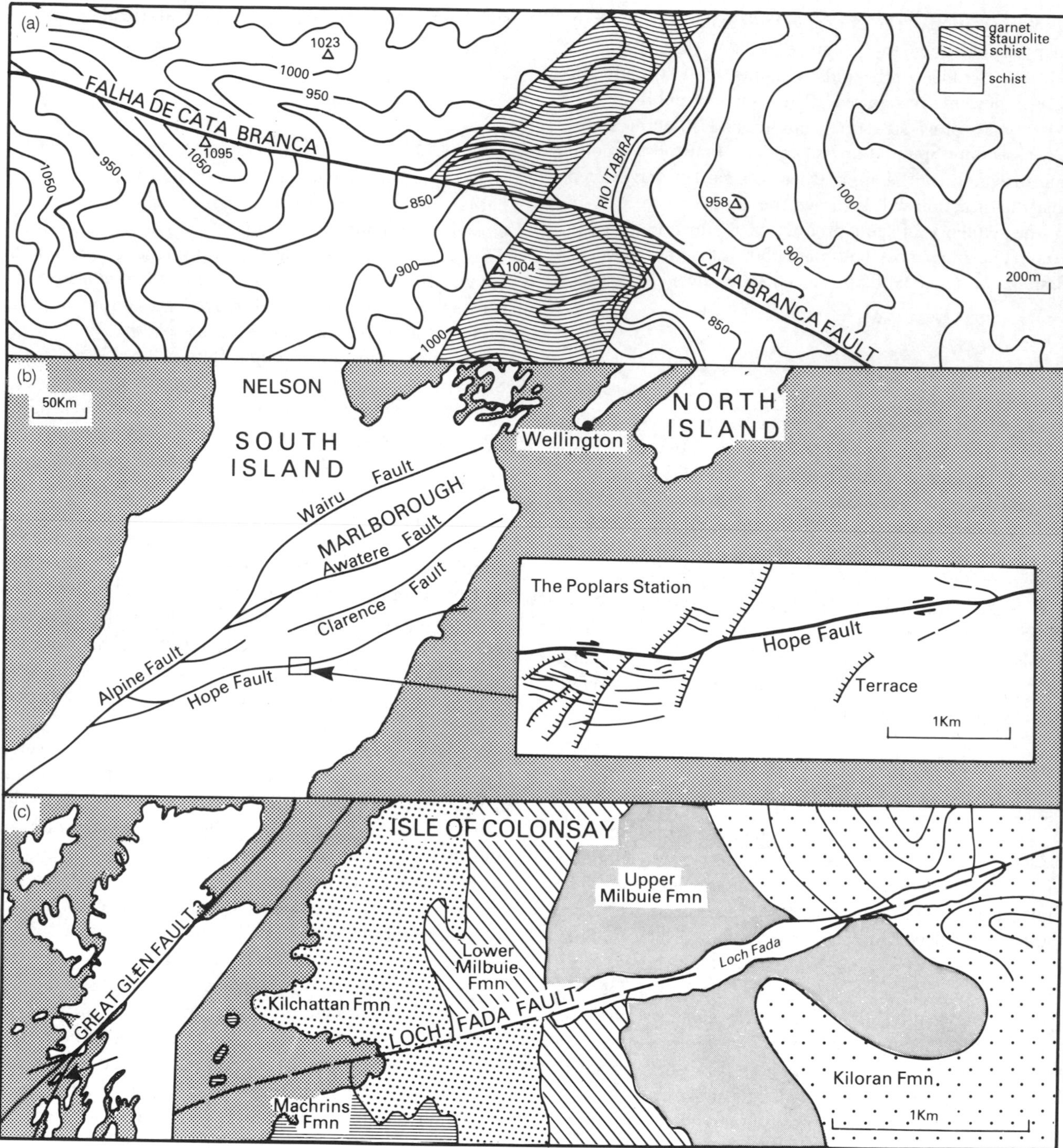
(a)
1023
1000
950
FALHA DE CATA BRANCA
1095
1050
950
1050
850
900
1004
1000
RIO ITABIRA
958
1000
900
850
CATA BRANCA FAULT
garnet staurolite schist
schist
200m
(b)
50Km
NELSON
SOUTH ISLAND
NORTH ISLAND
Wellington
Wairu Fault
MARLBOROUGH
Awatere Fault
Clarence Fault
Alpine Fault
Hope Fault
The Poplars Station
Hope Fault
Terrace
1Km
(c)
GREAT GLEN FAULT
ISLE OF COLONSAY
Upper Milbuie Fmn
Lower Milbuie Fmn
Kilchattan Fmn
Loch Fada
LOCH FADA FAULT
Machrins Fmn
Kiloran Fmn
1Km

Fig. 10.7 The recognition of strike-slip faults on maps. (a) The Cata Branca Fault, W Brazil. The straight outcrops, in an area of rugged topography, indicate that the schists are oriented vertically. The fault displacement must therefore be strike-slip. Redrawn from Wallace (1965), by permission of the USGS. (b) The Alpine Fault system, New Zealand. The inset shows how displaced river terraces have been used to infer 160 m of post-Quaternary movement on the Hope splay. Redrawn from Freund (1971), by permission of the New Zealand Geological Survey. (c) The Loch Fada, Colonsay, splay of the Great Glen Fault, Scotland. Variably oriented formations are displaced by similar amounts, indicating a strike-slip fault.

may be dramatic features, but deducing their displacement histories is a challenge to the geologist.

10.5 Summary of chapter

1. Contraction faults, comprising reverse faults and thrusts, decrease the horizontal extent of a rock sequence.
2. Thrusts are low-angle dip-slip faults, along which the hangingwall has been upthrown, bringing older rocks over younger.
3. It is usually possible to make estimates from maps of the three-dimensional arrangement of thrusts, their sequence of development, and the amount and direction of displacement.
4. Extension faults increase the horizontal extent of a rock sequence. They contrast with thrusts in being low-angle *normal* faults – the hangingwall moved down the dip of the fault – and in bringing younger rocks over older.
5. Other characteristics of extension faults have much in common with thrusts.
6. Major strike-slip faults are typically steep, straight features, commonly long-lived and with large displacements.
7. They are conspicuous on maps, but the displacements can be elusive.

10.6 Selected further reading

Suppe, J. (1985). *Principles of Structural Geology*, Englewood, New Jersey, Prentice-Hall.
(Pp. 277–89 summarise the morphology of strike-slip, thrust and detachment faults.)

Ramsey, J. G. and Huber, M. I. (1987). *The Techniques of Modern Structural Geology, Volume 2: Folds and Fractures*, London, Academic Press.
(Session 23 is a thorough, modern account of the geometry of faults, much of which is highly relevant to more advanced map work. Session 24 explains the construction of restored sections.)

MAP 18 Glen Creek, Montana, USA

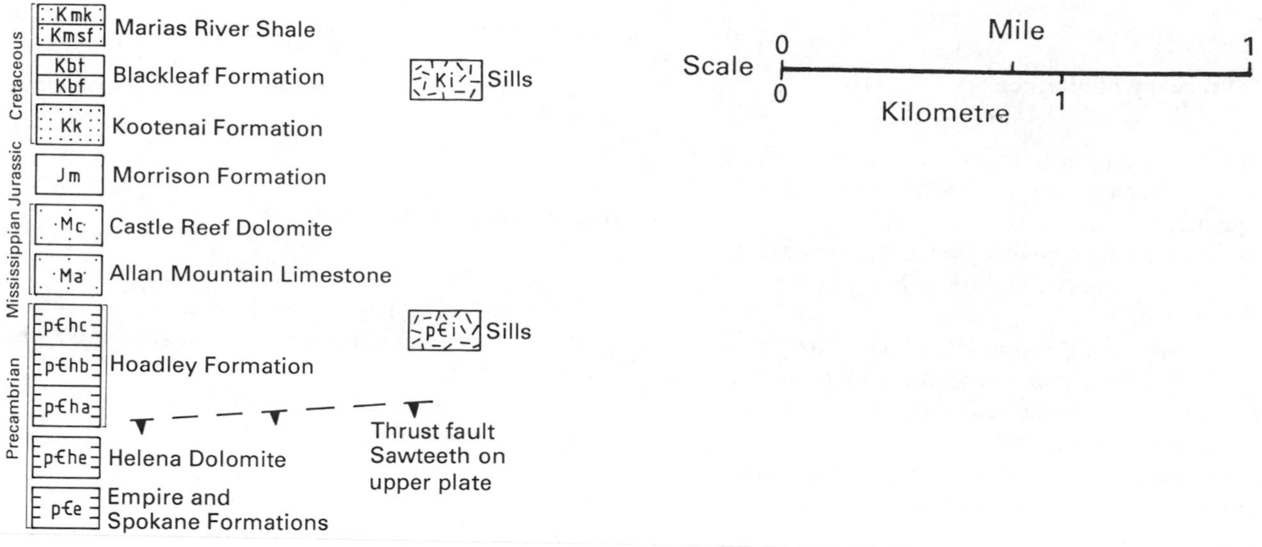

Cretaceous
Kmk
Kmsf
Marias River Shale
Kbt
Kbf
Blackleaf Formation
Kk
Kootenai Formation
Jurassic
Jm
Morrison Formation
Mississippian
Mc
Castle Reef Dolomite
Ma
Allan Mountain Limestone
Precambrian
p€hc
p€hb
Hoadley Formation
p€ha
p€he
Helena Dolomite
p€e
Empire and
Spokane Formations
Ki
Sills
p€i
Sills
Thrust fault
Sawteeth on
upper plate
Scale
Mile
0
1
0
1
Kilometre

The facing map is redrawn from the USGS map GQ-499 of Glen Creek, Montana, by permission of the USGS. It is of an area about 100 km WNW of Great Falls, in the easternmost ranges of the Rocky Mountains. The area therefore falls within the fold-and-thrust belt which dominates the eastern flanks of the Western Cordillera in much of N America, and it is a northwards extension of the area of thrusting introduced briefly in section 2.3.4 and portrayed on Plate 2.

Colouring some of the stratigraphic divisions on the map, particularly units Kbf and Kt, will help make their outcrop patterns more distinctive. What might the dashed line running through the central part of unit Kbf represent?

Looking at the relationship between outcrop and topography, and any map symbols, visualise the overall three-dimensional structure of the area. Draw two cross-sections at right angles to the dominant strike direction, one to represent the north of the area and one the southern part. In projecting the thrusts to depth bear in mind that they are not necessarily planes. Incorporate, for example, the symmetrical repetition of unit Kbt, possibly indicating a steepening of the thrust subsurface, and any coalescing of thrusts off the section line which may reflect changes in thrust dips. Number the thrusts on the cross-sections according to the sequence in which they are likely to have formed. How does the southern part of the area differ from the northern district?

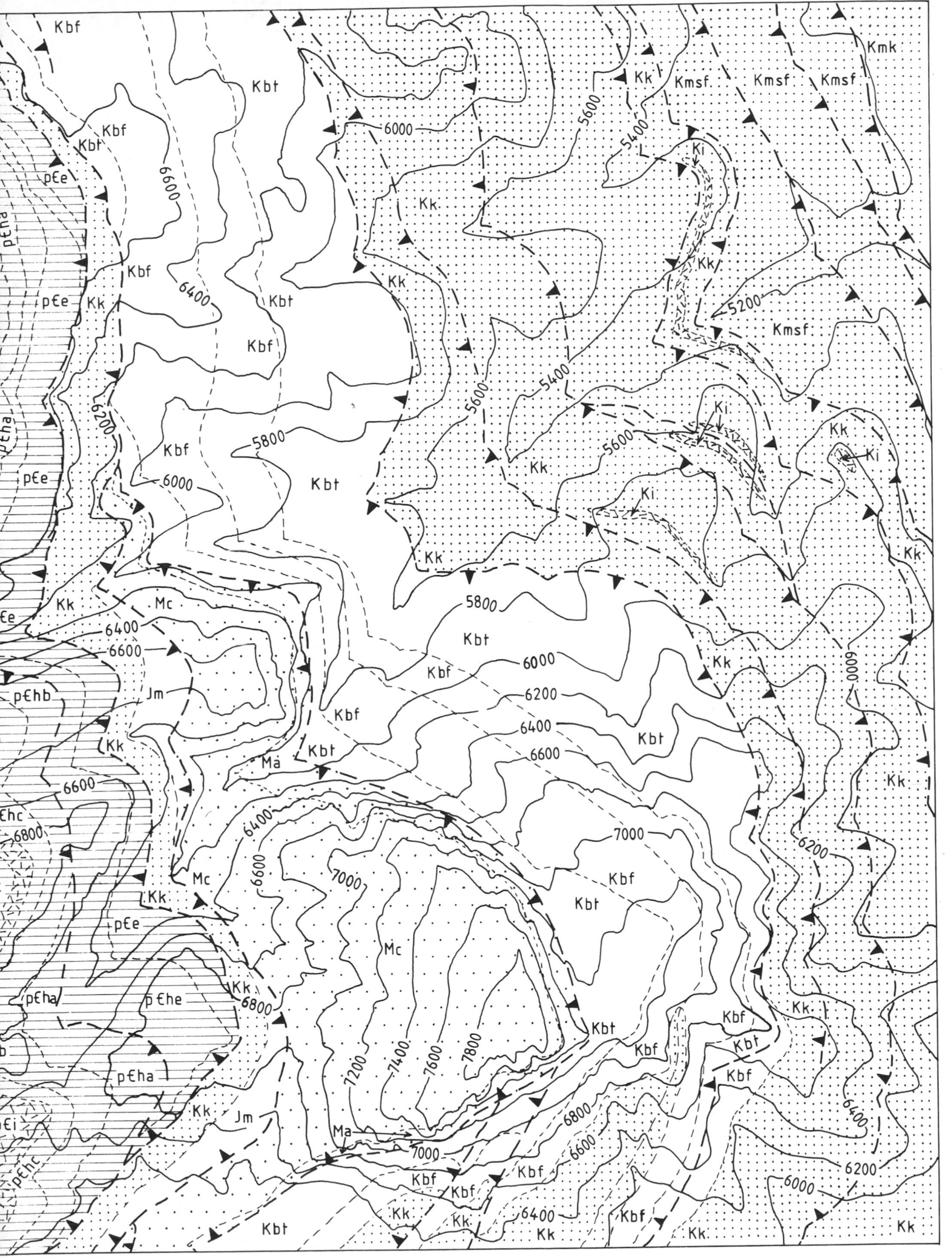

Kbf
Kbt
Kbf
Kbt
pЄe
pЄha
6600
Kk
Kmsf
Kmsf
Kmsf
Kmk
5600
5400
6000
Ki
Kk
Kbf
6400
Kbt
Kk
Kk
5200
Kmsf
Kbf
5400
5600
6200
pЄha
5800
Kbf
6000
Ki
5600
Kk
Kk
Ki
pЄe
Kbt
Ki
Kk
Kk
Mc
6400
5800
6600
Kbt
Kbf
6000
Kk
pЄhb
Jm
6200
6000
Kbf
Kk
Ma
Kbt
6400
Kbt
6600
Kk
6600
Єhc
6800
6400
6600
7000
Mc
7000
Kbf
Kk
Kbt
6200
pЄe
Mc
pЄha
pЄhe
Kk
6800
Kk
Kbt
Kbf
Kbf
Kbt
7200
7400
7600
7800
Kbf
pЄha
Kk
Jm
6400
Єi
Ma
7000
6800
6600
6200
pЄhc
Kbf
Kbf
Kbf
6000
Kbt
Kk
Kk
6400
Kk
Kbf
Kk
Kk

MAP 19 Hamblin Bay fault, Nevada, USA

The facing map is redrawn and simplified from a map by Anderson (1973), by permission of the USGS. It covers an area about 60 km east of Las Vegas, and is on the north shores of Lake Mead, created by the construction of the Hoover Dam, just southwest of the map area. Although the area falls into a region of the western USA dominated by large-scale extension faulting (the 'Basin and Range' structural province), some parts of the region show important strike-slip faults. In the present area, an andesitic volcano and associated dykes, known as the Hamblin–Cleopatra volcano, have been dismembered by faults, particularly the major Hamblin Bay Fault.

Discuss the evidence for the Hamblin Bay Fault having dominantly strike-slip displacement. Identify the sense of movement. Estimate the amount of strike-slip displacement.

Which other faults must also have a substantial component of strike-slip displacement?

Discuss the likelihood of the faults at Saddle Mountain being strike-slip faults.

What is the overall age of faulting in the area?

Is there any relationship between the orientation of bedding and proximity to a fault? What might this imply for the actual slip direction on some of the faults?

Further examples of faults on maps

Two faults appear on Map 7, of the 'north crop' of the South Wales coalfield. Comment on the displacement each must have produced to account for the present outcrop pattern.

Describe the fault which occurs in the northeast of Map 14 and affects the folded Millstone Grit.

The numerous faults in the southwest part of plate 2, of the western US, *tend* (there are exceptions) to curve with their concave side towards their dip direction. Judging by the relative ages of the rocks juxtaposed by the faults, distinguish the areas dominated by extension faulting from those with much contraction faulting.

Note that faults appear on all the coloured maps reproduced here, and that some of the questions accompanying Plates 5 and 6, of Sanquar, Scotland, and Heart Mountain, Wyoming, USA, concern the interpretation of faults.

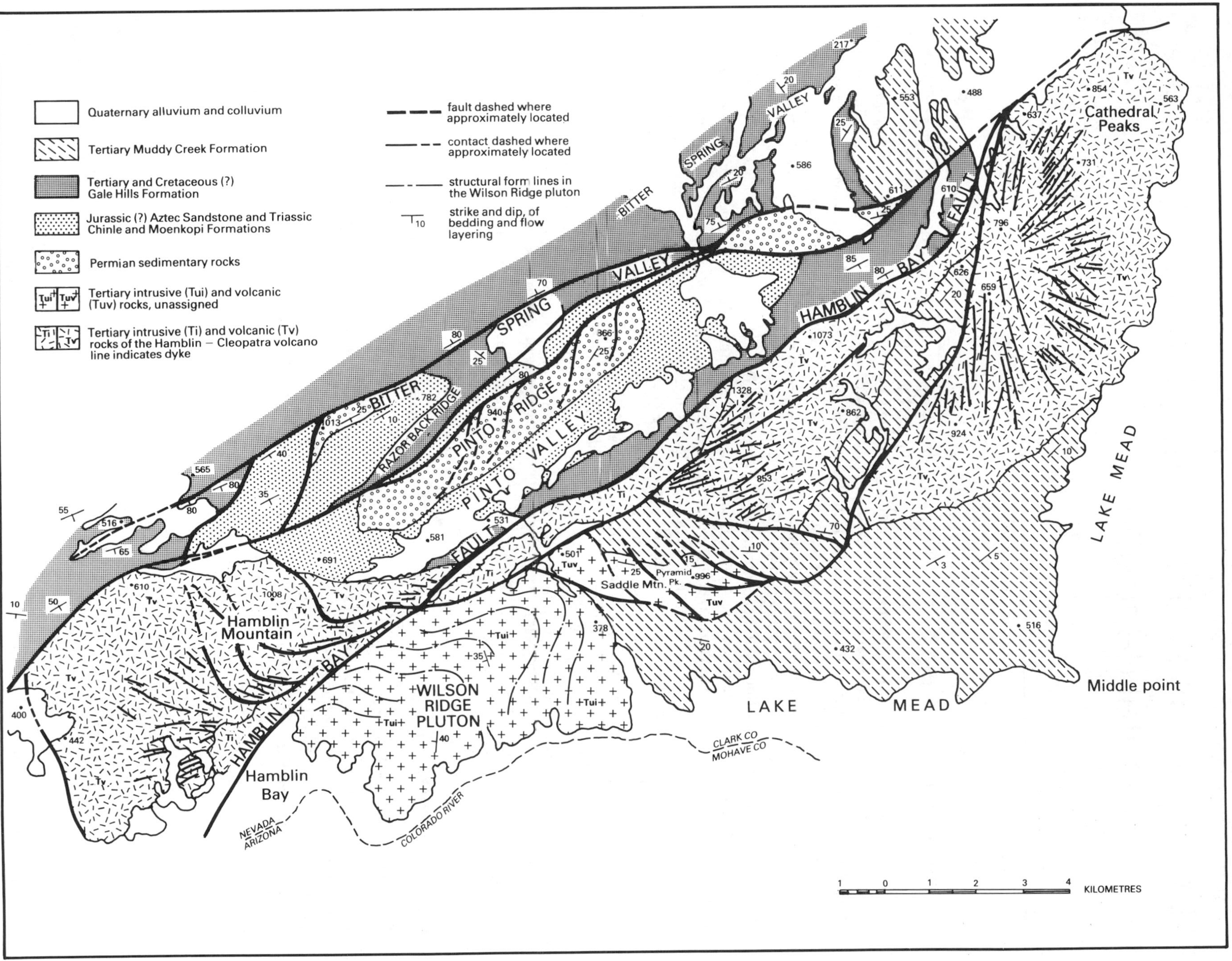

Quaternary alluvium and colluvium
Tertiary Muddy Creek Formation
Tertiary and Cretaceous (?) Gale Hills Formation
Jurassic (?) Aztec Sandstone and Triassic Chinle and Moenkopi Formations
Permian sedimentary rocks
Tertiary intrusive (Tui) and volcanic (Tuv) rocks, unassigned
Tertiary intrusive (Ti) and volcanic (Tv) rocks of the Hamblin – Cleopatra volcano line indicates dyke
fault dashed where approximately located
contact dashed where approximately located
structural form lines in the Wilson Ridge pluton
strike and dip of bedding and flow layering
Cathedral Peaks
LAKE MEAD
Middle point
LAKE MEAD
HAMBLIN BAY FAULT
BITTER SPRING VALLEY
RAZOR BACK RIDGE
PINTO RIDGE
PINTO VALLEY
Hamblin Mountain
Saddle Mtn.
Pyramid Pk.
WILSON RIDGE PLUTON
Hamblin Bay
CLARK CO
MOHAVE CO
NEVADA
ARIZONA
COLORADO RIVER
KILOMETRES

11 Igneous and metamorphic rocks; mineral deposits

11.1 Introduction

Most of the preceding sections have concentrated on sedimentary materials, which are stratified and readily organised into a sequence of map units. Each unit tends to have an overall tabular shape, being bounded at its top and bottom by roughly parallel surfaces, which enables three-dimensional interpretations from maps and sections. We have, however, to be more cautious with non-sedimentary materials, for their shape can be much less regular. It is with these that this chapter is concerned.

In the brief survey of these non-sedimentary materials which follows, the same themes constantly recur. How regular is the bulk form of the material depicted on the map? How likely is it to be tabular? These three-dimensional aspects can be awkward, but on the other hand non-sedimentary materials do lend themselves to another kind of interpretation – the chronological sequence in which they formed. This idea, introduced during this chapter, is expanded in chapter 12.

11.2 Igneous rocks

11.2.1 Volcaniclastic rocks

The tendency for volcaniclastic material to adopt a tabular shape is variable. At one extreme, volcanic ash which travels large distances before slowly settling will produce a continuous thin bed-like form, whereas debris which jostles around in the throat of a volcano will form an irregular mass quite unlike a bed. In between these two extremes are many kinds of volcaniclastic rock with varying bulk forms.

In general, fine-grained air-fall deposits adopt a bed-like form, mantling the land surface on which they settle. If the topography is smooth, the top and bottom surfaces of the layer will be virtually parallel, and the normal three-dimensional extrapolations can be applied. If the material settles on a dissected land surface, there may be rapid thickness changes, though these may not be discernible except on large-scale maps. If there are repeated volcanic explosions, a sequence of volcaniclastic layers will be built up. If there is little time for renewed erosion between the volcanic events, the dissected relief will become subdued as the successive deposits preferentially fill in the topographic lows. Figure 11.1a shows river erosion revealing a sequence of volcaniclastic deposits.

Coarse-grained air-fall material tends to travel less far, and there is usually more of it. The deposits may have a roughly tabular shape, but they will not be extensive, and if they lie on the volcano's flanks, they may have primary dips of up to 40°. Some volcaniclastic material is very localised. Patches of agglomerate on a map may be indicating choked volcanic necks; fan-shaped masses may be avalanche deposits. All these deposits can be dramatically changed by renewed volcanism or the swift erosion that can accompany eruptions. The outcrop patterns of these near-source volcaniclastic materials can be complex.

Despite all these difficulties, the field surveyor will usually have been able to divide the volcaniclastic materials into map units and to establish their sequence of production. Hence, most geological maps treat any volcaniclastic materials in the same way as sedimentary rocks, and they may appear on the key in their appropriate stratigraphic position. They may be given a special ornament or colour, and perhaps a letter symbol to indicate their particular lithology, but in other ways they will be treated as a sedimentary unit of the same age.

11.2.2 Magmatic rocks

The representation of lava on maps, and its interpretation, has much in common with volcaniclastic deposits. If the lava is highly fluid, it can flow large distances, filling valleys and eventually blanketing the land surface. Thus, it forms a mass of overall tabular form. The first lava may form an unconformity with the bedrock over which it flows (cf. section 2.3.2) and then a sequence of lava flows can be built up. Erosion of a series of lava flows can produce a characteristic stepped or 'trap' topography, which may be apparent on larger scale maps.

Viscous lavas are analogous to near-source volcaniclastic material. Though they will have travelled little, it may be

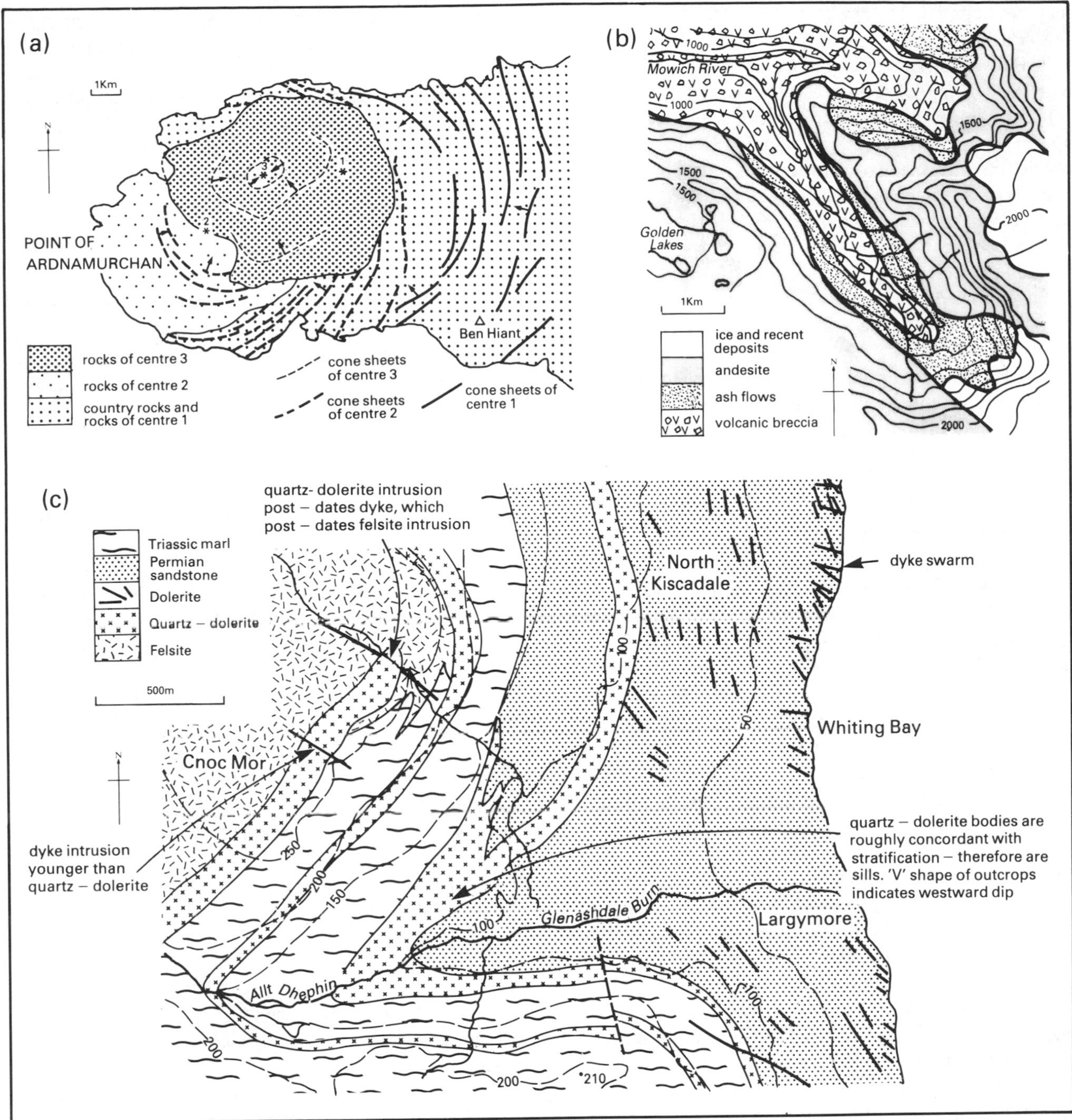
(a)
1Km
N
POINT OF
ARDNAMURCHAN
Ben Hiant
rocks of centre 3
rocks of centre 2
country rocks and rocks of centre 1
cone sheets of centre 3
cone sheets of centre 2
cone sheets of centre 1
(b)
Mowich River
1000
1500
2000
Golden Lakes
1Km
ice and recent deposits
andesite
ash flows
volcanic breccia
N
(c)
quartz- dolerite intrusion post – dates dyke, which post – dates felsite intrusion
Triassic marl
Permian sandstone
Dolerite
Quartz – dolerite
Felsite
500m
N
North Kiscadale
dyke swarm
Whiting Bay
Cnoc Mor
dyke intrusion younger than quartz – dolerite
quartz – dolerite bodies are roughly concordant with stratification – therefore are sills. 'V' shape of outcrops indicates westward dip
Glenashdale Burn
Largymore
Allt Dhephin
100
150
200
250
210

Fig. 11.1 Examples of the appearance on maps of volcaniclastic rocks and minor igneous intrusions. (a) Cone-sheets (arrows show dip directions), around three different volcanic centres. Ardnamurchan, W Scotland. Based on Richey (1961). (b) Rapid stream downcutting through a volcaniclastic sequence. Note that the valley gradients on the volcano slopes exceed the rock dips and hence contravene the normal 'V-rule' (section 6.3.2). Redrawn from USGS Map I-432, Mount Rainier National Park, Washington, by permission of the USGS. (c) Minor igneous intrusions, Isle of Arran, SW Scotland. Simplified from the BGS One-Inch Arran Special sheet. (a) and (c) reproduced by permission of the Director, BGS: Crown/NERC copyright reserved.

possible from their shape on a map to deduce the direction of flow. Note that they can have abrupt terminations which can resemble faults on maps. Individual lava flows of the same type are not normally distinguished, but collected together to form a single map unit. This, like the volcaniclastics, may be given a particular ornament; it may or may not appear in the key at its appropriate stratigraphic position.

Erosion of volcanic areas may expose bodies of magmatic material which failed to reach the land surface before solidification. If the masses are irregular in form, they will appear on maps as patches, distinguishable from volcaniclastic rocks, such as agglomerates, only by consulting the map key to establish their igneous nature. In three-dimensions the boundaries are likely to be steep, reflecting the ascent of the magma from depth, but detailed interpretation will be precarious.

The masses can be of more regular form and indeed are commonly quite tabular, in which case they are conveniently referred to as igneous **sheets**. **Sills**, being concordant with the layers of sedimentary or other material which envelop them, appear on maps just like a regular sedimentary rock unit, and are subject to all the same geometrical principles (Fig. 11.1c, section 2.3.5). Note that sills need not *everywhere* be concordant to the adjacent beds. Small stretches where the top and bottom of the sill cross cut the adjacent layering can be a helpful distinction from a lava flow.

Dykes are commonly conspicuous on maps. Being discordant sheets, they cut across the adjacent outcrop pattern, and typically being steep to vertical features, they produce on maps a characteristic narrow strip-like pattern (section 2.3.5). Patterns of dyke orientation and distribution frequency show up particularly well on maps. They may occur profusely, in **swarms** (Fig. 11.1c); the dykes may be radial to the magmatic source (section 2.3.5); or they may circle it. They may dip towards the volcanic centre – **cone sheets** (Fig. 11.1b) – or they may be vertical – **ring dykes**. If topographic contours are shown on the map it should be possible to interpret which of these types is present from their interaction with the dyke traces. A famous example of a beautifully executed geological map which shows all these features is discussed in section 14.3.6.

Igneous **plutons** are typically very conspicuous on maps. They form large, commonly irregular to roundish patches which bear no obvious relation to the surrounding rocks. Small-scale maps can usefully show the regional distribution of the igneous bodies and their relative shapes and sizes (Fig. 11.2a). Large-scale maps may show details within the pluton, for example, lithological variations, xenolith distributions, and joint patterns (Fig. 11.2b). These may prompt interpretations from the map on the origin and emplacement of the igneous mass.

Interpretations of the three-dimensional shape of a pluton will be precarious, but it may be possible to make some speculations. If the boundary trace is reasonably regular, it suggests some regularity in three dimensions, and tentative structure contours could be drawn (Fig. 11.2c). The most typical configuration will be a steeply dipping, gently curved surface. Any deviations from this may be apparent from the map trace. A wriggling boundary trace would suggest a three-dimensional irregularity that would make interpretation futile. It is best, if there is doubt, to treat the pluton boundaries as vertical. Intrusive bodies intermediate in size between pluton and dykes and sills can have all kinds of shapes, with various combinations of steep and flat boundaries.

11.3 Metamorphic rocks

The extent of any thermal metamorphism associated with an igneous body can be effectively shown on a map (Fig. 11.2c), but it is not always done. It should not be assumed, especially on small-scale maps, that because no metamorphic rocks are shown adjacent to an igneous body, there was no thermal effect. On the other hand, some large-scale geological maps show the different kinds of thermally produced metamorphic rocks, normally appearing as a series of zones, roughly concentric around the heat source. The rock type of each zone will be specified in the key in the usual way.

An alternative approach is to show on the map not the actual kinds of metamorphic rocks, but the areas where there has been thermal change. There may, for example, be a shaded zone to represent the extent of thermal metamorphism around an igneous body, or different ornaments may be used to depict greater or lesser degrees of change. A common device is for the map to show a line which is labelled in the key as something like 'outer limit of thermal metamorphism' away from the heat source. However the thermal metamorphism is depicted, most of the interpretive steps that can be made require further knowledge of metamorphic processes.

The representation of regional metamorphism on general geological maps presents more difficult problems. Some maps, particularly small-scale and older maps, group together diverse metamorphic rocks into one map unit, in which case little can be done in the way of interpretation. Other maps show the distribution of the different rock types.

To what extent their three-dimensional arrangement can be interpreted depends mainly on two factors. First, it depends on how well the original form of the rock masses is preserved. If they are still recognisably a succession of tabular bodies, albeit now metasedimentary in nature, then the same geometric principles as for non-metamorphosed sedimentary rocks apply. Thicknesses can be measured, outcrop patterns assessed, cross-sections drawn, etc. That the map units are of quartzite and schist rather than sandstone and shale makes no difference to the principles of mapwork. Similarly, if the original bulk form of meta-igneous rocks is still discernible, then the remarks of section 11.2 apply. Second, there is the complicating factor of deformation. Regional metamorphism is typically ac-

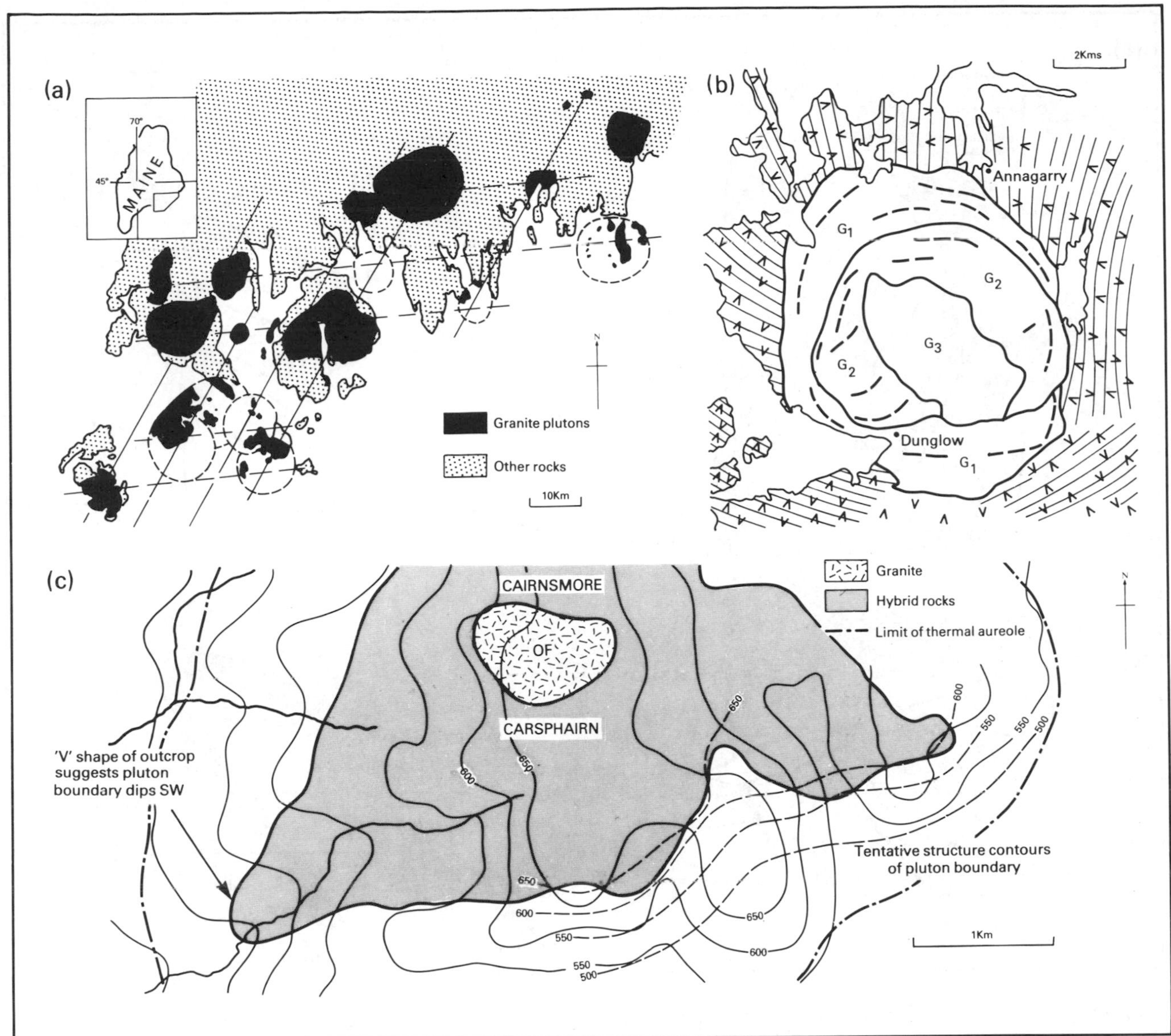
(a)
70°
45°
MAINE
MAINE
Granite plutons
Other rocks
10Km
(b)
2Kms
Annagarry
G1
G2
G3
G2
Dunglow
G1
(c)
CAIRNSMORE
OF
CARSPHAIRN
Granite
Hybrid rocks
Limit of thermal aureole
'V' shape of outcrop suggests pluton boundary dips SW
Tentative structure contours of pluton boundary
1Km
650
600
550
500

Fig. 11.2 Some aspects of plutonic igneous rocks on maps. (a) Map showing areal distribution of plutons, Maine, USA. In this example, the straight dashed lines were used to suggest a reticulate distribution pattern. Based on Chapman (1968). (b) Some pluton details. The pluton is comprised of three granites, G_1–G_3, with xenolith alignments shown by dashed lines. The Rosses complex, Donegal, Eire. Based on Pitcher and Berger (1972). (a) and (b) used by permission of John Wiley and Sons. (c) The three-dimensional arrangement of a pluton boundary, Cairnsmore, S Scotland. Note also the representation of the extent of the thermal aureole. Redrawn from Deer (1935), by permission of the Geological Society, from 'The Cairnsmore of Carsphairn Igneous Complex', W. A. Deer (1935), *Quart. J. Geol. Soc. London*, **191**.

companied by ductile deformation (section 8.1), producing structures such as folds. The deformation can be intense, and it can happen repeatedly. Exceedingly complex outcrop patterns can result. Such structures on maps can be disentangled but by methods which are beyond the scope of this book.

11.4 Mineral deposits

Many kinds of mineral deposits are dealt with on maps by the methods already discussed. For example: gypsum beds, limestone for cement, and coal seams are effectively sedimentary rocks; slate and marble are metamorphic rocks;

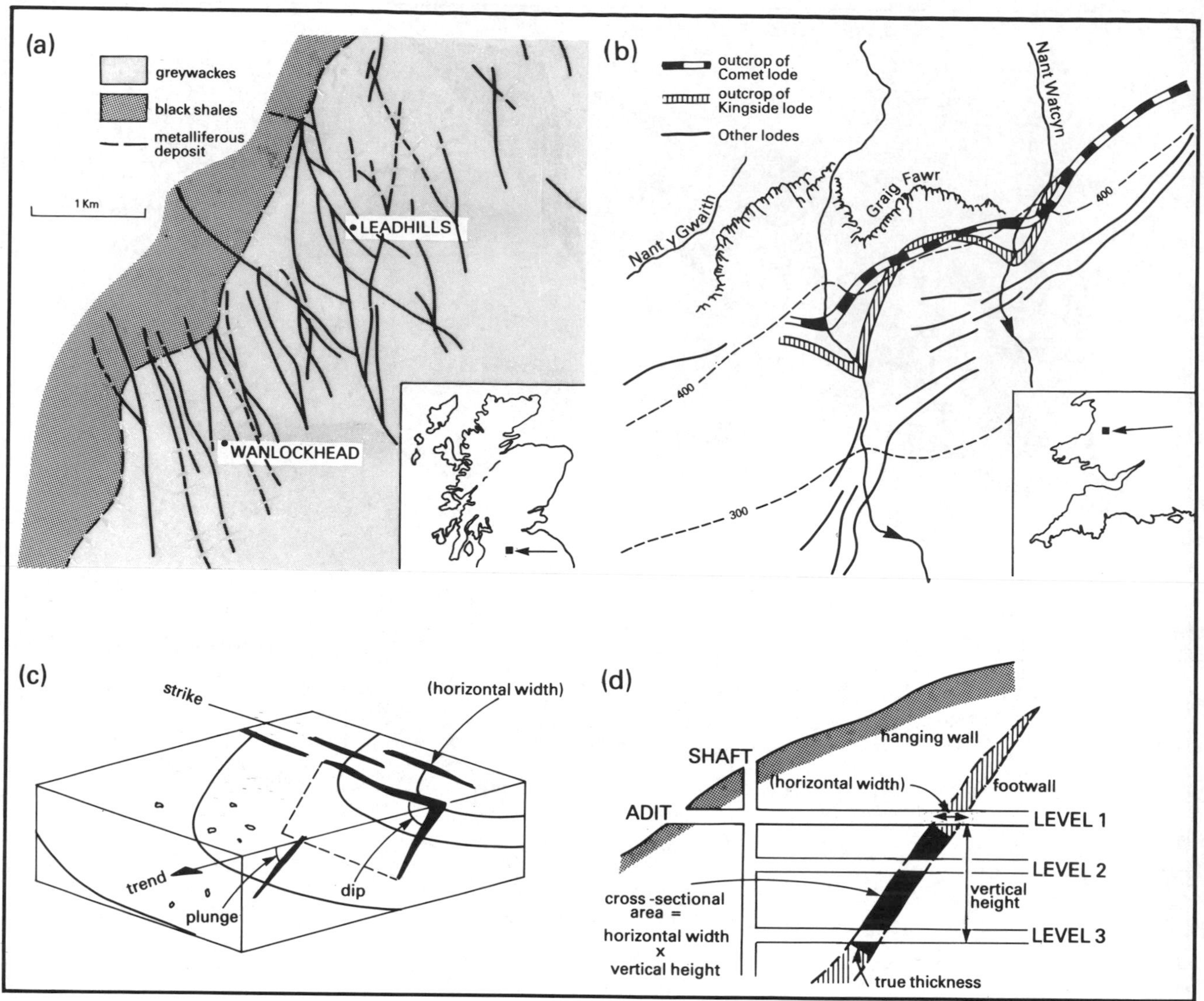

(a)
greywackes
black shales
metalliferous deposit
1 Km
LEADHILLS
WANLOCKHEAD
(b)
outcrop of Comet lode
outcrop of Kingside lode
Other lodes
Nant Watcyn
Graig Fawr
Nant y Gwaith
400
400
300
(c)
strike
(horizontal width)
trend
plunge
dip
(d)
hanging wall
SHAFT
(horizontal width)
footwall
ADIT
LEVEL 1
LEVEL 2
vertical height
cross-sectional area = horizontal width x vertical height
LEVEL 3
true thickness

Fig. 11.3 Some aspects of ore deposits on maps. (a) Narrow metalliferous deposits oblique to map units, therefore likely to be veins. Straight outcrops suggest steep dips. Note the localisation near a lithological junction, and a NNW–SSE pattern of orientation. Redrawn from Dunham *et al.* (1978), by permission of the Institute of Mining and Metallurgy. (b) Veins of differing orientations (lode is an old term for vein). Kingside lode makes tighter 'V'-shaped outcrop across valley than Comet lode, suggesting a shallower dip. Based on Jones (1922). (c) Similarity between orientation terminology for veins and other geological planes and lines. (d) Some mining terms commonly used on maps, and a simple method for assessing the cross-sectional area of a dipping vein.

and many construction and road stones are igneous rocks. Metalliferous deposits, however, occur in a wide variety of forms, and it becomes particularly important in mapwork to establish any three-dimensional regularity of the body.

Most disseminated or replacement ores are of highly irregular shape and their manipulation on maps requires advanced techniques (e.g. see Badgley, 1959, chapter 6). However, it may be useful to establish whether or not the ores have a particular areal or stratigraphic distribution, which maps and sections should make clear. Few kinds of ore deposits will be very regular, but there may be an approximation to a shape that can be dealt with. A map should readily show if the masses are concordant with the host rocks, as in the **stratiform deposits** that are the source of much copper, lead, zinc, and iron. On the other hand, any discordance of the ore bodies can also provide useful information. Discordant tabular bodies, often called **veins**, usually have a more or less systematic distribution and orientation (Figs 11.3a,b) and are commonly associated with faults. Some ores are concentrated where dif-

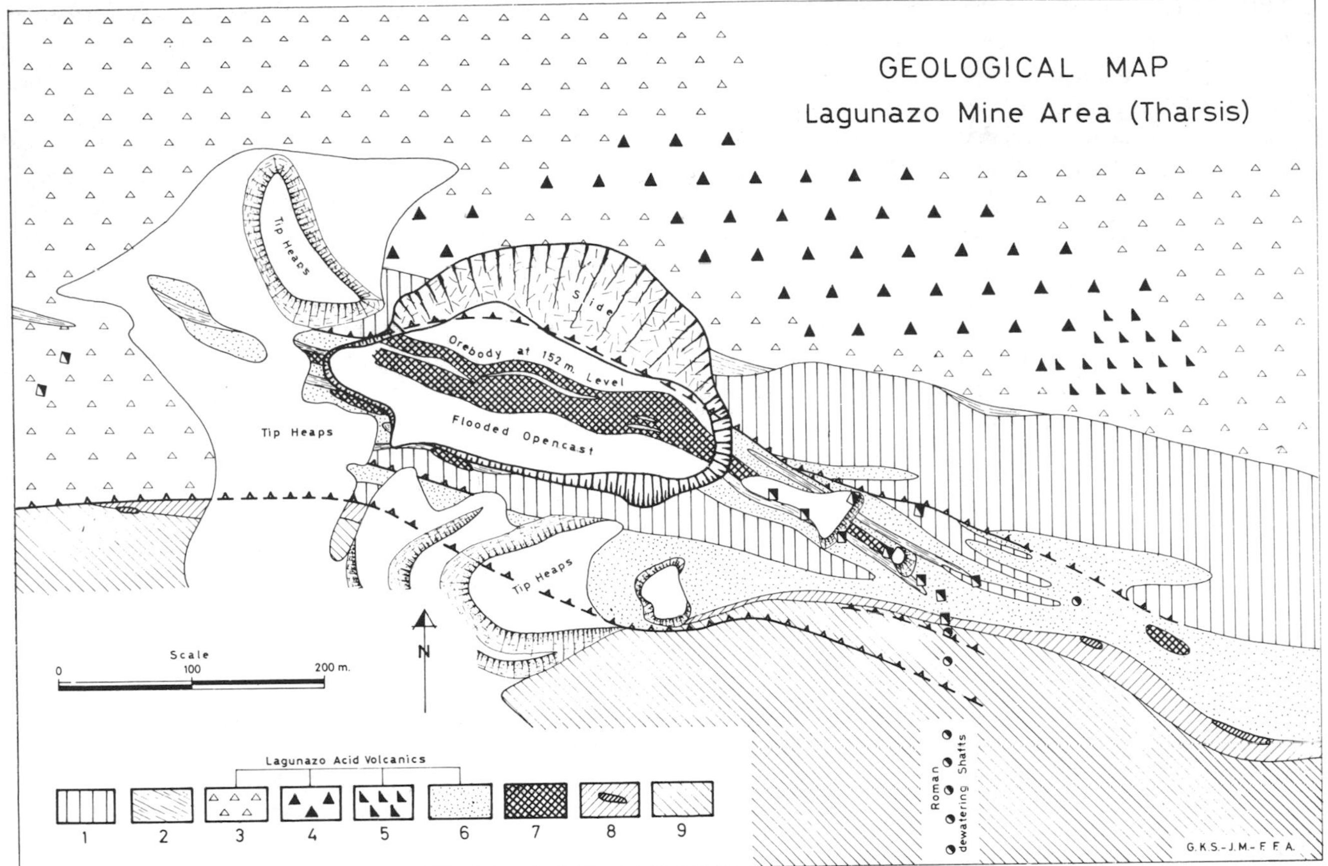
GEOLOGICAL MAP
Lagunazo Mine Area (Tharsis)
Tip Heaps
Side
Orebody at 152 m. Level
Flooded Opencast
Tip Heaps
Tip Heaps
Scale
0
100
200 m.
N
Lagunazo Acid Volcanics
1
2
3
4
5
6
7
8
9
Roman dewatering Shafts
G.K.S.-J.M.-F.F.A.

Fig. 11.4 Example of a map of a mining area, Lagunazo, Tharsis, Greece. Note the amount of man-made and other superficial deposits obscuring the bedrock geology, and the orebody being shown as it appears subsurface. Reproduced from Strauss *et al.* (1977), by permission of Springer-Verlag.

ferent fault sets meet. The commonness of the association with faults is illustrated by inclined veins having a hangingwall and a footwall (cf. section 9.2 on faults). A basic terminology for map-work with veins is given in Figs 11.3c,d. If the discordant mineral deposit is reasonably regular in form, it should be possible to make underground projections on its location, orientation, and shape, and perhaps even to make some rough volumetric estimates on ore reserves.

The kinds of maps with sufficient accuracy for useful commercial predictions are outside the scope of this book, but it is worthwhile mentioning several general points regarding maps of mineral deposits. Some orebody maps are extremely large-scale. In general, metrication is still the exception rather than the rule, and somewhat strange units such as furlongs and fathoms may be used. The topographic datum is unlikely to be sea-level, but instead some prominent local feature, perhaps a mine entrance. Man-made features connected with mining operations, such as dumps and ponds, may obliterate much of the surface geology and dominate the map. This is usually not a difficulty in practice, because subsurface information may well be supplementing the surface data. In fact, many maps of mining areas omit the overall surface geology altogether and show the actual orebodies as they appear underground, at one or more specified depths (e.g. Fig. 11.4).

Be careful when working with thicknesses of orebodies on maps. The true thickness of an inclined vein is measured at right angles to its walls (Fig. 11.3d), analogous to a map unit (section 4.4.), and so a correction will have to be made to the outcrop width. However, mining geologists sometimes refer to the horizontal width of a vein as its thickness, as it is this value that is encountered during mining. Figure 11.3d also shows a simple graphical method of utilising the horizontal thickness of an inclined body to obtain its cross-sectional area. With knowledge of the extent of the body in the other horizontal direction, which will be measurable from the map, it becomes a simple matter to calculate the volume of the deposit. This would, of course, be a very rough value in terms of actual ore reserve, and other factors, particularly the percentage of useable material, would have to be taken into account to obtain a more meaningful figure.

Underground mineral deposits are usually worked by sinking a vertical or steeply inclined **shaft** which connects a series of tunnels. These are driven horizontally at a particular altitude, and are known as **levels** (Fig. 11.3d). Large-scale maps of areas with mineral deposits commonly show the locations of shafts and **adits**, where levels intersect with the land surface. Mine maps commonly show the geology of the orebody at each mine level. The tunnel walls may provide information in the vertical plane to help control the drawing of cross-sections. The mining geologist will normally work with a whole series of cross-sections and maps for each of the underground levels, and so should have a closely controlled picture of the mineral deposit in three dimensions. Mine maps therefore differ somewhat from normal geological maps, but all the same geometric principles are employed in their use.

Attempts to find new orebodies will be helped by any knowledge of how the known deposits formed. Hence, in addition to working with the orebodies in three dimensions, it becomes necessary to project back in geological time. When during the geological evolution of the area were the ores formed? What were the circumstances at the time of their deposition? We come now to another great use of geological maps – the interpretation from them of geological history.

11.5 Summary of chapter

1. Volcaniclastic rocks are commonly presented on maps in the same way as sedimentary units, though the extent of possible three-dimensional interpretation is much more variable.
2. The distributions of magmatic bodies show well on maps.
3. Tabular masses of magmatic rocks, such as lava flows, sills, and dykes, can be treated using the same three-dimensional principles as for sedimentary rocks, but the methods are of limited application to irregular bodies.
4. Maps are useful for showing the areal extent of thermal metamorphism, but representation of regional metamorphism requires special treatment.
5. Metalliferous mineral deposits can be stratiform, and treated like sedimentary units, or irregular in form.
6. Some three-dimensional interpretation of mineral veins may be possible, and their relationships with faults discerned.
7. Large-scale mineral deposit maps may employ special techniques of representation.

11.6 Selected further reading

Compton, R. R. (1985). *Geology in the Field*, New York, Wiley.
(Has chapters on volcanic, plutonic and metamorphic rocks, parts of which are relevant to mapwork.)

Roberts, J. L. (1982). *Introduction to Geological Maps and Structures*, Oxford, Pergamon.
(Chapter 6 includes a discussion on the portrayal of igneous rocks on maps.)

MAP 20 Corndon Hill, Shropshire, England

The facing map shows part of the intrusion of basic igneous rocks which form Corndon Hill, about 8 km east of the town of Montgomery. The map is redrawn, by permission of the Geological Society, from Blyth (1943). The intrusion appearing here is one of a number of small igneous masses which appear on Plate 1. The Corndon body is at [SO3196].

Judging from Plate 1, are basic intrusions the only manifestation of igneous activity in this area? What is the overall arrangement of the rocks of the area? What indications are there on Map 20 that the Corndon intrusion may have modified the structure of the country rocks?

Construct structure contours for the upper surface of the igneous body. Comment on what appears to be the form of the igneous mass.

Construct a cross-section across the body in the south of the area, where the lower surface is also exposed. Approximately how thick is the igneous mass here? Assuming this thickness applies in the north of the map area, comment on the form the body must have, in order to account for its outcrop shape.

Say what you can about the three minor faults that effect the igneous margin in the southeast of the map area, e.g. whether they are strike-slip or dip-slip faults, and their senses and amounts of displacement.

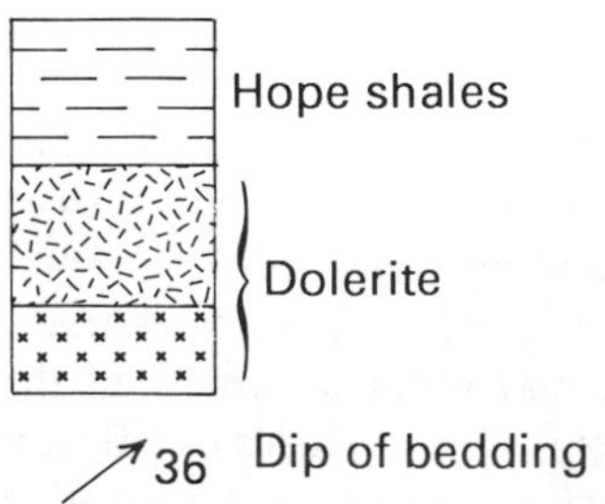
Hope shales
Dolerite
36 Dip of bedding

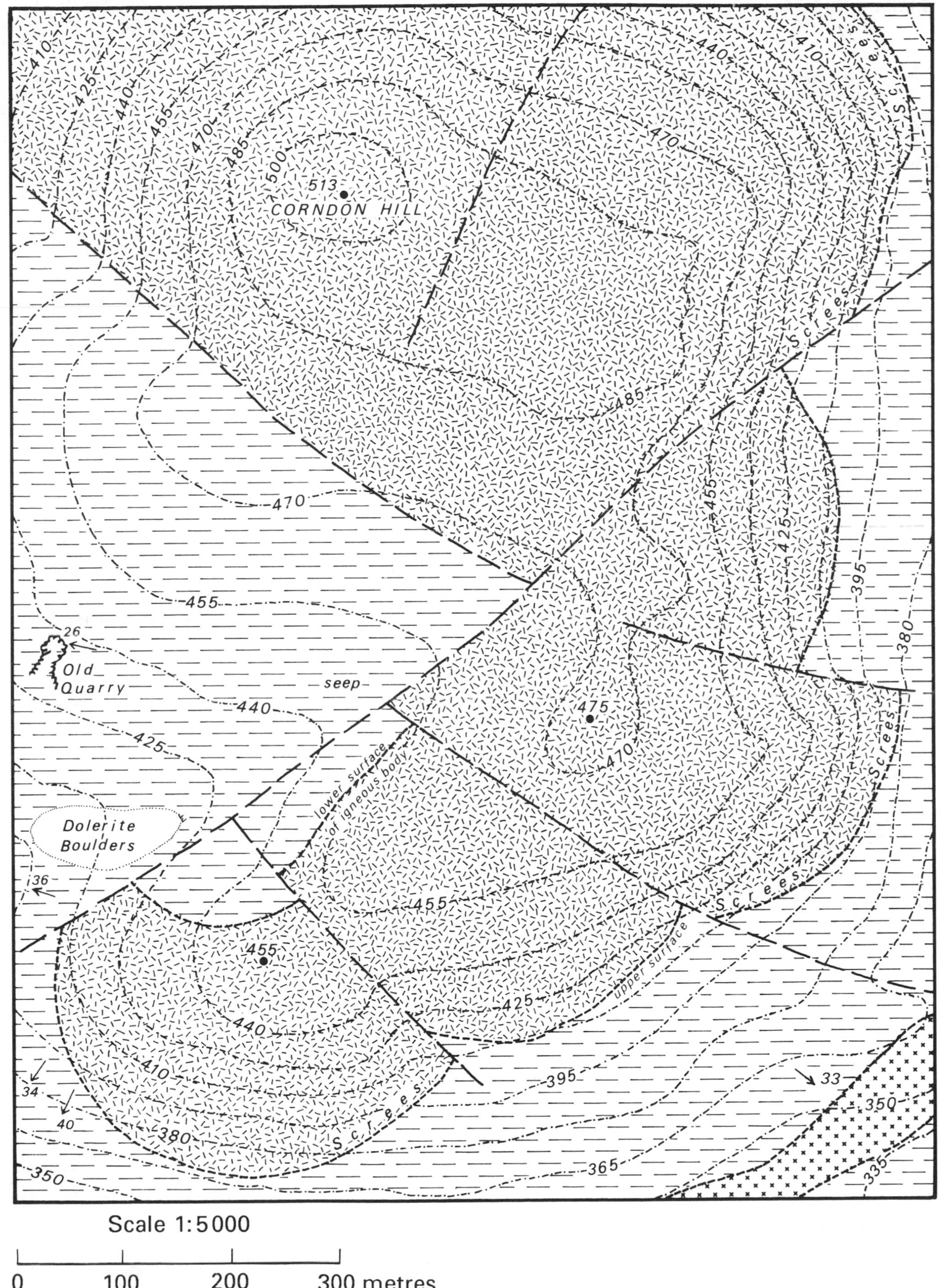

513
CORNDON HILL
Old Quarry
seep
Dolerite Boulders
475
455
lower surface of igneous body
upper surface
Screes
Scale 1:5000
0
100
200
300 metres

MAP 21 Southern Alps, New Zealand

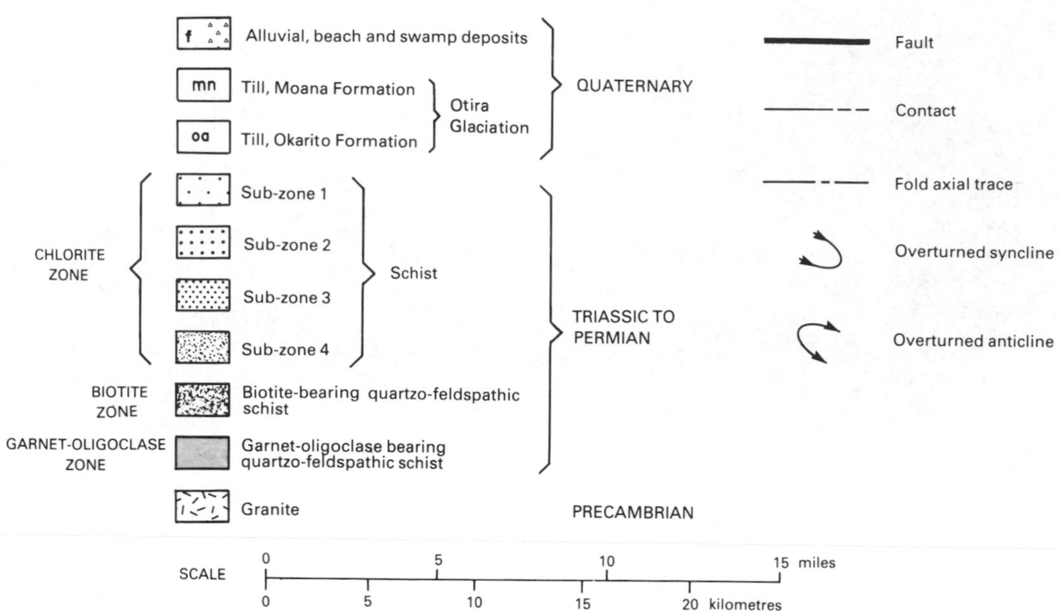

Alluvial, beach and swamp deposits
Till, Moana Formation
Till, Okarito Formation
Otira Glaciation
QUATERNARY
CHLORITE ZONE
Sub-zone 1
Sub-zone 2
Sub-zone 3
Sub-zone 4
Schist
BIOTITE ZONE
Biotite-bearing quartzo-feldspathic schist
GARNET-OLIGOCLASE ZONE
Garnet-oligoclase bearing quartzo-feldspathic schist
TRIASSIC TO PERMIAN
Granite
PRECAMBRIAN
Fault
Contact
Fold axial trace
Overturned syncline
Overturned anticline
SCALE
0 5 10 15 miles
0 5 10 15 20 kilometres

The facing map is redrawn and simplified from a part of the 1:250 000 Sheet 20, Mt Cook, of the Geological Map of New Zealand, by permission of the Geological Survey of New Zealand. Most of the rock units are based on differing grades of metamorphism, as reflected in the mineralogy. The metamorphic grade increases from chlorite subzone 1 through to the garnet–oligoclase zone. It can be assumed here that higher grades reflect deeper levels of burial, hence the metamorphic zones represent a kind of stratigraphic sequence.

In view of the major contrast in geology either side of the Alpine Fault, and the overall shape of its trace, what kind of fault is it likely to be?

What is the regional orientation of the units southeast of the Alpine Fault? What structure is shown by chlorite subzones 1 and 2 around the Dobson River?

Which is likely to be the downthrow side of (a) the fault running NNE–SSW between the Clarke and Wills Rivers, and (b) the fault running SSW from Mt Sinclair [362527]? Assuming that the chlorite subzones are of approximately constant thickness, why might the outcrop of subzone 2 around [352513] be wider than around [361513]?

Why might the outcrop width of subzone 1 increase southwards?

Which occurred later, the folding or the faulting?

Is there any relationship between the structure of the area and its drainage?

Sketch a cross-section to illustrate the overall structure of the region.

Further examples of non-sedimentary materials on maps

Describe the form of the following: the banded rhyolite mass on Map 6, of the Boyd Volcanics, Australia; the base of the quartz porphyry that appears on Map 15, of Aspen, Colorado, USA; and the various igneous bodies that are present on Map 19, of the Hamblin Bay Fault, Nevada, USA.

Note that igneous and metamorphic rocks and a metalliferous vein appear on Plate 5, Sanquar, Scotland. Plate 7, of Marraba, Australia, and the questions given there, are very largely concerned with igneous and metamorphic rocks.

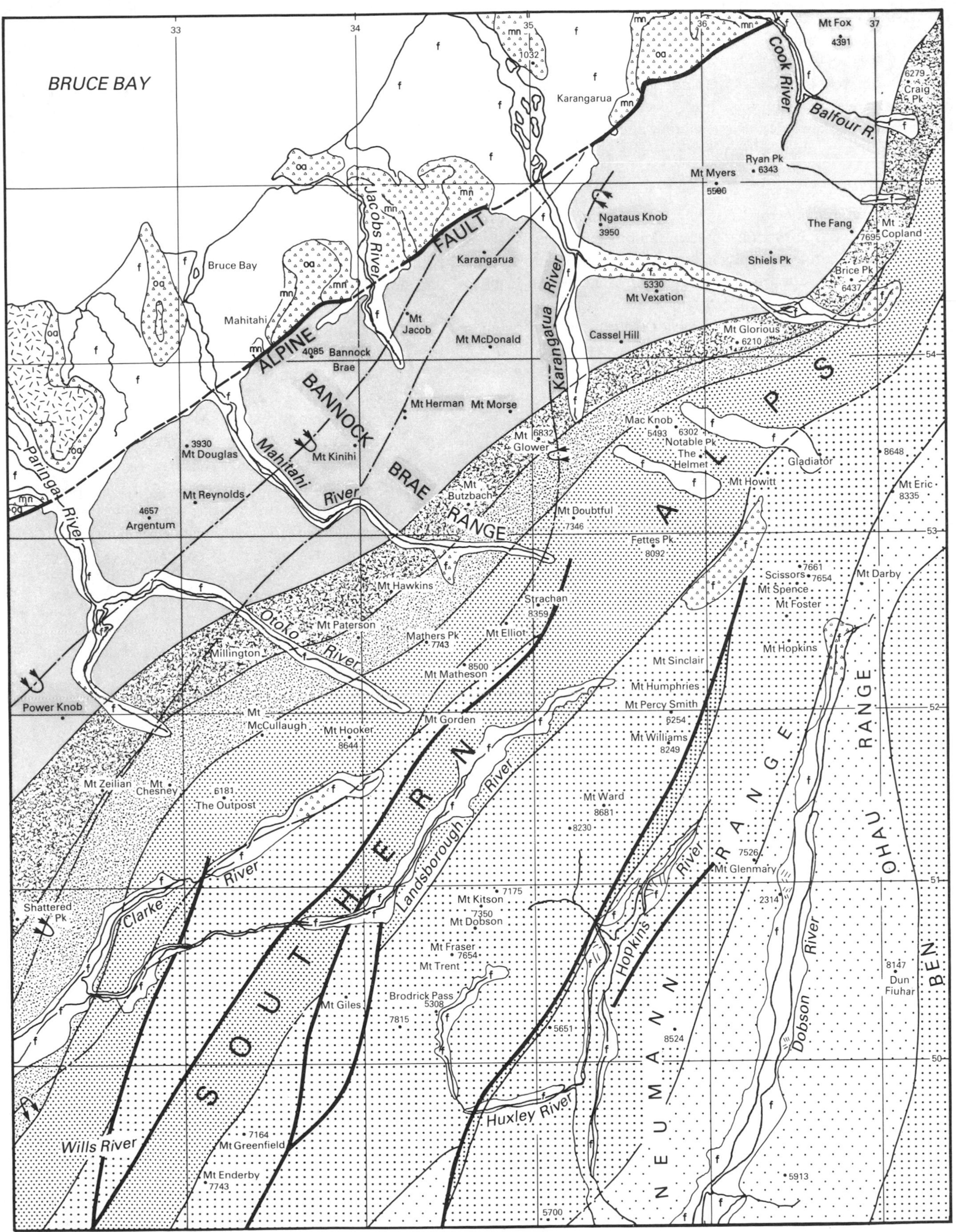
BRUCE BAY
ALPINE FAULT
BANNOCK BRAE RANGE
SOUTHERN ALPS
NEUMANN RANGE
BEN OHAU RANGE
Bruce Bay
Mahitahi
Karangarua
Mt Fox
4391
6279 Craig Pk
Cook River
Balfour R.
Ryan Pk 6343
Mt Myers
Ngataus Knob 3950
The Fang
Mt Copland 7695
Shiels Pk
Brice Pk 6437
5330 Mt Vexation
Cassel Hill
Mt Glorious 6210
Mt Jacob
Mt McDonald
4085 Bannock Brae
Mt Herman
Mt Morse
Jacobs River
Karangarua River
Mahitahi River
Paringa River
Otoko River
3930 Mt Douglas
Mt Kinihi
Mt Reynolds
4657 Argentum
Mt Glower 6832
Mac Knob 5493
6302 Notable Pk
The Helmet
Gladiator
8648
Mt Howitt
Mt Eric 8335
Mt Butzbach
Mt Doubtful 7346
Fettes Pk 8092
Scissors 7661 7654
Mt Spence
Mt Foster
Mt Darby
Mt Hawkins
Strachan 8359
Mt Paterson
Mathers Pk 7743
Mt Elliot
Millington
8500 Mt Matheson
Mt Sinclair
Mt Hopkins
Mt Humphries
Mt Percy Smith
Power Knob
Mt McCullaugh
Mt Hooker 8644
Mt Gorden
6254 Mt Williams 8249
Mt Zeilian
Mt Chesney
6181 The Outpost
Mt Ward 8681
8230
7526 Mt Glenmary
2314
Landsborough River
Clarke River
Shattered Pk
7175 Mt Kitson
7350 Mt Dobson
Mt Fraser 7654
Mt Trent
Hopkins River
Dobson River
8147 Dun Fiuhar
Brodrick Pass 5308
Mt Giles
7815
5651
8524
Huxley River
Wills River
7164 Mt Greenfield
Mt Enderby 7743
5913
5700
1032
33
34
35
36
37
55
54
53
52
51
50

MAP 22 Honister Slate Mine, Cumbria, England

The map opposite is of the underground workings which until very recently were used to extract the Ordovician Honister Slate for roofing material. The map, adapted and redrawn, is used by permission of Sir Alfred MacAlpine plc.

Four different levels are shown, connected by a NW–SE incline. The elevations of the floors of the levels are indicated in metres above a local datum. The levels have worked along the base of the Honister Slate, which has a reasonably consistent orientation and a remarkably constant thickness of 10 m. Construct structure contours for the top of the Honister Slate.

What is the overall strike and dip of the unit?

Construct an accurate cross-section to show the true dip of the unit and the location of the different levels.

Consider the following, largely hypothetical, mining programme. It is proposed to open a new level southeast of level 3, to be called level 2. There has to be at least 10 m horizontal distance from other levels to avoid the risk of roof collapse. Indicate on the section and map your proposed location and route for level 2.

What is the disadvantage of continuing level 4 in the SSW direction being followed when it was terminated? What might be a better direction in which to continue this level?

Level 5 was stopped when it met fault rocks and the slate unit was absent. If the level had been continued past the zone of fault rock, would it have met rocks above or below the Honister Slate? Indicate on the map the direction in which the level should be driven in order for it to retrieve the slate unit.

Indicate on the map, on the basis of the locations of the fault rock and any displacements of the structure contours, where the fault trace is likely to run. What is the stratigraphic throw of the fault?

In the south branch of level 6, the fault can be seen to dip at 70° to the east. Draw a cross-section across the fault at this point, in the true-dip direction of the fault, and indicate the top of the slate unit either side of the fault. What is the throw of the fault? Why is it that the value differs slightly from the stratigraphic throw?

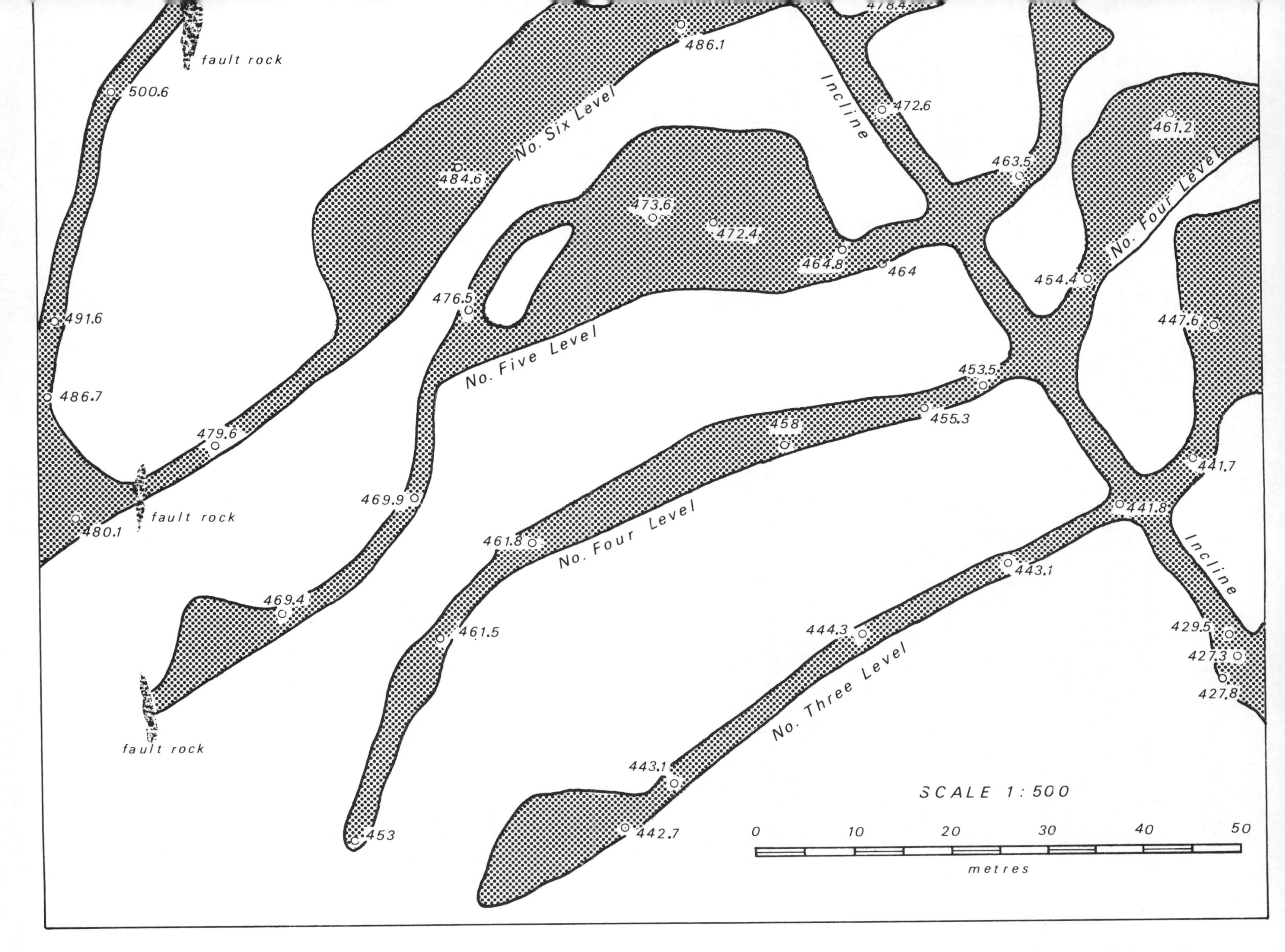
fault rock
500.6
491.6
486.7
480.1
fault rock
479.6
fault rock
469.4
469.9
476.5
484.6
No. Six Level
486.1
Incline
472.6
463.5
473.6
472.4
464.8
464
No. Five Level
453
461.5
461.8
No. Four Level
458
455.3
453.5
454.4
No. Four Level
461.2
447.6
441.7
441.8
443.1
Incline
444.3
No. Three Level
443.1
442.7
429.5
427.3
427.8
SCALE 1:500
0
10
20
30
40
50
metres

MAP 23 Gwynfynydd gold mine

This map, adapted by permission from the unpublished surveying of John Ashton, PhD, is of the Gwynfynydd mine, 4 km north of Dolgellau, N Wales. A number of gold-bearing quartz veins are sufficiently rich in gold to have tempted miners over many centuries and, by tradition, to have provided the material for numerous Royal wedding rings. The veins, given individual names such as Chidlaw, Collett, Main, and New veins, commonly occur along the faults, which displace the host Cambrian sedimentary rocks.

The map opposite shows the workings of the Chidlaw Vein at three different levels: 1, 2, and 6. Good potential control on the three-dimensional geology is provided by the information recorded at these three different elevations.

Construct an accurate N–S cross-section across the eastern part of the map to incorporate the information at all three levels. Project the Chidlaw vein between the levels. What is the overall orientation of the vein? (Note that a N–S section is not necessarily in the true dip direction of the vein.)

Indicate on the section the location of the Trawsfynydd fault at level 6. Project the course of the fault up to level 2. (Note that the cross-section is oblique to the fault.) How well does the projected location compare with that inferred from level 2 on the map, i.e. how planar is the Trawsfynydd fault?

If the Gamlan Flags-Clogau Shales boundary were projected onto the cross-section, what approximate orientation would its trace show?

Extrapolate on the map the Gamlan–Clogau junction northwards from level 2 to where it should occur at level 6. (Remember that the levels are at different elevations. By analogy with the trigonometric method for finding the depth to a dipping unit (section 4.5 and Fig. 4.9a), here knowing the dip angle and elevation difference, the horizontal distance can be calculated.) Any discrepancy between the predicted location of the junction and that shown on the map can presumably by accounted for by a fault, seeing as the geology either side of the parts of level 6 fails to correspond.

Using the predicted map locations of the junction and its orientation, and assuming that the known orientation of the Chidlaw vein represents that of the fault, find (a) the stratigraphic throw, and (b) the downthrow shown by the fault.

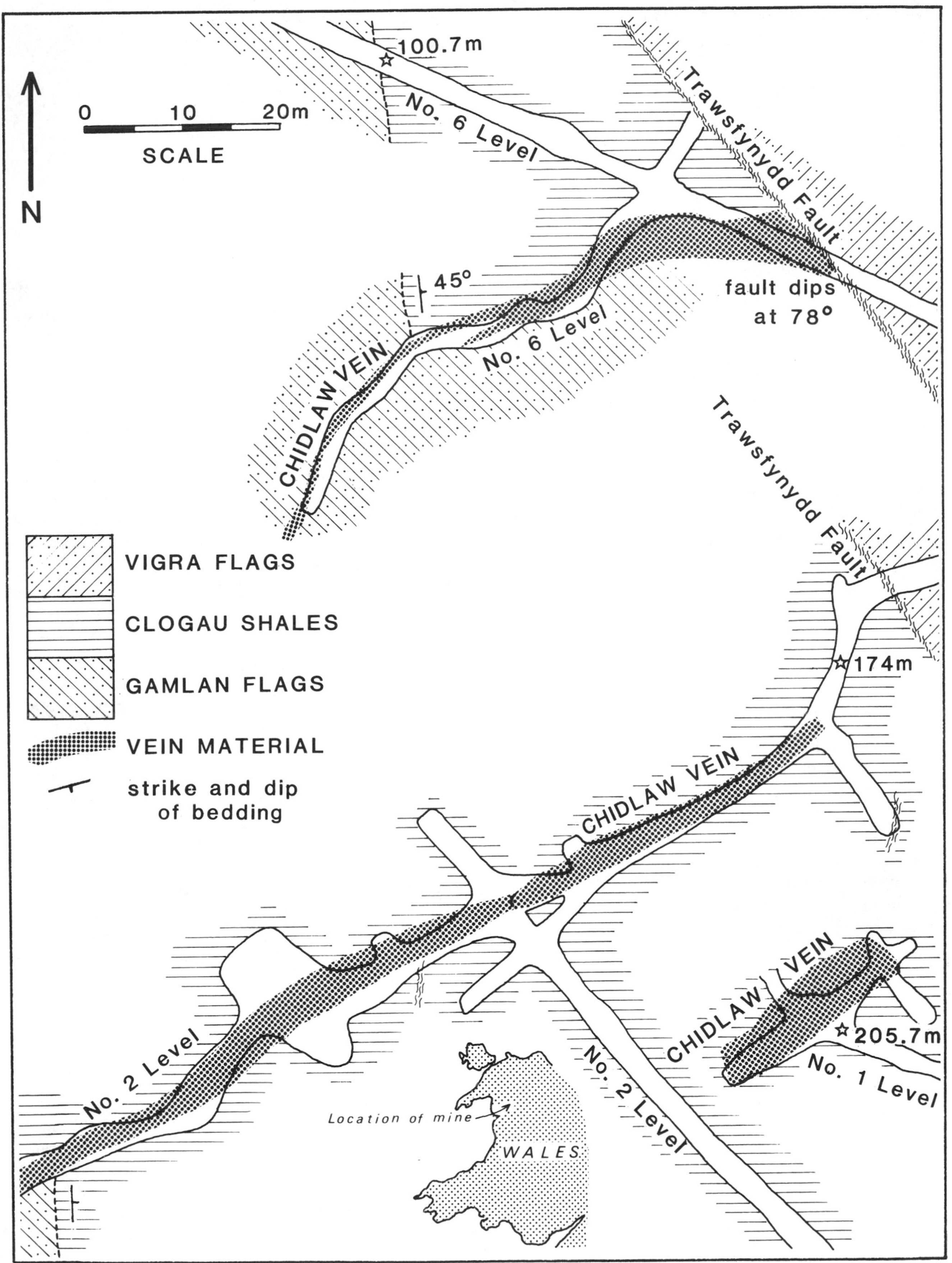

100.7m
0
10
20m
SCALE
N
No. 6 Level
Trawsfynydd Fault
45°
fault dips
at 78°
CHIDLAW VEIN
No. 6 Level
Trawsfynydd Fault
VIGRA FLAGS
CLOGAU SHALES
GAMLAN FLAGS
VEIN MATERIAL
strike and dip
of bedding
174m
CHIDLAW VEIN
CHIDLAW VEIN
205.7m
No. 1 Level
No. 2 Level
No. 2 Level
Location of mine
WALES

12 Geological history from maps

12.1 Introduction

The previous eight chapters have developed methods for the three-dimensional interpretation of maps. We look now at maps in a further dimension – the geological past. For the outcrop patterns on maps can reveal much of how the rock arrangements evolved through time; they enable interpretations to be made on the geological history of the map area, even the reconstruction of past geological environments. The timings that are derived from maps are usually relative, although reference to an absolute time scale may allow real dates to be assigned together with the establishment of time intervals and some idea of the rates at which events proceeded.

This kind of interpretation of the geological past typically involves dealing with a variety of geological processes. This chapter looks in turn at the kinds of interpretations that can be made from sedimentary successions, deformed rocks, and non-sedimentary materials. Of course, on a typical geological map, each of these aspects does not occur in isolation; their interaction has to be studied. This is one reason why geological maps are so central to geology.

Reconstruction of the geological evolution of a map area is of great academic importance, for surely the understanding of how an area became the way it is must be one of the fundamental objectives of geology, but it can be of applied significance too. If the geological circumstances which prompted the formation of some material of commercial interest can be deduced, it becomes easier to discover further occurrences. The petroleum industry makes much use of reconstructing past sedimentary environments to help focus on those areas where oil might be found.

It will become apparent that often the history of features seen on the map can be interpreted in more than one way. This is because we are dealing with map *interpretation*. The geologist has to weigh in his or her mind the evidence on the map, and decide on a preferred interpretation. There is no right or wrong solution available to us. Even experienced geologists may disagree on the most likely interpretation. However, Nature tends to do things in an uncomplicated manner. You should aim for the interpretation which explains most features in the simplest way.

12.2 Sedimentary successions

The idea that sediments are laid down on top of each other, forming a pile with successively younger deposits higher up, seems almost self-evident to us now, although the idea does appear to have first dawned only about two hundred years ago. Because of it, we are in a position to work out the relative ages of a series of sedimentary units shown on a map. If the beds are flat, those units that are topographically higher will be younger, and dipping beds become younger in the dip direction. The sediments above an unconformity must be younger than the rocks below.

However, the above statements assume that the succession is 'right way up'. Rock successions can be tilted past the vertical, leading to inversion of the sequence. This

Fig. 12.1 (opposite) Examples of the interpretation of geological history from maps. (a) Annotated map of Republic, Michigan, USA. (b) Sedimentation and folding perhaps related to faulting. Localisation of coal measures (d^{c1}–d^{c3}) adjacent to fault, restriction of folding to Carboniferous rocks, and increased dips towards fault all suggest folds are local responses to fault movement, perhaps synchronous with sedimentation. Near Alloa, Scotland. Redrawn from the BGS 1:50 000 Stirling sheet, by permission of the Director, BGS: Crown/NERC copyright reserved. (c) Lenses of limestone pebble conglomerate within (now metamorphosed) mudrocks may represent distributary channels on a submarine fan. Lake Bomoseen, Vermont, USA. (d) Suite of granite plutons post-dates folding, a common sequence in orogenic belts. Hill End, Australia. Based on Powell *et al.* (1976). (e) Variations in outcrop width of 'Smiddy Ganister' sandstone are not paralleled by other units, therefore probably represent primary thickness variation, perhaps reflecting deposition in channels. Moor House, North Pennines, England. Based on Johnson and Dunham (1963).

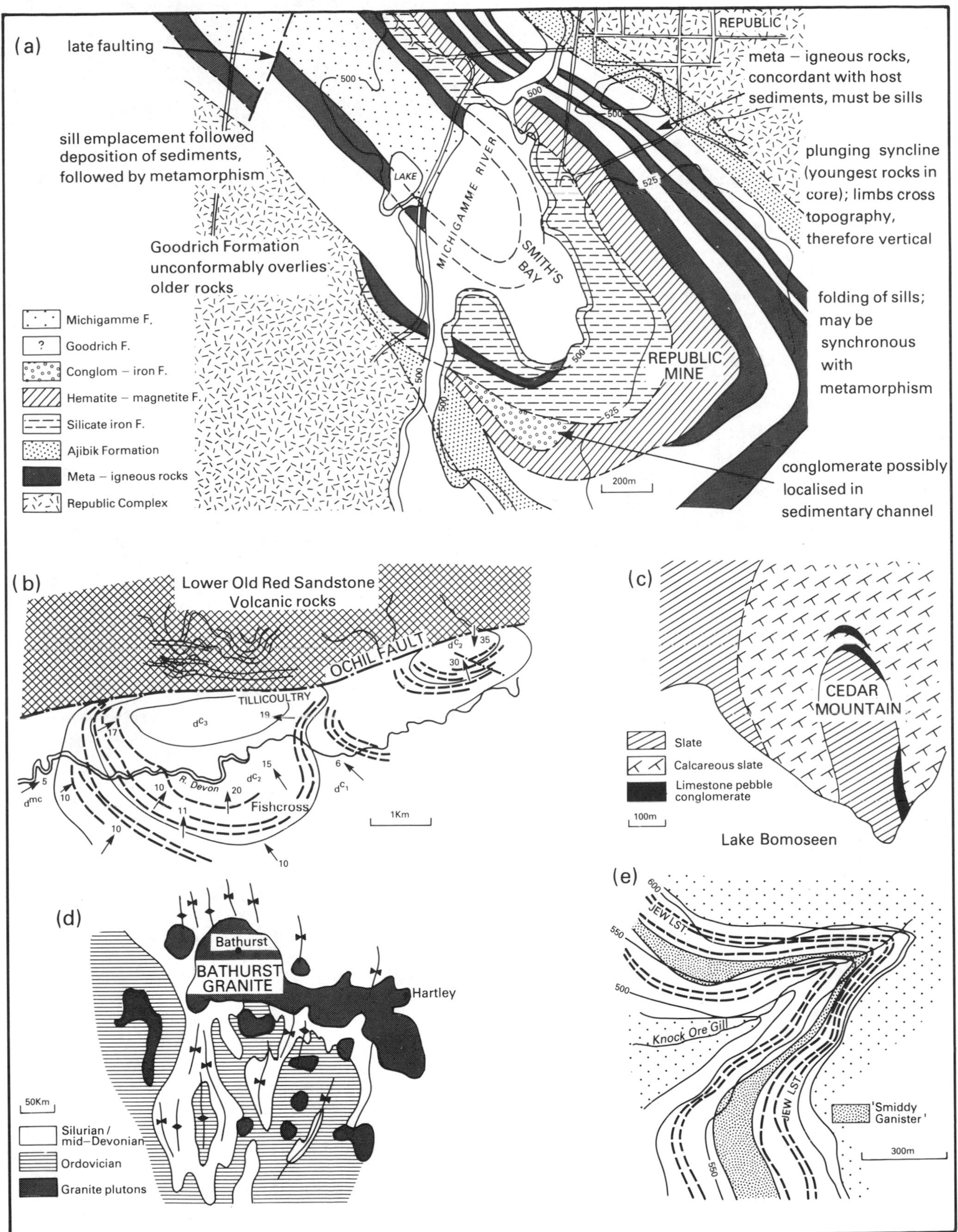
(a)
late faulting
REPUBLIC
meta – igneous rocks, concordant with host sediments, must be sills
sill emplacement followed deposition of sediments, followed by metamorphism
plunging syncline (youngest rocks in core); limbs cross topography, therefore vertical
LAKE
MICHIGAMME RIVER
SMITH'S BAY
Goodrich Formation unconformably overlies older rocks
folding of sills; may be synchronous with metamorphism
REPUBLIC MINE
Michigamme F.
Goodrich F.
Conglom – iron F.
Hematite – magnetite F.
Silicate iron F.
Ajibik Formation
Meta – igneous rocks
Republic Complex
200m
conglomerate possibly localised in sedimentary channel
(b)
Lower Old Red Sandstone Volcanic rocks
OCHIL FAULT
TILLICOULTRY
R. Devon
Fishcross
1Km
(c)
CEDAR MOUNTAIN
Slate
Calcareous slate
Limestone pebble conglomerate
100m
Lake Bomoseen
(d)
Bathurst
BATHURST GRANITE
Hartley
50Km
Silurian / mid-Devonian
Ordovician
Granite plutons
(e)
JEW LST.
Knock Ore Gill
'Smiddy Ganister'
300m

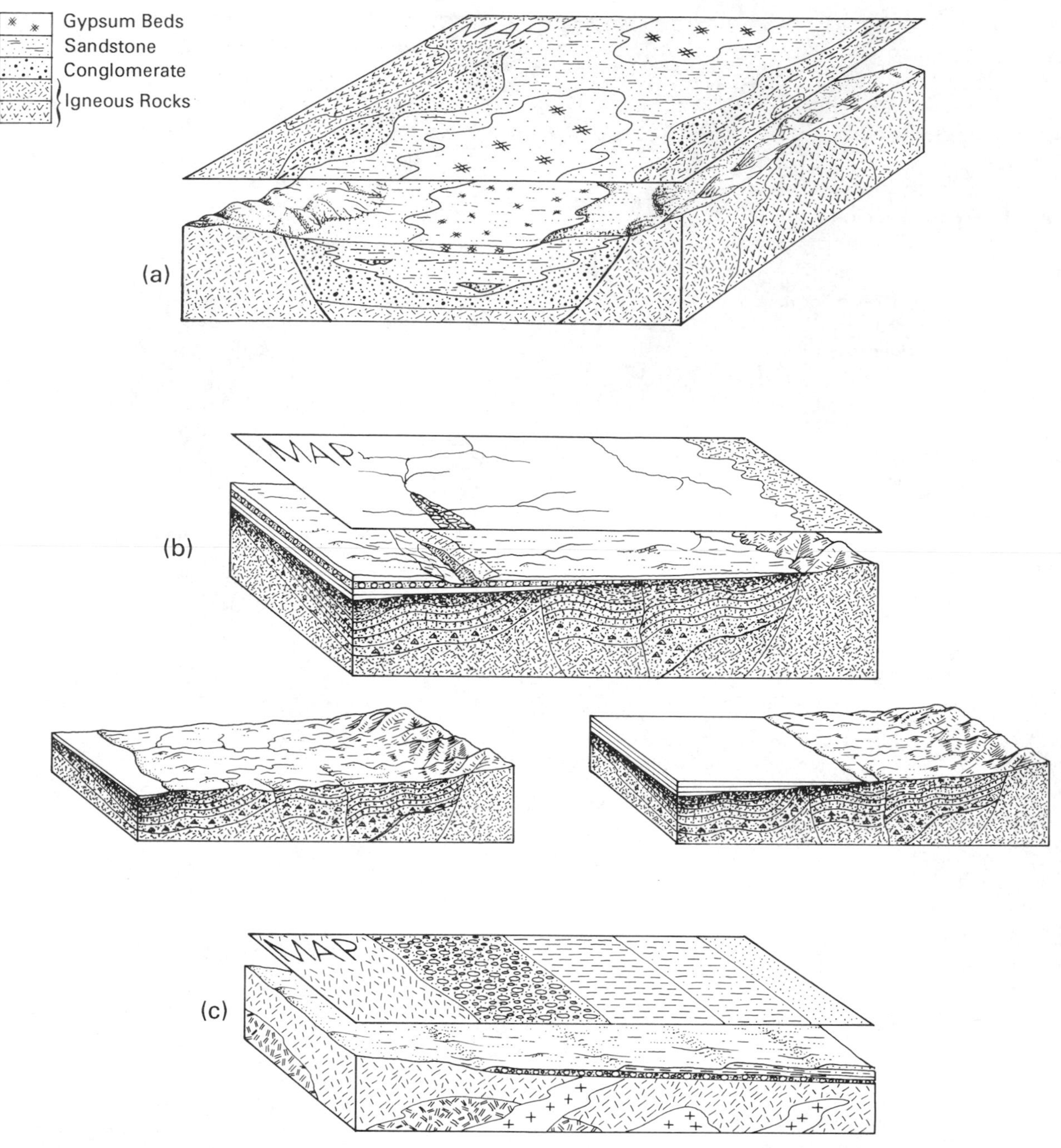
Gypsum Beds
Sandstone
Conglomerate
Igneous Rocks
MAP
(a)
MAP
(b)
MAP
(c)

Fig. 12.2 Aspects of geological history that may be interpreted from maps. (a) Sedimentary rocks on a map, with block diagram showing an interpretation of the depositional environment as a saline subaerial basin with alluvial fans. (b) Map showing unconformity with overlap (see section 7.4). The nonornamented unit extends further than the black unit, which is only revealed in present-day river valleys. Block diagrams show interpretation as a marine transgression. As the sea encroaches further, successively more extensive sediments are deposited. (c) Unconformity, with possible offlap. The map distribution of the sedimentary rocks could be due to present-day erosion fortuitously acting on once equally extensive units, but probably represents a marine regression. As the sea recedes from the land, successive deposits become less extensive.

happens particularly in areas of much folding, where entire fold limbs can become overturned. If the map shows signs of intense folding, or if the area is known to be within an orogenic belt, watch out for inverted successions. The **younging direction** is sometimes indicated on maps of such areas by a symbol (Fig. 4.2). Inverted sequences are largely outside the scope of this book, but note that they occur, for example, on Map 21.

Where units grade laterally or intertongue with each other, they must have formed at the same time. Such relationships may be indicated on the map key. Sedimentary units may vary in thickness across the map area. Make sure that this is a real variation, and not an effect of topography or bed dip (section 6.3), or of faulting. Thickness characteristics can give information on the environment in which the sediments were deposited. For example, conspicuous fluctuations may indicate deposition on a highly uneven floor or in channels (Figs 12.1a,b) whereas consistent thicknesses reflect stable sedimentation.

Knowledge of how different associations of sedimentary rocks come about can lead to reconstructions of the sedimentary environments (e.g. Fig. 12.2a). If an unconformity is present, analysis of the relations between the formations may prompt interpretations of the geological history of the area (Figs 12.2b,c; section 7.4). The relationships between sediments and structures can be informative. For example, sediment can thicken towards one side of a fault, especially a normal fault. This signifies that the fault was formed only shortly before the time of sedimentation. The upthrown side was able to provide a ready source of sediment, which banked up on the downthrow side, against the fresh fault scarp (Fig. 12.1c). If the units are present on both sides of the fault, but the progressively older ones show increased displacement, the feature is termed a growth fault (section 10.3.3). The implication is that the fault was moving during the accumulation of the sediments.

12.3 Deformed rocks

The detection and description of folds and faults on maps was discussed in sections 8.3 and 9.5. However, it may also be possible to make interpretations on the *timing* of the deformation. The first thing that can be said from a map is that the material must have been there before the deformation! That is, the folding or faulting must post-date the age of the rocks. Quite how much younger is a difficult matter. Deformation can occur soon after sediments were deposited, or long after they have been turned into rocks; the distinction would be virtually impossible to detect from a map. The duration of the stratigraphic divisions of most maps allows the formation of the rocks and their deformation to be accomplished within the same stratigraphic interval. Thus, it is certainly possible to have, say, rocks shown on the map as middle Permian in age deformed by a middle Permian fault. Of course, if rocks younger than Permian are affected by the same structure, then the deformation, too, has to be younger.

This key device in the interpretation of timings from maps, that of cross-cutting relationships, was introduced in section 2.3.5. If, continuing with the above example, beds of Jurassic age pass across the fault without displacement, then the fault movement had ended before Jurassic times. Although the principle is applicable to sedimentary rocks – an angular unconformity, for example, is a cross-cutting relationship – it is especially useful in interpreting igneous and metamorphic rocks and deformation sequences.

If one fault displaces another fault, then the former is the younger structure. A folded fault means that the fold is the younger structure. If, however, a fault which displaces a series of beds is folded, but to a lesser degree than the beds, it means that the faulting took place *during* the folding. Sometimes the relative timing has to be deduced through indirect logic. Suppose two separate igneous intrusions are known from the key to be of the same age. If one of them intrudes beds which overlie a fault, and the other is faulted, there must be two ages of faulting. Cross-cutting relationships are applied to map interpretation in endless permutations.

Regarding cross-cutting faults, there can be ambiguities. Make sure that the relationship is a sharp truncation. If the faults simply merge, they could have formed synchronously. If a unit is faulted but the adjacent one is not, this *may* indicate a depositional break (disconformity) in that there was enough time for faulting of the lowermost unit before formation of the upper one. On the other hand, faults do have to end somewhere. Movement along a fault is greatest along its central part and decreases outwards such that the fault tip may coincide with the boundary of the unit. Support for this interpretation may be provided by variable displacement along the fault. Many of the same considerations apply to folds. An area, especially one within an orogenic belt, can be subjected to more than one period of folding, although analysis of this situation is beyond this book.

If we are interpreting geological histories from a map that shows folds and faults, we naturally want to assign stratigraphic ages to their production. Cross-cutting relationships and reference to stratigraphic ages in the key may allow this but only to the extent that the relations are present on the map. Too often the fault of interest does not reach the rocks of critical age, or disappears off the edge of the map. Another separate structure that looks similar may provide the evidence. The question then arises as to what extent different structures can be grouped together as being of the same age. In general, groups of faults are likely to be different in age from groups of folds because the conditions during rock formation tend to favour either ductile or brittle structures (section 8.1). There are, however, many exceptions to this, for example, the hangingwall anticlines related to thrusts (section 10.2.1) and the rollover anticlines resulting from extension faults (10.3.2).

But how are groups of synchronous structures recognised? Folds of the same age tend to have similar characteristics. The axial surfaces are likely to be roughly parallel, and the fold attitudes and styles alike (section 8.2). Fold scale depends primarily on bed thickness, so is a less direct guide. If, for example, the map reveals a number of NE–SW trending, reclined to recumbent, moderately plunging non-cylindrical folds, they may well be of similar age. If folds are also present which are, say, E–W trending, upright cylindrical folds, it is likely that these structures formed in a different period of deformation. The relative ages of the two periods of folding may be discernible from the stratigraphic ages of the rocks affected. Similar considerations apply to faulting, in that one *kind* of fault tends to dominate at any one time, but there are many factors which can complicate these generalisations.

12.4 Non-sedimentary rocks

Detailed analysis of the genesis of non-sedimentary rocks is not usually possible on standard geological maps, but some interpretation might be possible. As discussed in section 11.2.1, investigation of volcaniclastic rocks has to take into account both the sedimentary and igneous processes that are involved. A map of a volcanic centre may prompt inferences in the way the ashes and tuffs accumulated. For example, a large *volume* of volcaniclastic material reflects major or protracted eruption whereas a large *area* covered by the material indicates an energetic, probably violent, explosion. But it may be difficult to establish these two amounts from a map, not only because the bulk form of the ejected material could be highly irregular, but also because such deposits are vulnerable to erosion. The type of volcanic rock may give clues to the environment of formation, e.g. pillow lavas indicate subaqueous, usually marine, eruption. The rocks may be cross-cut or interleaved with magmatic bodies, prompting interpretations of how the volcanic activity progressed through time.

The thing that igneous rocks lend themselves to on maps is the relative dating of emplacement. An intrusive igneous body has to be younger than the rocks it has intruded, and any deformation structures it cross-cuts (Fig. 12.1d). Conversely, it must be older than any features by which it is cross-cut. Any deposits which overlap onto the igneous body will also give a minimum age for emplacement. If the map covers an igneous complex, it may be possible to erect a detailed scenario of intrusive events. If something about the composition of the rocks is known from the key, it may be reasonable to speculate on the broad features of magmatic evolution.

Nevertheless, these methods may give a large stratigraphic time interval and it may not be possible to determine exactly when the intrusion took place. For the same reason the field surveyor may have been unable to pinpoint the stratigraphic age of the intrusive masses. Therefore, it is normal for igneous rocks to be shown on the map key with little or no indication of age and to be listed separately from sedimentary, volcaniclastic, and extrusive igneous rocks. It then falls to the reader to deduce what they can from the map about the age of the bodies.

Metamorphism of sedimentary rocks will usually have taken place long after deposition of the sediments, allowing time for their burial. Knowledge of the metamorphic conditions may allow some speculation on the time interval, but rarely can this be specified from maps alone. The map key may provide some information, but usually cross-cutting relationships are the only direct guide, i.e. metamorphic rocks being overlain by non-metamorphosed rocks. Igneous intrusions, assuming they formed at some depth, can be subjected to metamorphism at any time subsequent to their emplacement. It is common during regional metamorphism for the rocks also to be subjected to ductile deformation (e.g. Fig. 12.1e). Therefore, if folds are present on the map, they may well be synchronous with any regional metamorphism. If thermal metamorphism is indicated on the map note that the igneous mass which caused it may be partly or even completely buried. The present outcrop does not necessarily reflect the size and shape of the heat source at depth.

Regarding mineral deposits, the rocks in which they are found should disclose the overall nature of the mineralisation, whether they are sedimentary deposits, for example, or related to magmatism. But a general geological map is unlikely to reveal much about the conditions of mineralisation.

12.5 Reading a geological map

With the possibility outlined above of interpreting geological histories, in addition to all the three-dimensional aspects of earlier chapters, it will now be clear that there is a great deal to be achieved by looking at a map (e.g. Fig. 12.3). It is therefore wise to adopt a systematic procedure. A series of steps is listed below as a guide. The exact approach will depend on the purpose for which the map is being consulted and the kind of geology involved. When making a full inspection of a map it is usually worthwhile to jot down notes and make sketches as you work through the steps.

Note the map scale. Establish the regional location of the area.

Orient the map (i.e. determine the north direction).

Note the main topographic features. Trace the main drainage and watersheds. Note the topographic contour interval. Visualise the relief.

Examine the key very carefully. Note the variety of rock types and their stratigraphic distribution, the extent of information provided in the key, and any symbolism used. If the map is black and white, it may be useful to add colour to some of the units.

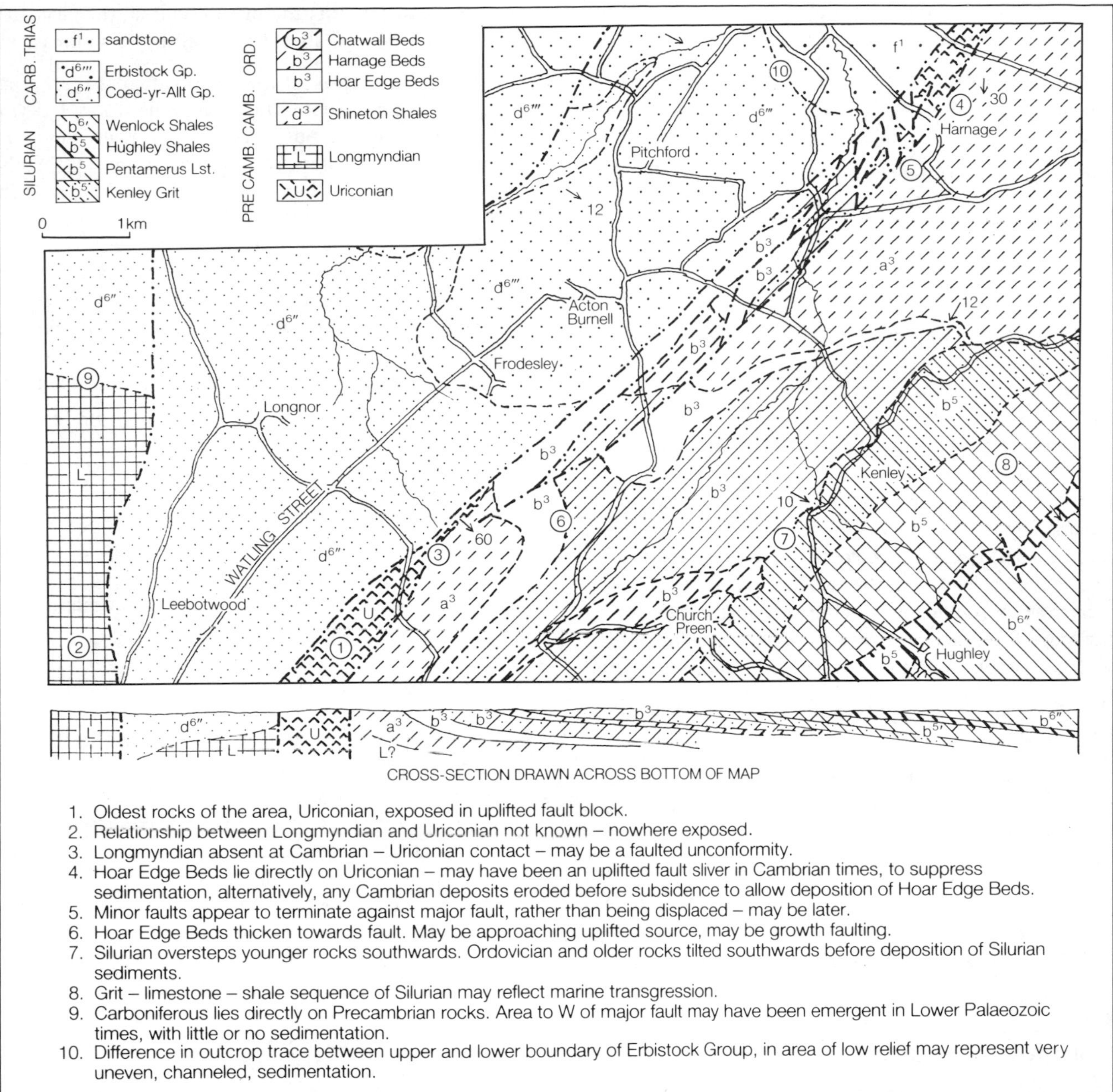

TRIAS
CARB.
SILURIAN
f¹ sandstone
d⁶‴ Erbistock Gp.
d⁶″ Coed-yr-Allt Gp.
b⁶ Wenlock Shales
b⁵ Hughley Shales
b⁵ Pentamerus Lst.
b⁵ Kenley Grit
0 1km
ORD.
CAMB.
PRE CAMB.
b³ Chatwall Beds
b³ Harnage Beds
b³ Hoar Edge Beds
d³ Shineton Shales
L Longmyndian
U Uriconian
Pitchford
Harnage
Acton Burnell
Frodesley
Longnor
Kenley
WATLING STREET
Leebotwood
Church Preen
Hughley
CROSS-SECTION DRAWN ACROSS BOTTOM OF MAP
1. Oldest rocks of the area, Uriconian, exposed in uplifted fault block.
2. Relationship between Longmyndian and Uriconian not known – nowhere exposed.
3. Longmyndian absent at Cambrian – Uriconian contact – may be a faulted unconformity.
4. Hoar Edge Beds lie directly on Uriconian – may have been an uplifted fault sliver in Cambrian times, to suppress sedimentation, alternatively, any Cambrian deposits eroded before subsidence to allow deposition of Hoar Edge Beds.
5. Minor faults appear to terminate against major fault, rather than being displaced – may be later.
6. Hoar Edge Beds thicken towards fault. May be approaching uplifted source, may be growth faulting.
7. Silurian oversteps younger rocks southwards. Ordovician and older rocks tilted southwards before deposition of Silurian sediments.
8. Grit – limestone – shale sequence of Silurian may reflect marine transgression.
9. Carboniferous lies directly on Precambrian rocks. Area to W of major fault may have been emergent in Lower Palaeozoic times, with little or no sedimentation.
10. Difference in outcrop trace between upper and lower boundary of Erbistock Group, in area of low relief may represent very uneven, channeled, sedimentation.

Fig. 12.3 Part of the BGS One-Inch Shrewsbury sheet, greatly simplified, with examples of observations relevant to interpreting the geological history of the area. Redrawn by permission of the Director, BGS: Crown/NERC copyright reserved.

Assess the overall stratigraphic distribution and the main outcrop patterns. (For example: are there any major unconformities? Are the map units horizontal, uniformly dipping, folded, faulted, or some combination of these?) Make a sketch which simplifies the geology but brings out the major features of the area.

Establish the main strike and dip directions. (You may need to sketch some structure contours to gauge the strike.)

Confirm the stratigraphic succession if it is provided in the key. Note any thickness variations or peculiarities. Watch for minor unconformities.

Deduce the main structures. Note the main points of shape and orientation (sketching structure contours may help), and any cross-cutting relationships. Can the structures be grouped, for example, according to style or stratigraphic age?

Note any igneous rocks (shapes of bodies, relative ages) and any features concerning metamorphic rocks.

Sketch or construct cross-sections as appropriate. Make any necessary corrections. Make any required measurements.

Sketch any particular significant relationships apparent on the map in order to emphasise them. Illustrate any significant structure contour patterns.

List the main stages in the geological evolution of the area.

12.6 Writing a map report

Sometimes a map is consulted out of general interest, sometimes for a specific reason. It is occasionally necessary to prepare a report of the geology of the area as apparent from the map for another person. For example, a company may be considering investigating the area and, before committing any money, requires some preliminary geological information. You, as a geologist, may be asked to summarise the geology from the available maps.

Such a report is mainly a matter of formalising in writing the steps listed above. A conventional order for dealing with the various topics has grown up, as follows:

Abstract summarises the main factual points made in the text of the report.

Introduction provides a brief introductory statement: gives the map location, scale, any characterisation, and the main geological features.

Stratigraphic succession briefly mentions each significant unit *in chronological order* (oldest first), grouping into systems if appropriate. Mentions lithologies and their distributions, thicknesses, unconformities, and any special features.

Structure mentions any dip variations; describes folds, faults. May well use cross-sections and sketches.

Igneous and metamorphic rocks

Economic geology

Geomorphology

Geological history lists the main events in the geological evolution of the area, in order, to serve as a summary.

This general order is, of course, modified as appropriate to the task in hand. Subheadings can be used also. It is vital that the report is rigorously organised. Equally important is that the writing is concise and to the point. Distinguish 'fact' from inference. For example, if you are discussing palaeoenvironments, timings of events, etc., distinguish clearly between these *interpretive* aspects and your *observations* from the map. Unless you have been instructed otherwise, you should assume the reader is a trained geologist, but completely unfamiliar with the map area.

Of course, for some purposes certain aspects of the geology may require particular attention. If the report is meant to address some specific question, it is important that the answer is provided straightaway at the beginning of the report. The sheer quantity of information derivable from a map can be impressive. Nevertheless, company managers are not usually interested in wading through pages of geological reasoning, brilliant though it may be. They want direct geological answers to their question.

12.7 Summary of chapter

1. Sedimentary successions lend themselves to the interpretation of relative ages and, to varying extents, the environments in which they were deposited.
2. Cross-cutting relationships between features are fundamental in deducing relative ages.
3. Structures of similar appearance and orientation may have formed at the same time. Folds and faults may fall into groups of differing ages.
4. The relative timing of igneous intrusion can commonly be established, but details of magmatic and metamorphic histories may be elusive from a map alone.
5. It is wise to adopt a systematic procedure for studying geological maps.
6. Reports on the geology of a map area should follow the conventional sequence of topics; they should be rigorously organised and concisely written.

MAP 24 Baraboo district, Wisconsin, USA (continued overleaf)

Pleistocene: Terminal moraine; Other glacial deposits and alluvium

Ordovician: Dolomite and Sandstone

Cambrian: Sandstone and Conglomerate

Middle Precambrian: Baraboo Quartzite

Early Precambrian: Rhyolite

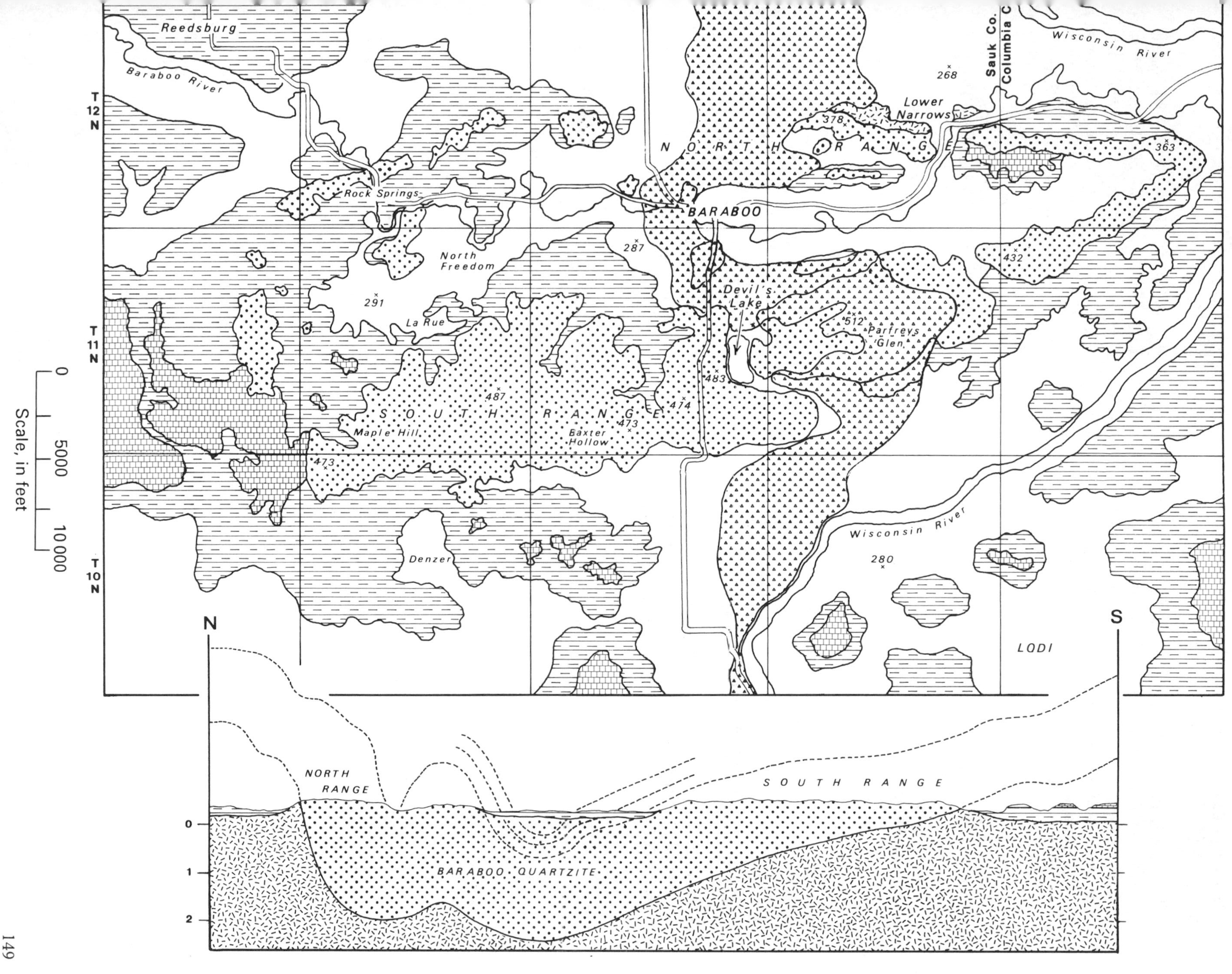

Reedsburg
Baraboo River
Wisconsin River
Sauk Co.
Columbia C
268
Lower Narrows
378
NORTH RANGE
363
Rock Springs
BARABOO
287
432
North Freedom
291
La Rue
Devil's Lake
512
Parfreys Glen
483
487
474
SOUTH RANGE
473
Maple Hill
Baxter Hollow
473
Wisconsin River
280
Denzer
LODI
T 12 N
T 11 N
T 10 N
0
5000
10 000
Scale, in feet
N
S
NORTH RANGE
SOUTH RANGE
BARABOO QUARTZITE
0
1
2

The map on the previous page is of a geologically famous area in central Wisconsin, USA. Early observations on the rock structures of the district were influential on the development of structural geology, and the list of teachers and students who have been drawn to the area has been referred to as a 'Who's Who' of American geology.

Little of the early Precambrian basement is exposed. The middle Precambrian rocks are represented by the upstanding ridges of the tough Baraboo Quartzite, and associated units are known from mine and well data. They are depicted on the cross-section by dashed lines. Note that the courses of the boundaries between the various bedrock units have been continued on the map below the terminal moraine.

Summarise the geological history of the area, paying particular attention to the structure of the Precambrian rocks and its relation with the Lower Palaeozoic rocks. Consider the glacial history. Why might the drainage patterns, with several gorges cut *through* the ridges of Baraboo Quartzite, be so little related to the Precambrian units? Suggest an explanation for the location of Devil's Lake. The Wisconsin River is thought to have once flowed approximately N–S through the Lower Narrows and the gorge containing Devil's Lake. Account for its change in course.

Further examples concerning geological history

Many of the black and white maps reproduced here lend themselves to the interpretation of geological histories, particularly maps 6, 9, 11, 12, 19 and 21. All the maps reproduced in colour incorporate interesting geological histories, most particularly Plates 5–8.

13 The production of geological maps

13.1 Introduction

This book is about working with existing geological maps, but an understanding and appreciation of such maps would be incomplete without some knowledge of what goes into their production. Many stages are involved, from the detailed field surveying required for large-scale maps, through the preparation of 'fair copy maps', and the design and execution of a final printed version. Greenly and Williams (1930, p. 99) list twenty-three steps; this chapter merely outlines what is involved.

There is another purpose to this chapter. Often, field surveying is seen as an endeavour which is completely separate from interpreting existing maps. Part of the reason is that the two procedures are commonly taught to students, for perfectly good logistical reasons, in quite separate courses, and the connection is not made. However, a thorough understanding of the three-dimensional behaviour of map units, and the genetic implications of the way they are presented, is as essential to field surveying as dealing with a published map. Moreover, a field map has to be compiled with the needs of the eventual user in mind. Attention will be drawn at several points in this chapter to the need for the finished map to be clear and visually attractive, as well as scientifically sound (Robertson, 1956). Such qualities cannot arise through cosmetic adjustment to the final document; the need has to be appreciated throughout the production of the map.

13.2 The field survey

Surveying to produce a geological map, or 'geological mapping' as it is often called, usually begins with the acquisition of a topographic base document on which geological data can be plotted. Very large-scale work, such as the production of mining maps, may well require the generation of a sufficiently large-scale base map at the same time as the geological survey, using the plane table methods described, for example, by Compton (1985). Where a topographic map of appropriate scale is already available, the geologist plots the information directly on to this, or onto air photographs (e.g. Barnes, 1981, chapter 3).

One of the first important judgements the geologist has to make in the survey is the basis on which to divide the rocks of the area into map units. Much of the geological mapping will be concerned with marking on the base map the course of these units, and particularly the boundaries between them. These will form the basic framework of the map. In reconnaissance work, it is common to use air photographs or satellite imagery (section 15.2.2) to locate boundaries, perhaps supplemented by traverses across the region.

In more detailed work, it is common to mark on the map the actual exposures of bedrock, so that the distinction between what has been observed and what has been inferred is clearly recorded. This can be done realistically only at scales of 1:10 000 and larger. In all methods, the sketching of cross-sections as the survey is progressing is necessary to keep clear the understanding of the three-dimensional geology. The various techniques are discussed in detail by the standard works on field mapping, e.g. Compton, 1985; Barnes, 1981; Mosely, 1981, Ahmed and Almond, 1981. Much of the summary given by Ramsay and Huber (1987, Appendix F) is relevant to general field mapping. Two points are emphasised here.

First, except in the rare case of perfectly exposed ground, the geologist will have to infer the course of the outcrops; to project traces between exposures, bearing in mind the *three-dimensional nature* of the boundaries; and to visualise how the boundary will interact with the ground surface. Commonly, the shortest route is unlikely. It is a matter of applying the principles of earlier chapters in reverse, e.g. drawing the trace to 'V' across valleys in the appropriate way (chapter 6). In large-scale mapping it may be possible to apply the principles of chapter 4 in reverse and sketch some structure contours from parts of a boundary that are well known in order to predict where the unexposed boundary is likely to run (Fig. 13.1).

Second, as already emphasised in section 1.3.4, the geological map is the result of *inferences* of many kinds by the surveyor. There may well have been some arbitrariness in the definition of the map units, and the surveyor will be

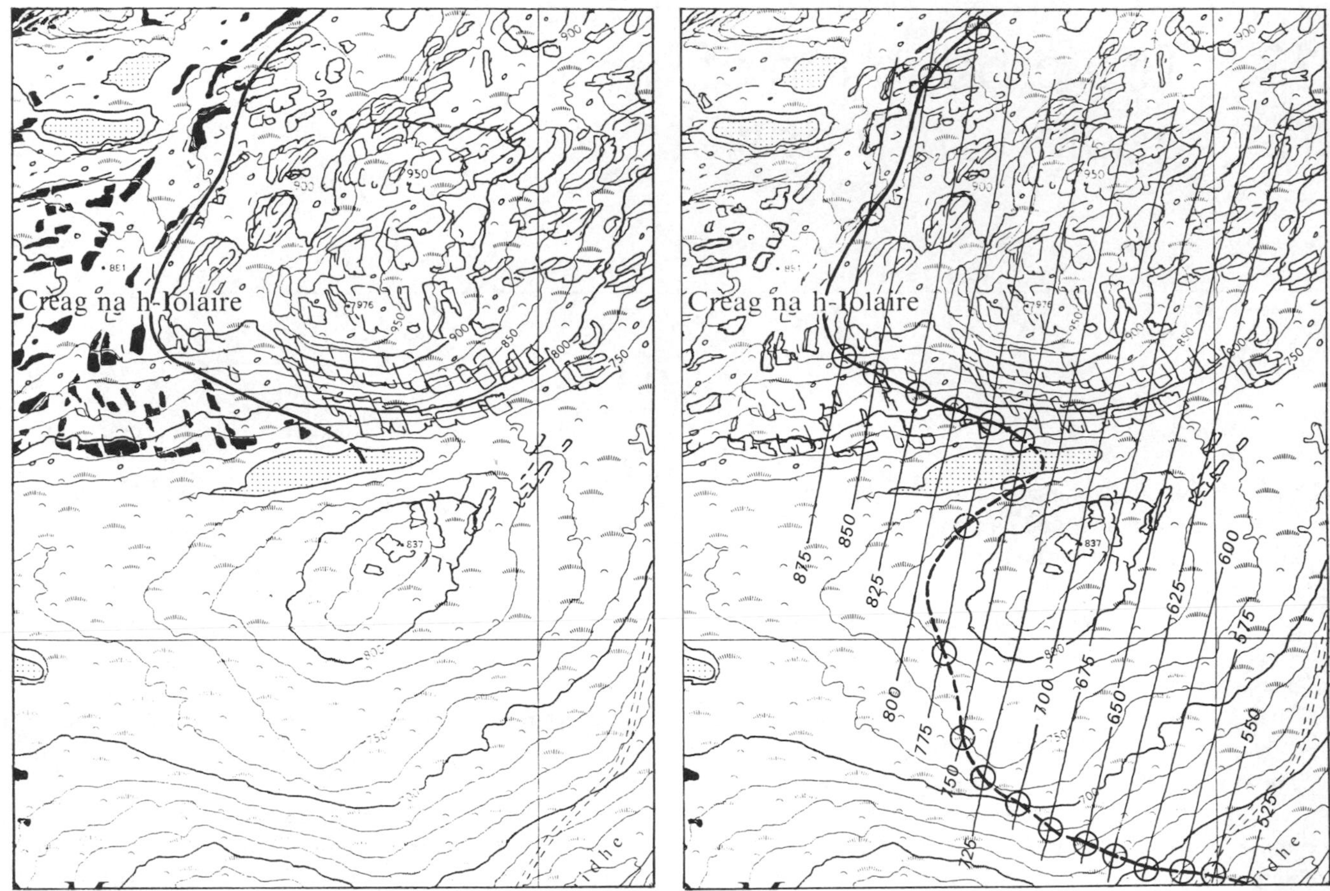
Creag na h-Iolaire
950
900
976
850
800
750
837
Creag na h-Iolaire
875
850
825
800
775
750
725
700
675
650
625
600
575
550
525

Fig. 13.1 Using structure contours to trace a surface through unexposed ground during geological surveying. (a) shows exposures of Torridonian sandstone, in black, and the overlying Cambrian quartzite, unornamented. Numerous exposures in the northern half of the area control the course of the junction between the two units. In the southern half, however, sparsity of exposure leaves the course unclear. (b) Structure contours, drawn from intersections (circled) of the trace known from (a) with topographic contours, are straight and evenly spaced, indicating a uniformly dipping surface. Extrapolating the structure contours southwards gives intersections with the topographic contours (circled) which enable a reasonable tracing of the junction in the southern area.

aware that implications for the geological history will arise from the judgement of the outcrop relationships. Although much of this book is about interpreting completed geological maps, it is important to remember that the map itself is an interpretive representation of part of the earth.

As the boundaries are plotted on the map, the outcrop patterns will begin to take shape, reflecting the geology of the area. The presence of structures, such as folds and faults, may be revealed. The surveyor may colour the field map to accentuate the outcrops, and may add supplementary information, such as orientation data, relevant topographic features, and perhaps some brief annotations. Much of these supplementary data will be recorded in the field notebook (e.g. Barnes, 1981, p. 91–4), which becomes an essential adjunct to the field map or, increasingly, on a computer-readable data sheet (section 15.2.3).

On completion of the survey, the geologist has a field map showing the outcrop pattern of the rocks, and the evidence on which the traces were based, with as much supplementary information as is consistent with clarity of the map. There will be some cross-sections developed during the survey, and he will have a notebook replete with data which are easily retrievable. All this information will probably be placed in some archive for future reference, either by the surveyor during follow-up work, by other workers, perhaps in different divisions of the company, or, in the case of a geological survey, by interested members of the public. Almost always it will be necessary to streamline all these data for easier dissemination, by producing a 'fair copy' geological map, probably supported by representative cross-sections and perhaps a written descriptive report.

The 'fair copy' map is a simplified version of the field map, which gives emphasis to the interpreted outcrop pattern, and gives selected representative supplementary information. Barnes (1981, chapters 8 and 9) discusses the nature and preparation of fair copy maps and cross-sections.

The geologist's field work may end with the submission of the field and fair copy document, but where the information is to be communicated widely, for example, published by a geological survey or as a research article, further steps are necessary.

13.3 Preparation of maps for publication

The following is in no way meant to be a set of instructions. It is merely a glimpse of what goes into completing a map for publication, to help the map reader have a greater understanding and appreciation of the final document.

13.3.1 Scale

The scale at which you see the published maps is not necessarily the scale at which the area was surveyed. For many purposes the field maps are considerably reduced. For example, it has been standard practice for the BGS to survey at 1:10 000, a scale highly convenient for the kind of accuracy and detail appropriate to a country the size of the UK and, while making these maps available for public inspection, to reduce them for publication to 1:50 000 (or, in pre-metric days, six inches to a mile field mapping for reduction to published one-inch maps). Plates 5 and 8, for example, were surveyed at a scale of six inches to a mile (1:10 650).

For the published document, the geologist has to decide what detail to retain. Mapping units may have to be grouped, and features excluded. Edward Greenly mapped parts of the island of Anglesey for the BGS at a scale of twenty-five inches to a mile. He later recalled that although this made it possible to record 170 different beds of jasper at one place, when the map was reduced to six inches to a mile for archiving, the number of jasper horizons had to be cut to 100, whereas the one inch to a mile map that was published (today at 1:50 000) could show only 45 jasper beds (Greenly and Williams, 1930, p. 382).

13.3.2 Boundaries

The geologist will have indicated on the reduced map which boundaries were observed and which inferred by using some system of dashed lines explained on the key (Fig. 4.2), and also will have ensured that boundaries have continuity with adjacent maps. Stories abound of the need to insert geological faults at the margins of a map in order to explain offset between the boundaries on adjacent sheets!

Some simplifications of the courses of the junctions may have been made to promote the clarity of the map; different weights of line may have been used to distinguish between depositional and faulted junctions; the final effect depends as much on the cartographic draftsman as the surveyor. Normal stratigraphic boundaries are best shown as a firm, but narrow, line, which unfortunately is not the case with some published maps.

13.3.3 Key and other information

Careful attention will have been given to the map key. The geologist will have decided how much information can be incorporated while maintaining clarity (e.g. Hageman, 1968). A stratigraphic column or vertical section showing thicknesses and relationships may have been added. Most maps include cross-sections on the map sheet. Maps published by official surveys often include a statement on authorship of the map, which can provide an interesting insight into the map's history. Some modern maps, such as the current BGS 1:50 000 series, include short descriptions and explanations of the geology next to the map; some USGS maps have lengthy descriptions on the reverse side of the sheet.

The design and layout of all these items should make a well-balanced whole. Modern BGS maps even have coloured frames. Returning to the map key, its main function, of course, is to explain the use of black and white ornament or colour on the map. The decision of how to represent each unit may seem a simple one, but it needs care to produce pleasing and effective results. There is, in fact, a fascinating and instructive history to the matter.

13.3.4 Ornament

The map units of an uncoloured map are normally ornamented to facilitate distinction between them. There have been attempts to standardise the patterns used. For example, Evans (1921) proposed that Precambrian rocks be given NW–SE ruled lines, Lower Palaeozoic rocks NE–SW lines, Upper Palaeozoic N–S lines, etc. Such systems have never caught on, except for certain patterns becoming associated with particular lithologies. It is common, for example, for limestones to have a 'brickwall' pattern, sandstones to be shown by various dots, and shales by dashes. Compton (1985, appendix 8) gives examples of some common ornaments.

13.3.5 Colour

Widely published maps have traditionally been coloured. The earliest maps, including those published in journals, were watercoloured by hand. The translucence of watercolours was ideal for allowing the other elements of the map to be easily examined, and in many cases, extremely pleasing effects were obtained. Some of them were very skillfully executed (e.g. Ireland, 1943). Many are now valuable collector's pieces.

However, there were serious snags. Such labour intensive methods greatly increased the cost of publication and restricted the number of copies. Some colours looked too dense and muddy, and broke the child's first rule of colouring – to 'not cross the line'! Mistakes were difficult to correct. The best colourists used a soaked map laid on wet newspaper in order to get even colours, but this lead to considerable distortion (Wilson, 1985). All this changed in the middle of the nineteenth century (section 14.3.4) when colour printing became used for geological maps.

Colours are so central to the effectiveness of a geological map that it does seem extraordinary that after about two hundred years of map-making there should still be such disparate colour systems. There seem to be four main approaches to choosing a colour scheme.

The first approach is largely aesthetic. The intention is to convey the outcrop patterns clearly, but in colours which are pleasing to the eye. The approach is often used in 'one-off' maps, which are not part of a wider effort such as those of the national surveys.

The second approach relates colour to the stratigraphic age of the rocks. The principles go back to a meeting of the International Geological Congress in 1881 but, although a number of European maps followed the guidelines that were agreed at the meeting, there has never been universal acceptance. In that scheme, each stratigraphic system was allotted its own colour which, apart from orange and red being reserved for igneous rocks and pink for metamorphic rocks, spanned the spectrum from the pale colours for younger systems to dark colours for older rocks. Although fine in theory, this did mean that whereas Tertiary rocks, for example, were assigned nice translucent yellows and Eocene deposits a pale yellow-green, Lower Palaeozoic and older rocks had to suffer dull, somewhat opaque colours. An analogous approach, though differing in detail, has traditionally been adopted by the US (section 14.3.5) and Canadian Surveys.

A third approach is based on the actual colours of the rocks themselves. Early map-makers such as William Smith followed this idea, and it has been influential on the colours used by the BGS. For example, the browns of the Torridonian and Old Red Sandstone, the oranges of the New Red Sandstone, and the dark grey of the Coal Measures seem to be based on this principle. The BGS maps of the region around Oban, W Scotland, portray the purples of the dark-red weathering volcanics, the dark blue-greys of the graphitic slates, dark greens of basic intrusives, and browns of the Old Red Sandstone deposits. Linton (1947) felt that such 'imitation of rock colours gave to the colour scheme a harmony which resulted in maps of real beauty . . . but that . . . it also imparted to many sheets an obscurity and gloom which made them almost impossible to read'. The same could be said of many of the French Bureau de Recherches Géologiques et Minières (BRGM) 1:80 000 sheets.

Fourth, some colours have come to be associated with certain lithologies. Blue has been used in many countries for limestone and calcareous deposits, and red for granites. Basic and ultrabasic igneous masses are commonly shown in dark greens or purples, and alluvium and other superficial deposits in pale cream. In addition to the colour, use can be made of various overprints, such as stipples and rulings, but this has to be done judiciously in order to avoid clumsy and opaque effects.

Whatever approach to colour and overprinting is adopted, it is imperative that the topographic base remains clearly legible. It is unfortunate that the BGS, perhaps because it has no control over the final production and printing of its documents, tends to issue maps with indistinct topography. Even on otherwise superb geological maps, such as the 'One-Inch' Bristol sheet and the 1:25 000 Snowdonia sheets, it can be difficult to read topographic information, such as contour lines. Linton (1947) criticised the maps being produced then for being 'quite opaque so that it is impossible to follow the contours beneath', and some modern examples seem hardly to have improved in this respect. The 1:50 000 map of Denbigh, for example, published in 1975, has such dark colours coupled with a heavily ruled overprint that it is impossible even to read some of the place names.

13.4 Map reports

Many geological maps are accompanied by a written report on the area. Traditionally, these were voluminous descriptions, highly detailed and technical. Some have made important contributions to geological knowledge, but they were hardly reading for the amateur.

The recent trend has been to produce shorter, more easily understood reports. For example, most French BRGM and Australian Bureau of Mineral Resources (BMR) maps now come in a plastic wallet, half of which contains the maps, and the other half contains a slim explanatory booklet. Some BGS maps are now following this format, and some of the explanations are specifically designed with the interested amateur in mind. Whatever their goal and format, such reports tend to follow the same organisational arrangement as those discussed in section 12.6. Some idea of what goes into preparing map reports is given by Compton (1985) and Blackader (1968).

13.5 Availability of maps

Ways of finding the geological map coverage of a specific area are reviewed by Martin (1973) and Pangborn (1971).

MAP DEALERS, producing lists, catalogues, and stocking maps of many countries of the world include:

The London Map Centre,
Cook, Hammond, and Kell Ltd.,
22/24 Caxton Street,
London SW1H 0QU

McCarta Ltd.,
122 Kings Cross Road,
London WC1X 9DS

Geoscience Resources,
1310 Rainey Street,
Burlington,
North Carolina 27215,
USA

Edward Stanford Ltd.,
12–14 Long Acre,
Covent Garden,
London WC2E 9LP

Geological Map Specialists,
49 Halfway Avenue,
Luton,
Bedfordshire LU4 8RA
England

UK Products of the British Geological Survey, and information, from:

Sales Desk,
British Geological Survey,
Keyworth,
Nottingham NG12 5GG

British Geological Survey,
Murchison House,
West Mains Road,
Edinburgh EH9 3LA

and BGS Regional Offices, Ordnance Survey agents, and booksellers

USA Products of the United States Geological Survey, and information, from:

(East of the Mississippi)

Branch of Distribution,
US Geological Survey,
1200 South Eads Street,
Arlington,
Virginia 22202

(West of the Mississippi)

Branch of Distribution,
US Geological Survey,
Box 25286, Federal Center,
Denver,
Colorado 80225

CANADA

Geological Survey of Canada,
601 Booth Street,
Ottawa,
Ontario K1A 0E8

AUSTRALIA

Publications Sales,
Bureau of Mineral Resources,
GPO Box 378,
Canberra ACT2601

NEW ZEALAND

Publications Officer,
Science Information Publishing Centre,
DSIR,
PO Box 9741
Wellington

Fig. 13.2 Some sources of geological maps.

Computer-based map indexing is the subject of vigorous current research (see section 15.2.4). Black and white maps which have been published in a book or journal can be photocopied, unless they are too big, but are subject to the usual copyright regulations. It may be possible to obtain a copy of the map by writing to the author if the address is given in any text which accompanies the map. Usually this would be the only way of getting a copy of an unpublished map.

The most widely available source of maps is the official geological survey of the relevant area. Usually this is a national institution, but some of the states of the USA, for example, have very active surveys. Obtaining information on current USGS products is discussed by Dodd *et al.* (1985), on US state maps by Fracolli (1985) and Fuller (1985), and current BGS map availability is summarised by Bain (1986).

Good bookshops may hold stocks of current official geological maps of their local area; otherwise these have to be ordered. Some addresses are given in Fig. 13.2. The general trend is for geological survey maps to be more attractively packaged and more widely available. Besides the name or number of the sheet your require, be sure to specify the scale. Some maps are available either folded, perhaps in a protective plastic wallet, or flat, normally delivered rolled up in a tube. With BGS maps you may have to specify 'solid' or 'drift' editions (section 1.3.2). Flat maps obviously avoid unsightly creases and are excellent for display purposes, but in any quantity create a major storage problem (section 15.2.4). Maps can be made more durable by mounting them on plastic or cloth (Groves, 1980).

13.6 Conclusions

A geological map shows so much more than just the distribution of rocks at the earth's surface. Besides all the projections into three dimensions and back into geological time that have been discussed earlier, this chapter has given a glimpse of the endeavours that lie behind a geological map. Many geological maps represent the culmination of numerous days of careful field survey and considered interpretation, as well as a best attempt to present all the information as elegantly as possible.

A good geological map not only represents the summation of geological understanding of that area at the time, but conveys it pleasingly to the reader. To extract from Edward Greenly's treatise on geological surveying (Greenly and Williams, 1930):

> Nature is beautiful; we are attempting a representation of her. A geological map is made to be looked at . . . let the process be a pleasant one. The surveyor should have kept beauty in view throughout his work. In its colour, as well as in its line, a geological map should be a thing of beauty.

MAP 25 Near Tywyn, Gwynedd, North Wales

The topographic map opposite is reproduced from the 1981 Ordnance Survey 1:10 000 map SH60SW, with the permission of the Controller of Her Majesty's Stationery Office, Crown copyright reserved. It is slightly enlarged here to 1:8000. The area is about 2 km east of Tywyn, N Wales, just off the region covered in Plate 1. The area comprises rocks of the Ashgill series of the Silurian; the continuation of the rocks can be seen on Plate 1 around [SH6603].

Within the Ashgill, a unit of slate known as the Narrow Vein is poorly exposed but has been quarried sporadically for roofing material. In quarries nearby, the unit can be seen to be of reasonably constant thickness and persistently oriented at 062/13° S. Exposures of the Narrow Vein in two of the small quarries are marked in black on Map 25, together with two natural exposures where only the top of the vein is exposed.

Using structure contours, locate the unexposed course of the Narrow Vein. (Begin with the two quarries and, say, the top surface of the vein. Establish the location and route of the 160 m contour, bearing in mind the known strike direction. Add other structure contours whose location can be derived from topography, say the 150 and 170 m values. Having established the spacing, add further structure contours, from about 200 to 130 m, checking their spacing against the known dip of the vein. Project the outcrop course between the two quarries. Repeat for the base of the vein.)

Repeat the procedure independently in the west of the area, using the two exposures of the top surface of the vein. You should find that the structure contours derived here fail to link readily with those drawn from the quarry information. Because the Narrow Vein is thought not to be folded in this district, the explanation may be the presence of a fault.

Suggest on the map where the trace of the fault may run, to best explain the structure contours, complete the Narrow Vein outcrop, and comment on the possible nature and displacement of the fault.

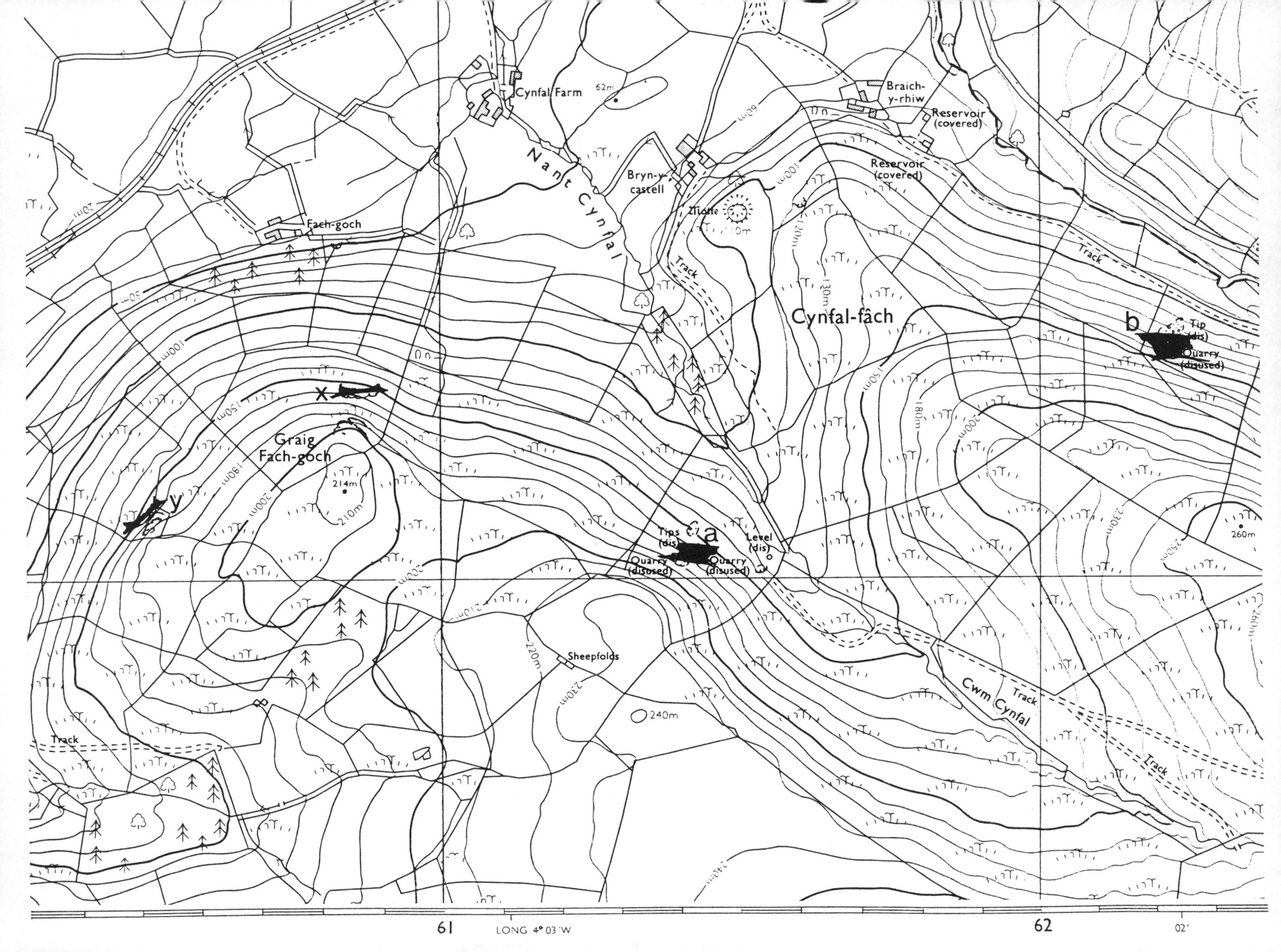

Cynfal Farm
62m
60m
Braich-
y-rhiw
Reservoir
(covered)
Reservoir
(covered)
Nant Cynfal
Bryn-y-
castell
Motte
100m
120m
130m
Track
Fach-goch
20m
50m
100m
150m
180m
200m
Cynfal-fâch
b
Tip
(dis)
Quarry
(disused)
x
y
Graig
Fach-goch
214m
210m
200m
Tips
(dis)
a
Level
(dis)
Quarry
(disused)
Quarry
(disused)
260m
230m
250m
260m
210m
220m
230m
Sheepfolds
240m
240m
Cwm Cynfal
Track
Track
Track
61
LONG 4° 03'W
62
02'

14 The heritage of geological maps

14.1 Introduction

There are facets of geological maps other than those discussed in the preceding chapters, such as the tremendous heritage they represent. The maps we use today have not always looked this way, and the earliest maps did not appear overnight. Geological maps have slowly evolved, in many ways reflecting the growth of geology itself. The first part of this chapter briefly outlines this history. Every geological map embodies parts of the story. The treatment here is brief, but references are provided which give much greater detail. Then there is the human aspect to maps. Many a geological map represents the culmination of much individual labour, and its production may have involved personal conflicts, adventure, even tragedy. There have been individuals and institutions who have contributed influential advances in map methods, and who have bequeathed magnificent maps. The second half of this chapter sketches the lives of six individuals in order to glimpse the personal stories that lie behind their maps and, because they all made influential advances, behind all maps. The choice of people is a rather arbitrary one, aimed at giving some chronological and geographical spread. Some very interesting persons and some very significant maps have had to be passed by.

14.2 A short history of geological maps

Maps of the earth's surface have long been made, but the arrival of geological maps was late, and slow. People had always *thought* about the earth but only when religious dogma was escaped and careful field observations made was the scene set for the advent of maps.

First came the *idea*. John Aubrey, famous for his archaeological discoveries at Stonehenge and Avebury, but called by a contemporary 'a shiftless person, roving and magotie-headed', wrote that he 'often times wished for a mappe of England, coloured according to the colours of the earth, with marks of the fossils and minerals'. Martin Lister, a physician living in York, in 1683 presented a paper entitled 'An ingenious proposal for a new sort of maps of countrys'. He described in some detail how the distribution of soils and rocks at the earth's surface could be displayed on maps so that 'something more might be comprehended'.

Then came maps which actually plotted the locations of minerals and rocks. They were approximate maps, lacking good information and an accurate topographic base. Some were better than others, so that it is unrealistic to specify the 'first' geological map. None had any concept of a sequential or a three-dimensional arrangement of the units. Two early examples were Packe's 1745 depiction of the hills around Canterbury, and Guettard's 1746 map of France (section 14.3.1). Later, Desmarest (1725–75) mapped in detail the basaltic lava flows of the Auvergne, France, showing their sequential arrangement, and the varied geology of the Transbaikal region of the USSR was surveyed by Lebedev and Ivanov between 1794 and 1798 (Pavlinov, 1984).

A tremendous advance in map-making was provided by William Smith (section 14.3.2). He was the first really to grasp the sequential arrangement of sedimentary rocks and depict it on maps with reasonable accuracy. He advertised the practical applications of geological maps. In 1815 he published his momentous map of England and Wales, arguably the most significant geological document there has been, and among the most treasured of geological collector's pieces.

Following this, geological maps began to appear thick and fast. Maps of parts of western Europe were published, with ever-improving detail and accuracy together with maps of entire countries. Another map of England and Wales appeared in 1819, which in its own way was also a remarkable achievement. The Geological Society of London had been formed in 1807 and its first President, Greenough, took on the job of compiling information from well-known geologists of the day to prepare a national geological map. Although it is Smith's map which is today most widely remembered, many regard Greenough's map as the better. MacLure's 1809 map of the eastern USA does not aspire to the cartographic heights achieved by Smith and Greenough, but is an extremely important document in American geological history.

All these maps were the works of private individuals and

societies. However, many of their authors stressed the value to applied geology of good maps, and it was inevitable that governments and public bodies would soon see the need for funding official geological surveys of their regions. There are competing claims as to which was the first official government survey. Guettard was receiving official money for mineralogical purposes in 1746 (section 14.3.1). MacCulloch carried out governmental geological work as early as 1811, and in 1826 was specifically instructed to make a geological map (section 14.3.3).

A geologist was attached to the Trigonometric Survey of India in 1818 (Eyles, 1950), and in 1823 Denison Olmsted of the State University of North Carolina was given $250 a year for four years to undertake geological excursions – perhaps the first use of US public funds for geology. Some remarks on geology and mineral resources had been made in the earlier reports of government expeditions such as the epic Lewis and Clark mission of 1805, but the comments were sparse and incidental. The North Carolina effort did not continue, neither did the State Geologist appointed in South Carolina the following year. The first fully functioning State Survey, soon producing a seven miles to an inch coloured state map as well as a significant advance in knowledge, was inaugurated in Massachusetts in 1830 (Merrill, 1924). A government-financed geological map of France was begun in 1825, completed in 1835 and published in 1841 (Eyles, 1950).

The Ordnance Survey in the UK took an increasing interest in geology, at first mainly in Ireland (Herries Davies, 1983). The Director apparently had the impression that if rock samples were collected from time to time by topographic map-makers, a geologist back at headquarters would be able to construct a geological map from the specimens (Wilson, 1985). Parcels of samples were actually dispatched from the field for this purpose. However, the impracticality of the idea is shown by the issue in 1827 of a seventy-page 'Directions for Geological and Mineralogical Observations', and the appointment of a 'Superintendent of the Geological Sciences in Ireland'.

Shortly after this, in London, what is now the British Geological Survey was born. In 1832, de la Beche (pronounced Beech) offered to make available for £300 the results of his own geological surveying of Devon, to add to the recently published Ordnance Survey maps of that county. De la Beche had been 'dismissed with ignominy' from military college in his youth, but had become an energetic and skilful geological observer. After some negotiation of conditions, a deal was agreed. At a rate of £37.50 for each of the eight sheets (Wilson, 1985) the geological survey was conducted at a cost many orders of magnitude less than it would be today. It worked well, and in 1833 de la Beche was offered a full-time position. The Geological Survey was established as a one-man department of the Ordnance Survey. Wilson (1985) describes what followed: a mixture of political manoeuvering, personality clashes, and shrewd appointments as de la Beche entrenched and expanded his position. By 1845 the Geological Survey employed twenty four scientists.

Geological mapping of the UK accelerated. By 1854, Wales had been surveyed at the one-inch scale, largely by the enthusiastic mapper A. C. Ramsay, who in the same year commenced the Survey's activities in Scotland. Mapping of superficial deposits began in about 1863–5; and the first Survey map of England and Wales was completed in 1883. By the turn of the century, most of Great Britain had been surveyed at the one-inch scale, apart from the Scottish Highlands. By this time it had become the aim, despite the altercations reported by Wilson (1985, chapter 10), to survey the nation at the six-inch scale, for eventual reduction. In general, this approach continues today. It has led to impressive accuracy, but it is very time consuming. In fact, the survey has never been completed for the whole country. Despite its flying start, the BGS is still pursuing its goal.

In the first half of the nineteenth century many parts of the world were geologically mapped, at the reconnaissance level, for the first time. Ireland (1943) gives a list. Detailed maps of small areas continued to proliferate. They were produced by learned natural historians and by amateurs. The day when geological mapping would be limited to technical experts was still far distant.

All this took place in the era of hand-colouring. This produced maps of highly variable colouring standard, and restricted their distribution, despite whole teams of colourers being employed, often apparently, rather poorly paid ladies (Wilson, 1985). Colour printing of geological maps began in 1851, after some unsuccessful false starts (Ireland, 1943). This made an immense difference to the availability of maps. The contrast is reflected in the prices these antique geological maps command today – hand-coloured maps fetch a considerable premium.

As the nineteenth century progressed, geological surveys were set up in more and more countries. Greenly and Williams listed over 50 in 1930. Some of these were to have a curtailed future, if only because the country itself ceased to exist. A Geological Survey of Canada was established in 1842, under William Logan. He returned to Canada after work for the British Survey in South Wales (Bassett, 1969a). Merrill (1924) recalls that when Logan began his work in Canada: 'a large part of the country was wilderness, without roads, and there were no maps. Little was known of the region beside the coast-line, of the geology practically nothing. From dawn to dusk he paced or paddled, and yet his work was not finished, for while his Indians (often his sole companions) smoked their pipes around their evening fire, he wrote his notes and plotted the day's measurements'. Since that time the Geological Survey of Canada has become a major organisation, with a prodigious output. Although Greenly and Williams (1930) felt that 'the whole system of publication of this survey appears to be complicated and difficult for an outside person to understand', the publications today are well catalogued and handsome maps have been produced.

In Australia various state surveys were established between 1856 (Victoria) and 1896 (W Australia) (Darragh, 1977), eventually leading to the formation of a coordinating body, the Bureau of Mineral Resources. The Geological Survey of New Zealand was formed in 1865.

Geological work in the United States had steadily progressed for several decades, and by the later part of the nineteenth century the west was rapidly being opened up, with several Territorial Surveys competing to reveal its geology (e.g. Bartlett, 1962; see section 14.3.5). Coordination became imperative, and in 1879 the USGS was established (e.g. Rabbit, 1980a). From the start this organisation had the responsibility for both the topographical and geological surveying of that country. As Linton (1947) has pointed out, this coordinated effort gave an immediate advantage over the European counterparts, where often the geological surveys had to make do with the base maps produced for a different purpose by a separate institution which was somewhat insensitive to the geologists' needs. The growth of the USGS has been awesome, its output enormous. But its products have always been well catalogued, its maps models of clarity and consistency.

At the same time as the launching of government surveys, in many places learned societies were being founded, each commonly publishing its own journal. Until recently, these learned journals formed the main vehicle for individual geologists to publish geological maps. The *Quarterly Journal of the Geological Society of London*, for example, contains numerous maps of many parts of the world. Such journal maps have to be folded up if they are at all large, and few are in colour, but they represent tremendous advances in knowledge.

Many geological companies realised the need for systematic investigations of their geological properties. Maps of mineral prospects, detailed mine maps, quarry maps, all were produced, sometimes in great detail, but usually for the private use of the company. Exploration for oil spawned a host of new cartographic techniques, especially concerning the subsurface geology.

Many of the principles that came into being in the early days of geological maps have carried through to today. The methods are greatly refined, but making a geological map is still basically the same endeavour with the same goals. However, the increased specialisation of modern earth science has encouraged today's journals to print articles on more specialised aspects of geology. Thematic maps (section 15.4) abound in them. Similarly, the efforts of geological surveys have diversified such that only a portion of the staff are engaged on basic surveying. This is also a reflection on the increased efficiency of surveying methods (section 15.2.1) and the power of modern instrumental techniques. It does not imply any diminishment of the central importance of the geological map.

14.3 The contributions of some individuals

14.3.1 Jean Etienne Guettard (1715–86)

Guettard was a great observer. At a time when thinking about the earth was still based on a mixture of religion and speculation, Guettard was a tireless collector of *facts*. He was a pioneer in seeing the value of displaying observations on a map. His maps were a long way from the kinds of thing we expect today, but it was a bold start.

As a child, Guettard was interested in natural history, especially plants. He trained as a doctor but continued to collect plant specimens. He became struck by how their occurrence appeared to depend on certain minerals and rocks. Eventually, it was the 'mineral substances' themselves, and *their* distribution, that came to dominate his interest. Guettard was a very energetic collector of information. He travelled widely in France, visiting mineral localities, observing all the time, and assiduously reading all the literature that was available to him. Unfortunately, as Rappaport (1969) put it: 'The talent he most conspicuously lacked was that of generalisation, of seeing the implications of his own observations.' He desperately needed some way of organising and presenting his vast amount of data.

With time, Guettard began to suspect that there may be some sort of pattern to the distribution of the mineral deposits. Rock classification was in those days a hazy affair, but he began to think that rocks, too, were not distributed haphazardly. The three kinds of rock he recognised, which he called 'sandy', 'marly', and 'schistose', seemed to occur in broad bands. He thought that if he could establish the 'determinate trend' of these bands, it would be possible to *predict* the kinds of rock in unknown country. But how could he illustrate this?

Guettard hit upon the idea of marking the mineral deposits and rocks on a map. He had little to guide him on how to do it. What little there had been done on similar lines was probably not known to Guettard. So he took an existing map of France, and used symbols, mainly chemical ones, to mark the locations of mineral deposits, and added a few fossil localities. The distribution of his three rock types was indicated by an engraved shading. The rocks did, indeed, fall into bands. His *Memoire et Carte Minéralogique* was presented in Paris in 1746 and published in 1751 (Geikie, 1905).

At a stroke, the map enabled Guettard to organise, synthesise and communicate his information, and to test his ideas. He had stumbled upon what were to become vital functions of geological maps. There was now no stopping him. On his first map, the three rock bands stopped at the English Channel, and Guettard predicted that they would reappear in England. He searched the literature for supporting information – reading no English, he had to rely on what had been translated – and convinced himself that he was right. So, on to a map of England went the same system of symbols and engraving. He tackled next, still relying on literature, the whole of Western Europe, from Iceland to the Mediterranean, and, later on, the Middle East and North America.

His maps were well received. This 'new kind of map' was deemed to open up a new field for geographers and naturalists, providing a link between the two subjects. Guettard extolled the practical value of his maps, for example, their use in locating further supplies of good building stone and durable road material. He felt sure that the maps would lead to a unified understanding of the earth. He was, however, dissatisfied with the accuracy of his work, saying, 'If you will only let me have a proper map of France, I will undertake to show on it the mineral formations underneath.' With the help of a young man called Lavoisier, destined to become the great chemist, and later on Monnet, Guettard went on to complete sixteen detailed sheets of France and a large report. The *Atlas et Description Minéralogique de la France* was published in 1780 (Rappaport, 1969).

Clearly, Guettard had made a great step in the direction of geological mapping. But can his maps be called 'geological maps'? Probably not, in a modern sense. They were, at best, approximate, partly because the base maps of the time were insufficient for accurate work, partly because much of his geological information, even in France, was second-hand. But there is a much more fundamental shortcoming: the maps were strictly two dimensional. There was no attempt to show the relationships between units, either geometrically or stratigraphically.

It is probably not that Guettard had no comprehension of geological relationships, more that he felt it involved too much inference. For Guettard, almost obsessed by the importance of observation, believed that if something were not factual it should not be shown on a map. As we have seen in this book, the modern geological map, in contrast, is intrinsically an interpretive document.

The point is well illustrated by a disagreement during the preparation of the 1780 Atlas. Lavoisier had grasped the importance of stratigraphic sequence, and realised that it may lead to an understanding of geological history. He had assembled some stratigraphic columns with this in mind, compound ones, drawn from various localities. This was all too speculative for Guettard, not the kind of thing he wanted on his maps. In addition, Lavoisier would have liked to infer more about distributions: 'It is only necessary to link all similar symbols by lines which would show not only the size and extent [of each deposit] but also their various points of intersection' (Rappaport, 1969, p. 283). However, Guettard, the senior man, had his way. Inference was not allowed on the map, although some of the sheets do have Lavoisier's compound sections in the map margin.

Before his death in 1786, Guettard published numerous, detailed papers, all based on his meticulous observations. But it is for his maps that he is most remembered. Besides illustrating geological distributions, he had pioneered the use of maps for data collection and synthesis, just as with modern maps. However, fundamental map problems were left untackled. The matters of dealing with the three-dimensional arrangement of rocks, of depicting stratigraphic sequence, and of combining inference with observation still lay ahead.

14.3.2 William Smith (1769–1839)

Smith is by any standards one of geology's greats. He first understood and communicated the idea of sequence in layered deposits and recognised their characteristic fossil assemblages, two concepts fundamental to stratigraphy. He was a pioneer of applying his geological knowledge: to finding underground water; to drainage schemes; to coal mines and canals. And he produced his epoch-making geological map. Much has already been written about the man, and his maps, but they are too significant not to be included here. Also, it is very relevant to the theme of this book that Smith apparently found writing awkward and difficult; it was through his maps that his perceptive geological knowledge and understanding were communicated.

Smith was born in Churchill, Oxfordshire, in 1769. His father was a blacksmith and his ancestors ordinary farmers – facts which became increasingly relevant when Smith encroached on a geological community dominated by the well-to-do. By the time he was eighteen, Smith was an apprentice surveyor at Stow-on-the-Wold and taking on increasing responsibilities. In 1792, while surveying coal properties, he lodged at Rugborne Farm, near High Littleton, seven miles southwest of Bath and 'began to think about the succession of the strata' (Eyles, 1969). This farmhouse he later called 'the birthplace of English Geology'.

According to Cox (1942), Smith was always 'ready to converse, with friend or stranger, upon many subjects, but usually reverting finally to his favourite topic – the strata of the earth and the application of their study to agriculture, mining and all words of public utility'. He began to realise that the geology of England is dominated by a regular succession of different strata, tilted towards the southeast. His continuing work furnished him with more and more evidence. Later critics said that Smith became over-obsessed with this belief, but the important thing for us is that he hit upon the idea of showing the arrangement on a map.

He drew a map of the area '5 miles round the city of Bath', one-and-a-half inches to a mile, which was 'coloured geologically in 1799'. In 1801 he produced two small maps of England and Wales to show the overall arrangement of the strata (Eyles, 1969). In the same year he issued a prospectus for a large-scale and accurate map of the strata of the whole of England and Wales. He began putting this together while continuing his various applied geological activities – supervising sinkings for coal, devising sea defences, etc. – and all the while amassing a fossil collection. This was displayed on sloping shelves in order to correspond with the beds in which they were found (Eyles, 1969).

Here we glimpse some of the obstacles which Smith had to overcome in order to publish what was to become his celebrated map. To start with, there was no topographical base map sufficiently uncluttered and accurate for Smith to use. He had to spend time and money persuading a London map engraver and publisher, John Cary, that his project was worthwhile enough to justify the preparation of a base expressly for Smith's purpose. And Smith did not have much money (Eyles, 1967). His nephew, John Phillips, later remarked that Smith's hearty laugh was a cover for his financial difficulties. Although making a reasonable living from his consulting work, with the Napoleonic wars in progress times were hard, and Smith was relying on his map to make him some money. After all, it was taking about fifteen years to collect the map data, carefully, single-handed, and without financial support. The cost of publishing the map became heavy. Each of the sixteen sheets had to be hand-coloured, and several artists had to be employed merely to do the colouring. Smith began to see that profits from the sales of his map would be thin. It was this situation which turned Smith to the idea of selling off his beloved fossil collection, a saga recalled in detail by Eyles (1967). It also meant tht even when the map did appear, it was to have a publication life of only four years.

Then there was the matter of the rival map, being assembled by Greenough for the Geological Society of London, and representing many of the leading geological figures of the day. Why, in 1812, did Greenough even contemplate such a map, when Smith's project was nearing completion? The question has been much discussed (e.g. Bailey, 1952). A friend of Smith's, John Farey, complained of the 'very unhandsome conduct of certain persons' in trying to strangle the sale of Smith's map. Greenough said he thought that Smith had abandoned his project.

Why did the Geological Society not lend its support to Smith's endeavour, rather than launch a rival project? Perhaps Smith would not have wished it; he was an independent man. According to his nephew, John Phillips, Smith had said: '. . . I foresaw that the truth and practicability of my system must be tested far and wide before its uses could be generally known and its worth duly appreciated. I thought, of course, no one could do this so well as myself . . .' (Bassett, 1969b). Also, Smith's working-class background had probably not gone unnoticed. Smith may have been a difficult fellow to work with, but one wonders if the stories behind some geological maps not only involve individuals and their personalities, but the circumstances of their birth. Smith had already stated his preference for 'Saxon and British words' rather than those contrived from 'dead languages', ruffling the feathers of the classically educated geologists of the time. Smith was not even invited to join the Geological Society until 1830, by which time recognition of his achievement was such that he could hardly be excluded.

Even seventy years later, Archibald Geikie, a later doyen of the geological establishment, was critical of Smith's uncultured approach. Geikie (1905) thought Smith's efforts were limited, and he saw them in the light of Smith's background:

> William Smith was tall and broadly built, like the English yeomen from whom he came. His face was that of an honest, sagacious farmer. His work, indeed bears out the impression conveyed by his portrait. His plain, solid, matter-of-fact intellect never branched into theory or speculation. His range of geological vision was as limited as his general acquirements.

Anyway, Smith's map did appear, in 1815. Not only was it the first geological map in any modern sense, it was of two entire countries, and the work entirely of one man. It embodied innovative principles, which are now fundamental to geology. There are sixteen sheets in twenty colours. At a scale of about five miles to one inch, the entire map occupies six feet by eight-and-a-half feet. The units are shown in their correct overall stratigraphic order, with the bases distinguished from the tops by a heavier tint. The inclined units even 'V' across the valleys in the correct way. Of course, there were mistakes and shortcomings; Challinor (1970) gives a list. Many users felt it was soon superceded in accuracy and clarity by Greenough's map of 1819. Smith was aware of some of the inadequacies, and took the opportunity to improve the map at each printing (Eyles and Eyles, 1938).

It has been said that with Smith's effort 'the geological map had arrived'. The colours Smith chose had no little influence on succeeding maps, both in Britain and elsewhere (section 13.3.5). In fact, at first glance, Smith's 1815 map is not greatly different from the BGS Ten Mile map of today. Smith continued to produce beautiful maps. Between 1819 and 1824 he published a *New Geological Atlas of England and Wales*, comprising maps of twenty-one counties. Some were recently reprinted by the British Museum of Natural History. In 1828, Smith moved to Hackness near Scarborough, in Yorkshire, and four years later published a remarkably detailed and accurate map of the Hackness Hills.

Of Smith's great 1815 map, the Eyleses were able to trace in 1938 only about thirty copies still in existence, distributed among only twelve owners. It will never be reprinted: Eyles and Eyles (1938) record that, when in 1877 the owner of the sixteen copper plates, Edward Stanford, offered to sell them 'at trifling cost' to the Geological Society of London, there was no support for the idea. The plates were melted down.

14.3.3 *John MacCulloch (1773–1835)*

MacCulloch was one of the first persons in the UK to receive government funds for geological purposes. He made numerous pioneering geological observations, wrote a travel book which is still in print, and made the earliest published geological map of Scotland.

Topographical surveying early last century was still in the hands of a government military body, called the Board of Ordnance. It had been set up in medieval times to survey artillery installations. John MacCulloch, trained as a surgeon but attached to the Board of Ordnance as a chemist, also had an interest in geology. In 1811 he was given an official geological job to do (Eyles, 1950): he was sent to Scotland to find out what kinds of rock were safest for grinding gunpowder! In 1814, he was appointed geologist to the newly formed Trigonometrical Survey unit of the Board of Ordnance to examine certain aspects of Scottish geology. This unit subsequently became the Ordnance Survey of the UK. The appointment of MacCulloch arguably formed the earliest state geological survey.

In 1819 MacCulloch published what was to become a classic of travel literature and of Scottish geology, his book: *A Description of the Western Islands of Scotland.* An abridged version is still sold today. Challinor (1970) lists twenty-seven original geological discoveries contained in the book, many of them now fundamental to Scottish geology. Ten coloured geological maps were included, covering many of the Hebridean Islands.

Despite all this, the Head of the Board of Ordnance, the Duke of Wellington, terminated the geological appointment. MacCulloch returned to being official chemist, but continued his survey of Scottish geology *at his own expense.* Only after several years had passed did the Treasury restore MacCulloch's financial support. In 1826, he received government funds for the sole purpose of preparing a geological map. A new era in geology had begun. The need for official geological surveying had been realised, and funds earmarked for it. But even back then, patterns were being set of relationships with universities and of expense claims which are not unfamiliar today. For example, one of the best-known university geologists of the time, Robert Jameson, snubbed the official effort, saying that MacCulloch's Survey was 'utterly unknown to any public body in Scotland' (Eyles, 1950).

Regarding expenses, MacCulloch was to receive £2 a day while in the field, £1 a day personal costs, and 2 shillings (10p) per mile travel expenses. In his first field season MacCulloch claimed over 7000 miles of travel costs, plus costs of boat hires, guides, stationery, and 'pedemeters' for measuring distances 'on foot, horse and carriage'. The Treasury was embarrassed, having greatly underestimated what was involved in a geological survey. So MacCulloch had to account in detail for his movements and his costs: the auditor questioned his large mileages and the short time taken to cover them. MacCulloch replied that accountants failed to understand the nature of geological field work.

MacCulloch pressed on, apparently working long days, including Sundays, and being paid considerably in arrears. Then doubts began to arise in official circles about whether or not the map should be published. Murchison was unsure about the quality of the field notes, though he thought the 'sketch' of a map might be useful. The topographic base map was known to be inaccurate – MacCulloch later spent much of the first fifty pages of his 'Memoirs' abusing it. In fact, if the Highland and Agricultural Society of Scotland had not taken an interest in the map (Boud, 1985), it may have 'remained buried in the archive of a government department' (Eyles, 1937). MacCulloch may not have helped the situation himself, being, rather like William Smith, fiercely independent. Flett (1937) says that MacCulloch had the reputation of being short-tempered and difficult to agree with. He became increasingly bitter that his work was not being properly recognised.

However, the map eventually did appear, in 1836. It comprised four hand-coloured sheets, each 86 × 69 cm, at a scale of four miles to an inch (1:250 000), and used eighteen different colours. The main elements of Scottish geology show clearly. It is now a famous document, but it somehow typifies MacCulloch's dogged career that he did not live to see it published. He married, for the first time, when he was 62, the year before the map came out. Whilst on his honeymoon, MacCulloch was killed by a runaway carriage.

As a final irony, Eyles (1950) draws attention to the review of the published map in the *Scotsman* newspaper. The price of £5 for the map was thought high by the reviewer. Yet, the topographic base map sold for the equivalent of £4.50. MacCulloch's life work, a classic document on Scottish geology, was being deemed to be overpriced at 50p.

14.3.4 *John Phillips (1800–74)*

John Phillips saw and helped engineer the change from the restrictions of hand-coloured maps to the increasingly accurate and more widely available colour printed maps.

He was born on Christmas Day, 1800, at Marden, in Wiltshire. His father was from near Carmarthen, in Wales, but migrated to Oxfordshire, where he married the sister of no less a person than William Smith. John Phillips lost his father when he was seven, and his mother soon after, and therefore came under the care of his Uncle William. When Phillip's schooling was finished, he went to live with Smith, in a house 'full of maps, sections, models, and collections of fossils'. He began to accompany his uncle on long walks, and on what would today be called consulting work. In this way, Phillips learned his geology.

In 1824, Phillips accompanied his uncle to York, where

Smith was giving a series of lectures, and he became interested in the fossil collection of the Yorkshire Museum. Phillips was eventually appointed Keeper to the Museum, and lived in the old museum buildings now known as St Mary's Lodge until 1853. During this time, Phillips was a busy man. He was instrumental in setting up the British Association for the Advancement of Science, had periods as Professor of Geology at King's College London, and Trinity College Dublin, and published much on the geology of Yorkshire, including several maps. He coined the names for the stratigraphic eras – Palaeozoic, Mesozoic, and Cenozoic. He advertised the pleasures of geology, encouraging people to ramble in the hills and valleys of Yorkshire 'for a better knowledge of its natural beauties'. Phillips seems to have been an amiable and easy-going fellow. Perhaps this is why he could get along with his somewhat prickly uncle. And, during his time at York, Phillips introduced to Britain a major advance in map production.

He had witnessed the delays his uncle had experienced before publication of the 1815 map (section 14.3.2). The hand-colouring of each copy of that map took about a week, and added greatly to the cost. John Phillips learned of the new German technique of lithography, where, through the antipathy of grease and water, a picture drawn in ink on fine stone can be pressed on to a sheet of paper. He learned the art of drawing on stone, and lithographed pictures for his uncle (Butcher, 1983). The plates in Phillip's 1841 work on SW England are lithographed by William Monkhouse, who operated in Lendal, York, close to Phillip's residence. Butcher (1983) remarks that the two seem to have struck up a friendship, so that when in 1849 Phillips began compiling a general work on the geology of Yorkshire, it was Monkhouse who lithographed the thirty-five plates. The book, *Geology of Yorkshire*, appeared in 1853, and one of the plates was a geological map of Yorkshire *lithographed in colour*. This is the earliest known colour-printed map in Britain (Butcher, 1983).

Colour printing of maps had been attempted in Europe for over a decade using various combinations of tin foil and cardboard masks, but there were always problems where the colours met (Ireland, 1943). Different stones were tried for the different colours, with varying degrees of success. Phillip's map employed four stones for the black, blue, red, and yellow inks, with which he was able to generate fourteen shades. The results were acceptable, although Butcher (1983) comments on the 'widespread and patchy discolouration' of the first edition of the map. The second edition, published in 1855, was an improvement.

In these infant days of colour-printing, the results were variable. Ireland (1943) cites an English 1853 map of N America as being 'poorly executed and much inferior to the excellent hand-coloured maps typical of the English publication of that date'. But the advantages of colour-printing were obvious and, as soon as the practical snags had been ironed out, the days of hand-colouring were numbered. John Phillips went on to become professor of geology at Oxford, organising the geological museum there, and to publish numerous works on geology, on other planets, even on the weather. But in many ways his main contribution to geology had been made while at York; this is certainly true of his contribution to geological maps. It is fitting that he was returned there to be buried. There is a memorial window to him in St Olave's Church, adjacent to where he lived.

14.3.5 John Wesley Powell (1834–1902)

John Wesley Powell – US Civil War soldier, Grand Canyon explorer, and government scientist – directed the USGS during its formative years. He was energetic in promoting the importance of geological maps to the government at a vital time, and was instrumental in establishing methods and standards which are apparent in today's maps of the USA and elsewhere.

Powell was born in New York state in 1834, four years after the arrival from England of his Methodist minister father. He took an early interest in natural history, studying it, and eventually teaching it. By 1860, civil war was looming in the US, and Powell, with his strong Methodist anti-slavery background, was one of the first to volunteer for Lincoln's army. He quickly rose in rank, already showing his leadership talents. At the Battle of Shiloh, while raising his arm to signal 'fire', he was badly shot. His arm had to be amputated. Within months, however, he was back in the action, with his love of geology intact. According to a colleague (Rabbit, 1980b), while marching his regiment through new areas, Powell would 'familiarise himself with the geology'. He was in the trenches at the Battle of Vicksburg, at the same time collecting rocks and fossils for the Illinois State Museum.

At the end of the war, Powell, tough and war-hardened, and with administrative and scientific experience, looked for employment – and excitement. He took a geology teaching job in Illinois, which provided the former but not the latter. The unexplored west was beckoning. The great rivers attracted Powell, and especially that last largely unknown place – the Grand Canyon of the Colorado. And so, while retaining his teaching position, he organised an expedition there. It was largely self-financed, and it was ill-thought out. Faull and Faull (1981) remarked that 'at the time it could have been reasonably viewed as a reckless and pig-headed adventure', although 'in retrospect we know it was the beginning of a great survey'.

Excitement it certainly provided. Boats were lost, and the food turned rancid. The crew got sick. One day, what was left of their clothing caught fire at the campground, and the explorers had to continue their journey half-naked. At one point, Powell fell while climbing the canyon wall, but managed to grab a jutting ledge. He dangled over the canyon, hanging by his single arm, while a colleague scrambled to the only accessible point above Powell, but out of reach. A barometer case was stretched down, but it also failed to reach Powell. Finally, the colleague took off his 'drawers' and lowered them down. Powell let go of his vital handhold, being momentarily suspended over the canyon before grasping the rescuing underpants.

The crew grew increasingly despondent. They were exasperated at Powell being continually captivated by the geology and oblivious to their dire situation. One member wrote about Powell that 'if only he can study geology he will be happy without food or shelter, but the rest of us are not afflicted with it' (Bartlett, 1962). Eventually, three of the group decided to leave the expedition. They managed to climb out of the canyon, whereupon they were shot by Indians.

Information accumulated about the natural history and Indian culture of the canyon, though not a great deal about the geology. The individual mainly responsible for the geological surveying was one of the three that had been shot, and in any case, the surveying equipment had been lost in the river. However, beautiful ink drawings were produced (see Fig. 6.1) with sufficient care and detail to bring out the main configurations of the rocks (Powell, 1895).

A rumour spread that the entire party had drowned in one of the rapids. The story appeared in several national newspapers, with an obituary to Powell included. As a result, when the bedraggled expedition reappeared, having navigated the canyon, Powell got national publicity beyond his dreams. Fame came instantly, together with funding for more exploration. A second expedition brought back considerably more geological information, and led to a complete topographic map of the region, and also tremendous popular interest. Powell was a national hero.

At this same time, other government surveys were operating in the west, and conflicts of interest began to develop. Congress saw fit to consolidate activities, and in 1879 established the USGS (Rabbit, 1980a). The first director did not enjoy the politics involved in such a position and after only two years resigned in favour of Powell. He had the right administrative and political qualities, as well as common support. He assembled round him a group of exceedingly able scientists, on whose advice he could draw and on whose work he could rely. Powell, himself, did little more in the way of surveying, indeed geology remained as only one of his interests. He was, however, committed to the fundamental importance of geology and geological maps, and was adamant on the necessary standards of accuracy and presentation.

Powell established a series of committees to consider just how geological mapping should be executed, and how the map is best produced. The results were radical. For example, accuracy of the topographic base map was deemed paramount, and it had to be contoured. Hachuring and shading, so much in vogue elsewhere, were out. The typeface, symbols, colours, etc. of the topographic map were carefully designed, not as an end in themselves, but to produce a base on which other data, particularly geological, could be shown effectively. Such a coordinated approach was unknown in Europe, where the geological surveyors had to make do with the base maps they were given.

Powell's committees gave a lot of thought to the nature and status of the map units, and designed a colour scheme based on several criteria. At first, the approach was 'to follow common usage', which was essentially the William Smith approach of mimicking the colour of the natural rock. After four years of attempts, this usage was deemed to be 'vicious and bad' (Powell, 1881). An 'entirely new colour scheme' was to be employed. For example, by a logical system of printing the spectrum colours, plus brown and grey, in spaced lines of various combinations of orientations, 'several hundred distinctions for the clastic rocks' were demonstrated to be feasible. Colour-printing of hieroglyphic-like symbols, with various weights, sizes, and closeness, gave several hundred distinctions for the Archaean alone. A scheme of letter symbols was devised to facilitate further distinction of the units, and also in case the colours should fade with map use. The 'explanation of colours' conventionally employed was replaced by a new kind of map legend designed to help each map be self-explanatory and of maximum value to all kinds of users.

These ideas were immediately put into operation by the USGS. Under Powell's directorship, these innovative, high standard maps began to pour out. At the same time, new subdivisions of the Survey were founded. The USGS burgeoned into the world's premier geological organisation.

Meanwhile, Powell's strong opinions were brought to bear on broader concerns, such as organisation of the settling of the west and irrigation of the lands. These were emotive issues in a time of political delicacy. Powell had 'made warm friends and strong enemies' (Merrill, 1924), and eventually the latter won out. Powell resigned the directorship in 1894, although continuing his interests in Indian affairs. His health deteriorated, further surgery was required on his arm, and in 1902 he died and was buried in Arlington National Cemetry.

Today, the significance of his scientific ideas are being rediscovered (Rabbit, 1980a), and the romance of his military and exploring achievements glows brighter than ever. But his geological legacy lies mainly in maps. It is seen in every quadrangle produced by the USGS, and all the other national surveys which have followed the lead of that institution.

14.3.6 Sir Edward Bailey (1881–1965)

Edward Bailey had many parallels with J. W. Powell. For

example, both were infused with the importance of geological maps, both sustained serious war wounds, and both rose to become Director of their nation's Geological Survey. Unlike Powell, however, Bailey disliked the administrative aspects of Survey work, and was perfectly happy making maps, including some of the most outstanding maps ever produced by the BGS.

Edward Bailey was born weak, and suffered a sickly childhood. At school he was picked on by bullies, and took some cruel beatings. Bailey's reaction to this was to set about 'toughening himself up'. He did this in no small way, until he built up a mental and physical fearlessness which was to become a hallmark for the rest of his life, to the point of eccentricity. As an undergraduate student he would go for marathon walks at night, he took up boxing, and he would sleep all year with his bedroom window wide open and only a cotton sheet for a cover. He graduated in 1902 and applied to join the Geological Survey. Only two people were appointed that year, but Bailey was one of them, despite having broken the nose of the Director's nephew in an undergraduate boxing match.

To his great delight, Bailey was assigned to the West Highland unit. There, the complex geology and the difficult terrain were to be his delight for many years. Perhaps more importantly, he joined a team comprising three of the finest geologists the BGS has ever employed. Ben Peach and John Horne were fresh from their brilliant unravelling of the Moine Thrust region of northwest Scotland, and the field maps of the equally gifted C. T. Clough have often been cited as the standard against which others should be judged. The mapping training that Bailey received, and his sudden exposure to 'a jostling crowd of problems awaiting solution' exhilarated Bailey for the rest of his life. By his twenty-first birthday he was mapping independently for the BGS, and Bailey went on to be involved with many of the superb geological maps of the Scottish western seaboard.

Even so, for Bailey the maps alone were not sufficient. The accompanying memoirs were vital channels for Bailey to expound his imaginative interpretations of the geological histories of the surveyed areas. The memoir accompanying the map of Glencoe, for example, allowed the first detailed three-dimensional analysis of a volcanic caldera. It was a characteristic of Bailey's writing that terms were used exactly, and if no suitable terms existed, he would invent them – antiform and synform, for example. In addition, Bailey was beginning to publish the results of geological studies carried out in his own time – evenings, weekends, holidays – in journals other than official Survey publications. As we shall see shortly, the liberty to do this was to become to Bailey a principle of profound importance.

All was not plain sailing in these early days, though. Bailey's eccentricities were already raising eyebrows. Why was some of his fieldwork being done barefoot? And was he really conducting official Survey work *wearing shorts*? The hierarchy reeled, and informed Bailey that he was not wearing 'sufficiently formal attire'. Hearing this, Bailey promptly resigned, which rattled his senior supervisors even more. A special dispensation was produced which allowed Bailey to continue his work in shorts.

At the start of World War I, Bailey volunteered for duty, which took him away from his beloved Highlands; he was posted to an island off Plymouth. This did not part him from geology, however, for he immediately began surveying the island, the results of which he published after the war. He was eventually sent to the front line, and was badly wounded during the Battle of the Somme and later at Ypres. He sustained a badly damaged arm and lost an eye. He was later knighted for gallantry in battle.

After the war, Bailey was able to return to the survey of western Scotland, and was put in charge. Most significantly, in the present context, he was put in a position to complete a project he had been involved with off and on since 1907 – the mapping of the island of Mull and nearby areas. The finished one-inch map appeared in 1924, and the following year the accompanying two volume explanatory memoir was published. The map is superb. It has been called a 'landmark in the history of geological cartography'.

The intricate geology of the island of Mull, a deeply-eroded Tertiary volcanic complex, had presented a formidable scientific challenge, and it was tough terrain. Bailey was entranced, both with the routine surveying, and the gradual deciphering of the volcanic story that was hidden in the rugged mountains. His commitment to geology and oblivion to danger is reminiscent of J. W. Powell. On one occasion of prolonged heavy rain, the survey team was camped in a meadow which became flooded. The team was forced to leave during the night, only to realise the next morning that Bailey had not joined their evacuation. One of them waded back to Bailey's tent, to find the water lapping just inches below the level of the canvas camp bed. On the bed lay Bailey, happily reading a text book on physics.

The mapping of Mull has been called 'one of the most wonderful chapters of the geology of Britain'. When the map was published 'new lustre had been added to the Geological Survey' (Flett, 1937). The precision with which the intricate geology is portrayed, including over forty kinds of igneous rocks, is a joy to the eye. It is the kind of map that draws gasps when first seen. One can find criticisms – the density of the colours tending to obscure the topographic base, the oddly slanting annotations – but these are quibbles. Without doubt the Mull sheet represents one of the highest pinnacles of achievement of the BGS.

Nevertheless, Bailey was continuing to annoy his superiors with his machismo activities. He would soak his boots at the start of a day in the field, so that further wettings would go unnoticed. He was renowned for eating nothing more than a chocolate bar for lunch, or, if he had been supplied with more, eating it first thing to 'get it over with'. On one occasion Bailey received an official reprimand for leading his new Assistant Director through a chin-deep river, when he knew there was a perfectly good bridge just out of sight upstream.

But much more significantly than all this, in 1920 a Director was appointed to the BGS who felt that all his staff's scientific writings, whether or not they were related to Survey work, had to be vetted by him. This was completely contrary to the principle of scientific liberty cherished by Bailey. He became increasingly uneasy with the new regime. In turn, his Director became increasingly paranoid about enforcing his new rule. Things eventually came to a head. When Bailey was banned from looking at any of the Survey's field maps, even though they were available for consultation by the general public, it was the last straw. Bailey knew he had to move. He resigned, taking up the life of a university professor at Glasgow.

There, Bailey clearly enjoyed himself, travelling far and wide, coming up with innovative interpretations, and letting his geological imagination roam. He was one of the first in the UK to embrace a wild new theory which involved the continents actually drifting apart. He seized on the significance in rocks of 'way-up' indicators, was one of the first to recognise submarine slumping in rocks, and anticipated the concept of growth faulting.

Bailey had an unrivalled grasp of the three-dimensional aspects of mapwork. He began to apply his skills to geometrically difficult regions such as the Swiss Alps. The convoluted forms of the sections he constructed became nicknamed 'Bailey's bicycles'. He, himself, enjoyed a play on his first name in his paper entitled 'Eddies in mountain structure'. He formulated some of the methods for dealing with the outcrop patterns of structurally complex areas, and, following a visit to the Appalachians, helped promote the 'down-structure' viewing technique (section 8.3).

But all the time, despite the treasured scientific liberty which a university offered, it seems that the Geological Survey was still his first love. In 1936 he was invited to return as Director. Bailey accepted, but on his own conditions regarding research. As it turned out, he had little time to put his ideals into action before once again he and his Survey were plunged into supporting the national war effort.

In World War II, BGS geologists were not involved in the fighting, but in all kinds of strategic support work. Geological surveying was required for underground vaults, new airbases, temporary water supplies, etc. as well as sources of raw materials which could no longer be imported. These ranged from coal and iron to less obvious but vital needs – sand for sandbags, mica for electrical equipment, silica for optical glass, even sapphires for aircraft compass pivots. Bailey threw himself into his new responsibilities. He was later to be proud of the BGS war effort, and was eager to point out that its duties had been greatly facilitated by the fact that high-standard geological maps of the UK already existed.

During the war, the BGS office was evacuated, becoming the Civil Defence Headquarters. The geological maps and materials were shipped to North Wales for safety; the geologists, too, were moved. Except Bailey, that is. He found space sufficient for a temporary office on the topmost gallery of the Survey building and worked there throughout the London blitz. True to form, he seemed oblivious of the danger, even after he was 'temporarily buried by a V1 or Doodlebug' (Bailey, 1952).

At the end of the war, Bailey saw the need for the Survey to have a fresh look. Reorganisation was necessary, and Bailey felt that it was time for him to make way for new blood. He retired, although until his death twenty years later he continued actively in geology, publishing research papers and attending geological meetings – invariably wearing shorts! In 1948, there came to fruition one of his pet projects. Back in 1942 Bailey had been appointed to look after the geological aspects of a 'National Atlas'. He had arranged for the BGS to produce a map at the innovative scale of 1:625 000, or 'about ten miles to an inch'. The scale was selected in order that the land mass could be accommodated on 'two not over-large sheets'. The map was to carry a new kind of ten-kilometre grid. This was to help unify the two sheets and give easy correlation with larger scale maps which from then on were to carry a kilometre grid. This 'National Grid' would also provide a convenient and precise reference system for locations 'much more easy to employ than that given by longitudes and latitudes' (Bailey, 1952).

Most of the detailed survey data were already available on the one-inch sheets; it was largely a matter of compilation and reorganisation to fit the new scale. Bailey took the project to heart. The north sheet covered the Scottish Highlands and islands and he saw this part, especially, as his own. We can imagine him during those long dark evenings of the war, perhaps even with the sound of air-raids around him, drafting his map.

On its publication, the map was hailed a great success. Since then it has remained the standard geological map of Great Britain, and a model for many other national maps. Without a great deal of alteration, a second edition was published in 1957, and a third in 1979. Part of the south sheet of the map is, of course, reproduced here as Plate 2. The north and south sheets are widely available today for purchase. Also still sold are the one-inch maps of the Scottish western seaboard which Bailey helped produce. They remain the definitive maps of those areas (some now photographically enlarged to 1:50 000), especially the celebrated Mull map. The legacy to geological maps of Sir Edward Bailey remains very tangible.

15 Current trends in geological maps

15.1 Introduction

In many ways geological maps have changed little during the couple of hundred years of their existence. The last chapter mentioned improvements such as the advent of colour-printing, refinement of ornament and increase in detail, but a geological map produced today would probably be quite intelligible to, say, William Smith. Suddenly, however, the rate of change has begun to accelerate. The purpose of this chapter is to touch on some aspects of these developments.

The changes are mentioned here in three groups. First, there are the various applications of new technologies. Details are outside the scope of this book, but some examples are mentioned of the radical changes which are taking place in surveying methods, map production, and the handling of map data.

Second, there are tentative but potentially significant changes in the form of geological maps. These are largely attempts at showing the arrangements of the rocks at depth at the same time as their superficial distribution.

Third, there is continuing growth of maps which present a special aspect of the geology of an area, or are designed with a particular purpose in mind. All these are 'geological maps' in that they are concerned with the geology of an area, but they fall outside the normal meaning of a map showing general rock distributions at surface. The latter kind of map, the conventional geological map, is therefore now taking on a new role as a central coordinating document for these specialised maps.

15.2 New technologies in geological maps

15.2.1 Field surveying

The traditional methods of field mapping were outlined in section 13.2. Much geological surveying still consists of the geologist going into the field in the time-honoured way to make the observations on which the map will be based. But now there is an expanding battery of technological aids. Logistical support while in the field may involve methods of rapid transport and instant communications unknown to the early surveyors. The topographic base map is likely to have involved an assortment of high-technology devices in keeping it accurate and up-to-date. The geologist may locate positions on the base map using infra-red or laser instruments. In these kinds of ways the geologist is being helped by new technology even before beginning geological observations.

It is increasingly likely that observations will be recorded in computer-readable form, such as by answering standard multiple-choice questions or by completing a checklist. Storage and processing of the field data by computer tremendously improves accessibility of the information, and the flexibility of its use for different purposes. There are, however, distinct drawbacks to this approach. For example, restricting an experienced geologist to looking at a set of standard features runs directly counter to training and philosophy. A standardised approach may help expedite the routine surveying of little known areas, but it is often the recognition of unusual features of the rocks which leads to geological insights. Field data sheets will undoubtedly be more widely used as they are refined to combine the power of a computer-based approach with the benefits of a field geologist's wisdom of experience.

These days the on-land geological surveyor now has access to a range of subsurface data which will help construction of the map. No longer does the surveyor have to rely on topographic information and observations at the exposures, but can call on geophysical and geochemical methods to help interpret the underground arrangement of the rocks. Drill-core and seismic data may be available, especially in areas of commercial interest. Off-shore geological maps, of course, rely very heavily on subsurface techniques.

15.2.2 Remote sensing

Aerial photography has long been used in the construction of geological maps. Small-scale and reconnaissance maps, in particular, have benefited and it continues to be a vital tool. Various supplementary techniques of airborne imagery continue to be developed, for example, side-looking airborne radar and shuttle imaging radar are proving particularly useful.

Satellite imagery is a newer technique, still growing in applicability as the technology improves. It has so far proved most useful for geological mapwork in the surveying of arid areas that have well-exposed, contrasting rock types. Here, the areal extent of different rocks may be directly visible on the images, leading readily to the generation of outcrop patterns. It is usually necessary to confirm identification of rocks on the ground. However, with continuing research on the radiation-absorption properties of differing rocks and minerals, and the development of new kinds of sensors, it may become possible to survey some areas directly from satellite images.

Remote sensing is less useful for geological mapping where there is soil cover, and still less useful where there is a vegetation cover. It is possible for a computer to manipulate and enhance the remotely acquired data in order to extract the maximum information, but so far in these kinds of regions it is linear features, rather than the actual rocks, that have proved most tractable. Hence, in humid regions such as the UK and the eastern USA, it is for locating straight outcrop boundaries, and particularly faults, that satellite imagery is being increasingly used.

15.2.3 Computer methods in map manipulation and production

Storing in a computer the information on which a map is based opens great possibilities for increasing the power and flexibility of maps. It becomes possible to have the computer print out a map to a specified scale, form, and resolution; to keep it up-to-date; and to enhance, remove, and manipulate the data. This trend is already established in some commercial work, and is rapidly being applied elsewhere.

So far, however, computers have been little used to carry out the initial construction of geological maps. This is partly for reasons of cost, but also for practical reasons. Some of the obstacles are very relevant to the themes of this book. For example, the computer readily accepts standardised information observed at specific field localities (section 15.2.1), but fundamental to the geological map is the form of the outcrops *between* localities. The experienced geologist notes, albeit subconsciously, a host of features between exposures that aids in locating the boundaries between rock types.

It was put colourfully by Hutchison (1975):

> The geologist does not stop at one point A, look down at his feet and record all significant data within a radius of three metres of his feet, then close his eyes and walk blindly onwards for a hundred metres then stop, look down, open his eyes at point B and record all data within a radius of three metres. Instead he is more concerned in the first instance in establishing the relationship between data set A and data set B, and recognizing (using his own inboard computer) whether or not there is a difference, and if so, what its nature might be. Each hour and each day in the field is spent working essentially interactively with the rock patterns to build up a picture of the field setting.

Moreover, as we have abundantly seen in earlier chapters, it is the form of the outcrop which helps reveal the three-dimensional configuration of the rocks and their geological history. These aspects have to be borne in mind when the boundaries are drawn (section 13.2). In other words, it is the information between localities which is essential to the geological map but which remains difficult for a computer to handle. According to Gold (1980, p. 171): 'It is, and will probably remain, difficult to produce good final geology maps without considerable manual intervention'.

However, once the outline of the map has been constructed, it is a different story. The locations and shapes of lines on the map can be converted to a numerical form acceptable to the computer, a procedure called **digitising** the map. It can be done either by following the lines manually with a digitising pen which is connected to an electrical grid on which the map is laid, or by placing the map on a digitising table which scans the map. In both cases electrical impulses feed the data to the computer. Digitising can be a time-consuming process but once carried out the computer can rapidly process the information as required. It could, for example, change the map scale or projection, add or subtract information, select certain parts of the map area, or combine the entire area with that of adjacent maps.

Computer programs are now available which allow cross-sections to be constructed rapidly from digitised maps, and vice versa. Section lines and vertical scales can be varied; structure and stratigraphic sections can be interchanged; multiple sections can be transformed to fence diagrams and block diagrams, with various projections and perspectives (chapter 5). Other constructions such as structure contour or sub-crop maps can be carried out. The manipulations are executed extremely swiftly. Trial and error can be employed: if a particular form of map or cross-section is displayed on a screen and seen to be unsatisfactory, it can be modified before printing. Additional underground information such as seismic sections and well logs can be readily incorporated. Not surprisingly, it is the oil companies that are making most use of these facilities. The kinds of data they work with are very amenable to this treatment, and their needs are specific and easy to define.

Consider, for example, a geologist investigating a petroleum reservoir and requiring the standard isopach and isochore maps (section 4.4) of the relevant formations. Working manually, this would involve consulting the well and seismic data, calculating and interpolating apparent and true thicknesses, and the construction of structure contour maps before visually overlaying and subtracting them in various permutations to obtain the thicknesses.

And some oil fields have scores of formations. Seismic and well information, however, is readily given to a computer, which can then assemble and interpolate the data into a three-dimensional grid system for storage. As required, any part of the grid can be instantly retrieved and any permutation of thicknesses, thickness ratios, thickness differences, etc. can be calculated and plotted for any specified stratigraphic intervals.

In addition to all the data manipulation, computers and related technology can greatly aid in the drafting of geological maps by adding ornaments, names, symbols, etc., and in the final printing. In fact this sort of equipment is rapidly becoming standard in the geological laboratory. As Wilson (1985, p.89) remarked: 'It is a sobering thought that while a draughtsman of the 1840's would have been able to take his place at a desk up to the late 1940's with little readjustment, a draughtsman of the 1940's would be completely lost in the drawing office of the 1980's.' Governmental geological surveys are rapidly increasing their use of these kinds of cartographic methods. For example, several BGS 1:50 000 maps have been produced partly by computer methods, such as the Abingdon, Merthyr Tydfil, and Swindon sheets. Loveland and Ramey (1986) discuss uses by the USGS of digitised map data.

So rapid is the rise in power of these manipulative programs and the sophistication of the output, that it is reasonable to ask if the content of the early chapters of this book will soon be redundant. This is extremely unlikely, for at least two reasons. First, the methods are expensive. The programs are costly to purchase and to run. The more realistic operations require substantial computing power and high-quality graphic output facilities. This is another reason why it is the oil companies that have benefited most from this approach – they can both afford and justify it. Second, it is only sensible that such expensive procedures, on which much may depend, are operated effectively. The equipment still has to be instructed on the manipulations to carry out. It has to be told along which line to draw the cross-section, on which surface to draw structure contours, etc. The rapid manipulation is merely an efficient means to an end. So the operator has to know what it is the computer is doing, and its limitations. The technology is removing time-consuming tedium, but it is making geological understanding more important then ever.

15.2.4 Map storage, indexing and retrieval

If you collect a few geological maps, keeping them somewhere is not going to be a problem, especially if they are folded. And you will probably be able to remember without much difficulty approximately what is included on each map. Consider, however, the problems faced by a library of tens of thousands of maps. Folded maps rapidly become damaged, especially along the creases, and unfolded maps are awkward to store and retrieve. The difficulties are especially acute when the map coverage of an area is not known. Sifting through collections of maps by trial and error is time consuming and wears the maps. And even the best designed storage cabinets have a habit of losing maps deep in their insides.

Hence, new methods of storing and portraying map information are being experimented with. One approach is to file photographs of the maps in some form of microfile or coloured microform. These can be inspected on conventional magnifying equipment, and only when a definite map selection has been made is the actual map taken out of store. Other systems being investigated involve storage in various microforms and on laser optical discs. But all these approaches require some initial information on the map coverage available.

Computer indexing of maps could help alleviate the problems of ascertaining the map coverage of an area of interest. If the computer stored not just the title, scale and sheet number of the map, but additional information on the map content – ranging from merely specifying the geographic coordinates of the area covered to a complete digitisation of the map – meaningful bibliographic searches could be conducted. Maps in books and journals could be included as well as governmental survey sheets. On instructing the computer of the area of interest, at least a listing of relevant map coverage could be obtained, perhaps together with a screen display of some elements of the map content. It is unlikely to be cost effective to have the computer actually print out the required map, and there could be copyright problems, but the potential for rapidly focusing on the exact map required is huge.

Unfortunately, the computing problems remain formidable. The systems required are likely to remain expensive, and outside the reach of smaller companies and libraries. The major oil companies already use simple forms of computer-based bibliographic search facilities for maps. How sophisticated and how widespread this approach becomes will depend ultimately on the financial considerations.

15.3 New forms in geological maps

Early geological maps showed the distribution of rocks at the earth's surface, and that is what geological maps show today. The eleborations and refinements discussed in previous chapters allow more to be interpreted from the distribution pattern, but it is only gained by interpretation. Efforts continue to show the three-dimensional arrangement of rocks more directly. Some approaches are mentioned here.

Posting maps show narrow stratigraphical columns on the map at representative localities. The mind's eye projects between adjacent columns to provide further visualisation of the third dimension. Any thickness variations or changes in structure will be evident. It is rather like including a partial fence diagram on the map. Unfortunately, the parts of the map behind the post are hidden from view. In fact this approach has found more success in showing at selected localities various parameters which are not normally shown on conventional geological maps. For example, vertical variations in porosity, engineering or geophysical characteristics, or chemical analyses can be listed for each site. Useful though this information may be (see section 15.4), posting these values hardly helps a more direct portrayal of the three-dimensional form of the rocks. Some geological maps include structure contours of one or more underground surfaces. This does assist visualisation of three-dimensional form, but is an extension of existing techniques rather than a new approach.

Maps have been attempted which show the distribution not of the single unit which appears at the earth's surface, but of a vertical sequence of units which is specified in the key. This approach is really feasible only where the sequences are not too variable or complex. It has been used, for example, in the near-surface glacial sequences of northern Illinois (Kempton, 1981). There the method was called 'stack-unit' mapping. The key indicates that a particular ornament or symbol represents not a single stratigraphic unit but, say, 5 m of unit A overlying approximately 10 m of unit B overlying 5 m of unit C. The approach has found applications in environmental and engineering geology maps, but so far has not gained widespread use.

Russian geologists, among others, have experimented with 'depth maps' (e.g. Milanovsky, 1984). These show, in addition to the rocks at the surface, the rock distribution at certain specified depths. The line symbols and the ornaments have to be chosen particularly carefully to prevent the patterns of the various depths from interfering with one another. The practical limitations are obvious: if more than a few depths are shown, or if the patterns are complex, the map rapidly becomes unintelligible. In any case, a measure of interpretation is still required to 'fill in' the structure between the levels provided. Milanovsky (1984) advocated the use of transparent overlays, one for each depth, but this is hardly a radical departure from traditional map forms. It may be that in the future there will be some completely innovative approach – making use of holograms, for example – but so far attempts at solving the problems of representing three-dimensional geological structure on a flat map have not met with success.

The attempts at portraying the rocks at depth have, however, spawned another variation on the form of the geological map. The position of the boundary line between two adjacent map units is usually shown as the result of interpretation (section 13.2); its location is rarely observed (see Kupfer, 1966). The certainty with which the surveyor places the boundary varies: for boundaries at depth it rapidly decreases. This has given rise to 'probability' maps, on which there is some statistical treatment of the likelihood of a given boundary being shown in the right place. Mileev and Yunakovskaya (1984) have argued that it is imperative that such probabilities be shown by line symbolism or narrow zones shaded according to the confidence interval ascribed to the boundary location. Several Russian maps have already incorporated this approach. It remains to be seen to what extent it is adopted in the West.

15.4 Specialised and thematic maps

A major trend which has been accelerating for some time is to modify the content of a geological map, either by incorporating extra information, or focusing on some special aspect. Some of these developments are mentioned here.

Geological maps are supposed to show rocks at the earth's surface, yet the vast majority of traditional maps are confined to the *land* surface; the sea is shown simply as one colour. Of course, until fairly recently we had little knowledge of rock distribution on the sea-floor, but now an important trend is for this information to be included also. The earth's surface is just that, whether or not it is covered by water.

It is likely that geological maps in the future will not be expected to stop at the present-day coastline, but show the mutual arrangement of both the on- and off-shore geology, as in the current BGS 1:250 000 maps. The coastline will almost certainly continue to be indicated, for maps can look very strange until the shape of a familiar coastline is recognised. It may be some time before the various principles described earlier in this book can be applied to maps of the seabed, because only in the best explored areas will the outcrop boundaries be known with sufficient accuracy. In fact it is in off-shore areas that the approach mentioned in section 5.1 is often utilised: information based on well and seismic data is first plotted on cross-sections and from these the geological map is derived.

The content of geological maps is changing in other ways, many inspired by the oil industry. The range of maps which emphasise the sedimentological characteristics of the rocks, with a view to helping interpret the environments of deposition, have long been known as **facies** or **lithofacies maps**, but are continually being refined and extended in application (e.g. Low, 1977). Special kinds of maps which are derived from normal geological maps have already been mentioned in section 7.6. Palaeogeological maps were introduced, together with the construction known as a sub-crop map. Section 3.4 illustrated maps which show the structure contours of a selected underground surface, and section 4.4 mentioned isopach and isochore maps. These latter maps are being extended, particularly by petroleum geologists, to produce maps that show, for example, formation thicknesses differences, net sand thicknesses, and net sand/gross thickness ratios, as well as such parameters as porosity, hydrocarbon saturation and reservoir shrinkage.

Other fields of applied geology are developing modifications of the basic geological map for their own purposes. Section 11.4 touched on mining maps (see also Herness, 1977). Engineering geologists have evolved maps which accentuate parameters of significance to construction projects. Although these properties may coincide to some extent with the units of a conventional geological map, the civil engineer is little concerned with three-dimensional arrangements or the geological histories that can be derived from them, so the units can be treated differently. For instance, a standard map may show two shale units in strikingly different colours to emphasise their different stratigraphic ages and all that implies to the geologist. An engineer will be much more concerned with whether or not the two shales have dissimilar compressibilities or shear strengths and where such parameters reach their optimum for construction. Varnes (1974) has discussed the ways in which engineering information can best be conveyed on geological maps.

An extension to these kinds of maps has come about in recent years as a result of increased awareness of the need to manage carefully the natural environment. Various kinds of **environmental geology maps** have been produced (Turner and Coffman, 1977). These portray aspects of the geology which need to be taken into account during environmental planning and the preparation of environmental impact statements. They may indicate, for example, areas vulnerable to landslip or surface subsidence, fault hazard zones, and areas of potential flood damage. They may indicate foundation conditions and likely excavation costs, areas of potential construction materials such as sand and gravel, and ground-water conditions relevant to extraction and waste disposal.

The use of environmental geology maps is strikingly illustrated by Robinson and Spieker (1978). Apart from the actual content, these maps differ from standard geological maps in other basic ways. They are intended primarily not for geologists, hence the construction and interpretations dealt with in this book are not appropriate, but for planners. Most environmental maps are actually a folio of several maps, each covering a particular aspect, such as construction resources, sand, gravel, limestone for cement, mudstone for brick-making, etc., engineering properties, pipeline siting, and ground-water resources. Hydrogeological aspects are so important in wise planning that some environmental geology maps concentrate on these, showing depths of bedrock, and various aquifer characteristics.

Such kinds of maps grade into true hydrogeological maps. These maps may show something of the geology at surface, with the key emphasising the hydrogeological characteristics of the rocks, together with further data such as structure contours or isopachs of important aquifers, contours of seasonal ground-water levels, and variations in ground-water purity. They are commonly produced by geological surveys in collaboration with other bodies that may be directly responsible for ground-water matters.

Maps of this kind, which are essentially geological maps but concerned with one particular theme, have existed for some time, but they are proliferating. They are becoming more technical, and more specialised. Tectonic maps accentuate the rock structures, especially folds and faults. Geochemical maps show the distribution of specified elements at the earth's surface, and geophysical maps depict variations in parameters, such as gravity anomalies, magnetic anomalies, and electrical resistivity. There are geothermal maps, metamorphic maps, geocryology maps, mineral resource maps and earthquake maps.

Such a list could go on. Thematic maps are of great use, and are burgeoning. Specialised maps are likely to continue to proliferate. This is, after all, an age of geological specialisation. However, there remains a central thread in all this – the conventional geological map. Invaluable though thematic and specialised maps may be, most of them are not particularly meaningful without reference to a standard geological map.

Geological maps will be increasingly produced and manipulated using the technologies and methods outlined in this chapter. But geological maps they remain. As this book has tried to emphasise, the purposes and principles are unaltered, and as important as ever. All the signs are that the geological map will remain the basic tool of the geologist.

15.5 Summary of chapter

1. The field surveyor has an expanding battery of technological aids to help him produce geological maps.
2. Remote sensing of different kinds is increasingly being used in geological mapping.
3. Computers are revolutionising the manipulation of map data, increasing the scope and reducing routine tedium, but making imperative operator understanding of the the principles involved.
4. Computers are beginning to help solve the problems of map storage and indexing.
5. Tentative attempts are being made at portraying more directly the three-dimensional arrangement of map units, and the probabilities involved with inferred boundaries.
6. Specialised and thematic maps continue to grow in range and usefulness, linked by the central thread of the conventional geological map.

15.5 Selected further reading

Kidd, C. M. (ed) (1985). *Maps in the Geoscience Community*, Proceedings of the Nineteenth Meeting of the Geoscience Information Society.
(Contains articles dealing with map indexing, storage and retrieval.)

North, F. K. (1985). *Petroleum Geology*, London, Allen and Unwin.
(Chapter 22 discusses the kinds of maps used in petroleum geology.)

References

Ahmed, F. and Almond, D. C. (1981). *Field Mapping for Geology Students*, London, Allen and Unwin.

Anderson, R. E. (1973). Large-magnitude Late Tertiary strike-slip faulting north of Lake Mead, Nevada, *USGS Professional Paper 794*.

Badgley, P. C. (1959). *Structural Methods for the Exploration Geologist*, New York, Harper and Brothers.

Bailey, E. B. (1952). *Geological Survey of Great Britain*. London, HMSO.

Bain, J. A. (1986). British Geological Survey maps and their availability, *J. Geol. Soc. London*, **143**, 569–76.

van der Bark, E. and Thomas, O. D. (1980). Ekofisk: first of the giant oilfields in Western Europe, in: *Giant oil and gas fields of the decade 1968–1978*, Halbouty, M. T. (ed), Tulsa, Oklahoma, Amer. Assoc. Petrol. Geol., 195–224.

Barnes, J. W (1981). *Basic Geological Mapping*, Milton Keynes, The Open University Press.

Bartlett, R. A. (1962). *Great Surveys of the American West*, Norman, Okla., Univ. Oklahoma Press.

Basset, D. A. (1969a). Wales and the geological map, *Bull. Nat. Museum of Wales*, **3**, 10–25.

Bassett, D. A. (1969b). William Smith, the Father of English geology and of stratigraphy: an anthology, *Geology, J. Assoc. Teachers of Geol.*, **1**, 38–51.

Beach, A. (1984). Structural evolution of the Witch Ground Graben, *J. Geol. Soc. London*, **141**, 621–8.

Billings, M. P. (1954). *Structural Geology*, 2nd ed, Englewood, New Jersey, Prentice-Hall.

Bishop, M. S. (1960). *Subsurface Mapping*, New York, Wiley.

Blackader, R. G. (1968). Guide for the preparation of geological maps and reports, *Geol. Survey of Canada, Miscellaneous Report. 16*.

Blyth, F. G. H. (1943). Intrusive rocks of the Shelve area, south Shropshire, *Quart. J. Geol. Soc. London*, **119**, 169–204.

Boud, R. C. (1985). The Highland and Agricultural Society of Scotland and John MacCulloch's geological map of Scotland, *Cartographica*, **22**, 92–115.

Butcher, N. E. (1983). The advent of colour-printed geological maps in Britain, *Proc. Royal Institution of Great Britain*, **55**, 149–61.

Butler, A. J. (1939) The Stratigraphy of the Wenlock Limestone of Dudley, *Quart. J. Geol. Soc. London*, **115**, 37–74.

Challinor, J. (1970). The progress of British geology during the early part of the nineteenth century, *Annals of Science*, **26**, 177–234.

Chapman, C. A. (1968). A comparison of the Maine coastal plutons and the magmatic central complexes of New Hampshire, in: *Studies of Appalachian Geology: Northern and Maritime*, Zen, E-an, White, W. S. and Hadley, J. B. (eds), New York, Interscience, 385–96.

Compton, R. R. (1985). *Geology in the Field*, New York, Wiley.

Cox, L. R. (1942). New light on William Smith and his work, *Proc. Yorks. Geol. Soc.*, **25**, 1–99.

Darragh, T. A. (1977). The first geological maps of the continent of Australia, *J. Geol. Soc. Australia*, **24**, 270–305.

Deer, W. A. (1935). The Cairnsmore of Carsphairn igneous complex, *Quart. J. Geol. Soc. London*, **191**, 47–76.

Dennison, J. M. (1968). *Analysis of Geologic Structures*, New York, Norton.

Dixon, H. R. and Lawrence, W. L., Jr. (1968). Structure of Eastern Connecticut, in: *Studies of Appalachian Geology: Northern and Maritime*, Zen, E-an, White, W. S. and Hadley, J. B. (eds), New York, Interscience, 219–29.

Dixon, J. S. (1982) Regional structural synthesis, Wyoming salient of western overthrust belt, *Bull. Amer. Assoc. Petrol. Geol.*, **66**, 1560–80.

Dodd, K., Fuller, H. K. and Clarke, P. F. (1985). Guide to obtaining USGS information, *USGS Circular 900*.

Dunham, Sir K., Beer, K. E., Ellis, R. H., Gallagher, M. J., Nutt, M. J. C., and Webb, B. C. (1978). United Kingdom, in: *Mineral Deposits of Europe. Volume 1: Northwest Europe*, Bowie, S. H. U., Kvalheim, A. and Haslam, N. W. (eds), London, Inst. Mining and Metall. and Mineral. Soc., 263–317.

Earp, J. R. (1938). The Higher Silurian rocks of the Kerry district Montgomeryshire, *Quart. Journ. Geol. Soc. London*, **94**, 125–60.

Elliot, D. and Johnson, M. R. W. (1980). Structural evolution in the northern part of the Moine thrust belt, NW Scotland, *Trans. Roy. Soc. Edinburgh*, **71**, 69–96.

Evans, J. W. (1921). The representation of stratigraphical divisions by shading, *Geol. Mag.*, **58**, 40–41.

Eyles, J. M. (1967). William Smith: the sale of his geological collection to the British Museum, *Ann. Sci.*, **23**, 177–212.

Eyles, J. M. (1969). William Smith (1769–1839): A bibliography of his published writings, maps and geological sections, printed and lithographed, *J. Soc. Bibliog. Nat. Hist.*, **5**, 87–109.

Eyles, V. A. (1937). John MacCulloch, F.R.S., and his geological map, *Ann. Sci.*, **2**, 114–29.

Eyles, V. A. (1950). The first national geological survey, *Geol. Mag.*, **7**, 373–82.

Eyles, V. A. and Eyles, J. M. (1938). On the different issues of the first geological map of England and Wales, *Ann. Sci.*, **3**, 190.

Faull, H. and Faull, C. (1981). *It Began with a Stone. A history of geology from the stone age to the age of plate tectonics*, New York, Wiley.

Fergusson, C. L., Cas, R. A. F., Collins, W. J., Craig, G. Y., Crook, K. A. W., Powell, C. McA., Scott, S. A. and Young, G. C. (1979). The Upper Devonian Boyd volcanic complex, Eden, New South Wales, *J. Geol. Soc. Australia*, **26**, 87–105.

Flett, J. S. (1937). *The First Hundred Years of the Geological Survey of Great Britain*, London. HMSO.

Fleuty, M. J. (1964). The description of folds, *Proc. Geol. Assoc.*, **75**, 461–89.

Fracolli, D. L. (1985). An investigation of preparation and costs for a state bibliography of geology, in: *Maps in the Geoscience Community*, Kidd, C. M. (ed), Reno, Nevada, Proc. Geoscience Information Soc., vol. 15, 117–24.

Freund, R. (1971). The Hope Fault. A strike-slip fault in New Zealand, *New Zealand Geol. Survey Bull.*, **86**, 1–49.

Fuller, H. K. (1985). Maps of maps – geological map indexes prepared by state geoscience agencies, in: *Maps in the Geoscience Community*, Kidd, C. M. (ed), Reno, Nevada, Geoscience Information Soc., vol. 15, 81–89.

Geikie, A. (1905). *The founders of geology*. Reprinted 1962, New York, Dover.

Gold, C. (1980). Geological mapping by computer, in: *The computer in contemporary cartography*, Taylor, D. R. F. (ed) Chichester, Wiley, 151–90.

Green, G. W. and Welch, F. B. A. (1965). Geology of the country around Wells and Cheddar, *Mem. Geol. Survey Great Britain 280*, London, HMSO.

Greenly, E. and Williams, H. (1930). *Methods in Geological Surveying*, London, Thomas Murby.

Groves, J. R. (1980). Step-by-step procedure for mounting maps on cloth, *J. Geol. Educ.*, **28**, 141–43.

Hageman, B. P. (1968). The reliability of geological maps, *Intl. Yearbook of Cartography*, **8**, 144–54.

Harrington, H. J. (1958). Geology of the Kaitangata Coalfield, *New Zealand Geol. Survey Bull.*, **59**, 1–131.

Harrison, J. M. (1963). Nature and significance of geological maps, in: *The Fabric of Geology*, Albritton, C. C., (ed). Stanford, California, Freeman Cooper and Co., 225–31.

Hayward, H. A. (1932). The geology of the Lower Greensand in the Dorking–Leith Hill district, Surrey, *Proc. Geol. Assoc.*, **43**, 1–31.

Herness, S. K. (1977). Subsurface representation in mining geology, in: *Subsurface geology. Petroleum, mining, construction*, LeRoy, L. W., LeRoy, D. O. and Raese, J. W. (eds), Golden, Colorado, Colorado School of Mines, 529–39.

Herries Davies, G. L. (1983). Sheets of many colours: the mapping of Ireland's rocks 1750–1890, Dublin, Royal Dublin Society.

Holmes, A. (1965). *Principles of Physical Geology*, 2nd edn, New York, Ronald Press.

Hudson, R. G. S. and Dunnington, H. V. (1944). The Carboniferous rocks of the Swinden Anticline, Yorkshire, *Proc. Geol. Assoc.*, **55**, 195–215.

Hutchison, W. W. (1975). Introduction to geological field data systems and generalized geological data management systems, in: Computer-based systems for geological field data, Hutchison, W. W. (ed). *Geological Survey Canada Paper 74–63*, 32–38.

Ireland, H. A. (1943). History of the development of geologic maps, *Bull. Geol. Soc. America*, **54**, 1227–80.

Jamieson, H. C., Brockett, L. D. and McIntosh, R. A. (1980). Prudhoe Bay –a 10-year perspective, in: *Giant Oil and Gas Fields of the Decade 1968–1978*, Halbouty, M. T. (ed), Tulsa, Oklahoma, Amer. Assoc. Petrol. Geol., 289–314.

Johnson, G. A. L. and Dunham, K. C., (1963). The geology of Moor House, *Monograph Nature Conserv.*, No. 2. London, HMSO.

Jones, O. T. (1922). Lead and zinc. The mining district of North Cardiganshire and West Montgomeryshire, *Spec. Rept. Miner. Resour. Gt. Br.*, **20**.

Jones, O. T. (1949) The geology of the Llandovery district. Part II: the northern area, *Quart. J. Geol. Soc. London*, **105**, 43–64.

Kempton, J. P. (1981). Three-dimensional geologic mapping for environmental studies in Illinois, *Illinois State Geol. Survey Envir. Geol. Note 100*.

Korn, M. and Martin, M. (1959). Gravity tectonics in the Naukluft Mountains of south-west Africa, *Bull. Geol. Soc. America*, **70**, 1047–78.

Kupfer, D. H. (1966). Accuracy in geologic maps, *Geotimes*, **10**, (7) 11–14.

Langstaff, C. S. and Morrill, D. (1981). *Geologic Cross-Sections*, Boston, USA, International Human Resources Development Corporation.

Lemoine, M. (ed) (1978). *Geological Atlas of Alpine Europe and Adjoining Alpine areas*, Amsterdam, Elsevier.

Levorsen, A, I. (1960). *Paleogeological Maps*, San Francisco, Freeman.

Linton, D. L. (1947). The ideal geological map, *Advancement of Science*, **5**, 141–49.

Lobeck, A. K. (1958). *Block Diagrams and Other Graphic Methods Used in Geology and Geography*, 2nd edn. Amherst, Maryland, Emerson–Trussell Book Co.

Loveland, T. R. and Ramey, B. (1986). Applications of US Geological Survey digital cartographic products, 1979–1983, *US Geological Survey Bulletin 1583*.

Low, J. W. (1977). Subsurface maps and illustrations, in: *Subsurface Geology. Petroleum, Mining Construction*, LeRoy, L. W., LeRoy, D. O. and Raese, J. W. (eds) Golden, Colorado, Colorado School of Mines.

McClay, K. (1987). *The Mapping of Geological Structures*, Milton Keynes, The Open University Press.

Martin, E. L. (1973). Geological maps, in: *Use of Earth Sciences Literature*, Wood, D. N. (ed). London, Butterworth's, 122–50.

Merrill, G. P. (1924). *The first one hundred years of American Geology*. Reprinted 1969, New York, Hafner Publ. Co.

Milanovsky, E. E. (1984). Evolution of the geological map relative to the development of geological sciences, in: *Contributions to the History of Geological Mapping*, Dudich, E. (ed). Budapest, Akademiaikido, 3–9.

Mileev, V. S. and Yunakovskaya, Y. V. (1984). Volumetric geological study and the cartographic presentation of its results, in: *Contributions to the History of Geological Mapping*, Dudich, E. (ed), Budapest, Akademiaikido, 10–14.

Mosely, F. (1981). *Methods in field geology*, Oxford, Freeman.

North, F. J. (1928). *Geological maps. Their history and development with special reference to Wales*, Cardiff, National Museum of Wales.

Page, B. M. (1966). Geology of the Coast Ranges of California, *Calif. Division of Mines and Geology Bull. 190*, 255–76.

Pangborn, M. W., Jr. (1971). Geologic maps. A contribution to geologic reference sources, in: *Geologic Reference Sources*, Ward, D. C., Wheeler, M. W. and Pangborn, M. W., Jr. (eds). Metuchen, New Jersey, The Scarecrow Press, 352–436.

Parkinson, D. P. (1936). The Carboniferous succession in the Slaidburn district, Yorkshire, *Quart. J. Geol. Soc. London*, **92**, 294–331.

Pavlinov, V. N. (1984). Evolution of geological mapping in connection with the development of natural sciences, in: *Contributions to the History of Geological Mapping*, Dudich, E. (ed), Budapest, Akademiaikido, 35–40.

Pitcher, W. S. and Berger, A. R. (1972). *The Geology of Donegal: a study of granite emplacement and unroofing*, New York, Wiley-Interscience.

Powell, C. McA., Edgecombe, D. R., Henry, N. M. and Jones, J. G. (1976). Timing of regional deformation of the Hill End Trough: a reassessment, *J. Geol. Soc. Australia*, **23**, 407–21.

Powell, J. W. (1881). Sur la nomenclature générale, sur le coloriage et les signes conventionnels des Cartes geologiques, *Intern. Geol. Congr., Compte Rendu*, 2nd session, Boulogne, 627–41.

Powell, J. W. (1895). *The Exploration of the Colorado River and Its Canyons*. Reprinted 1961, New York, Dover.

Rabbit, M. C. (1980a). A brief history of the US Geological Survey, *USGS Popular Publication.*

Rabbit, M. C. (1980b). John Wesley Powell, soldier, explorer, scientist, *USGS Popular Publication.*

Ragan, D. M. (1985) *Structural Geology. An introduction to geometrical techniques*, 3rd edn., New York, Wiley.

Ramsay, J. G. and Huber, M. I. (1987). *The Techniques of Modern Structural Geology. Vol. 2: Folds and Fractures*, London, Academic Press.

Rappaport, R. (1969). The geological atlas of Guettard, Lavoisier, and Monnet: conflicting views of the nature of geology, in: *Toward a History of Geology*, Schneer, C. J. (ed), Cambridge, Mass., MIT Press, 272–87.

Richey, J. E. (1961). *Scotland: The Tertiary Volcanic Districts*, 3rd edn, British Regional Geology, Edinburgh, HMSO.

Robertson, T. (1956). The presentation of geological information in maps, *Advancement of Science*, **13**, 31–41.

Robinson, G. D. and Spieker, A. M. (1978). Nature to be commanded... Earth-science maps applied to land and water management, *US Geological Survey Professional Paper 950.*

Rowland, S. M. (1986) *Structural Analysis and Synthesis: A laboratory course in structural geology*, Oxford, Blackwell.

Rudwick, M. J. S. (1976). A visual language for geology, *History of Science*, **14**, 149.

Smart, J. G. O. (1954). Notes on the geology of the Alton Pancras District, Dorset, *Bull. Geol. Survey. Great Britain*, **9**, 42–49.

Strauss, G. K., Madel, J. and Fdez Alonso, F. (1977). Exploration practice for strata-bound volcanogenic sulphide deposits in the Spanish–Portuguese pyrite belt: geology, geophysics, and geochemistry, in: *Time and Strata-bound Ore Deposits*, Klemm, D. D. and Schneider, H-J. (eds), Berlin, Springer-Verlag, 55–93.

Snyder, J. P. (1987). Map projections: a working manual, *USGS Professional Paper 1395.*

Travis, R. B. and Lamar, D. L. (1987). Apparent-dip methods, *J. Geol. Educ.*, **35**, 152–54.

Turner, A.K. and Coffman, D. M. (1977). Geologic applications in land use and environmental analysis, in: *Subsurface Geology. Petroleum, Mining Construction.* LeRoy, L. W., LeRoy, D. O. and Raese, J. W. (eds), Golden Colorado, Colorado School of Mines, 788–97.

Varnes, D. J. (1974). The logic of geological maps with reference to their interpretation and use for engineering purposes, *USGS Professional Paper 837.*

Ver Ploeg, A. J. and de Bruin, R. H. (1982). The search for oil and gas in the Idaho–Wyoming–Utah salient of the overthrust belt, *Geol. Survey of Wyoming Rept. of Investigations No. 21.* Laramie, Wyoming.

Vigneaux, M. and Leneuf, N. (1980). Géologie et Vins de France, *Bull. Inst. Géol. Bassin d'Aquitaine, Bordeaux,* **27**, 165–234.

de Villiers, J, (1983). Geology of the Helderberg, *Trans. Geol. Soc. South Africa*, **88**, 175–7.

Wallace, R. M. (1965). Geology and mineral resources of the Pico de Itabirito District Minas Gerais, Brazil, *US Geol. Survey Professional Paper 341-F.*

Willats, E. C. (1970). Maps and Maidens, *Cartographica J.*, **7**, 50.

Wilson, H. E. (1985). *Down to Earth. One hundred and fifty years of the British Geological Survey*, Edinburgh, Scottish Academic Press.

Winnock, E. and Pontalier, Y. (1970). Lacq Gas Field, France, in: *Geology of Giant Petroleum Fields*, Halbouty, M. T. (ed), Tulsa, Oklahoma, Amer. Assoc. Petrol. Geol. Mem. **14**, 370–87.

Woodward, L. A. (1984). Potential for significant oil and gas fracture reservoirs in Cretaceous of Raton Basin, New Mexico, *Bull. Amer. Assoc. Petrol. Geol.*, **68**, 628–36.

Woodward, N. B., Boyer, S. E. and Suppe, J. (1985). *An Outline of Balanced Cross-Sections*, 2nd edn, Studies in Geology vol. 11, Knoxville, Tennessee, University of Tennessee, Department of Geological Sciences.

Index

Page-numbers in **bold** type refer to main text entries.
Page-numbers in *italics* refer to figures.